Compliments
of Isabelle

1996

John Wolcott

WASTE TO WEALTH

A History of
Gas Processing
in Canada

by

Fred Stenson

ISBN 0-88925-583-0

Published by
Canadian Gas Processors Association/
Canadian Gas Processors Suppliers' Association
Calgary, Alberta
Canada

Second Printing, 1992

Printed and bound in Canada by
Friesen Printers
a Division of D. W. Friesen & Sons Ltd.
Altona, Manitoba R0G 0B0
Canada

TABLE OF CONTENTS

FOREWORD

Alberta practically floats on an underground ocean of gas. In the drilling of more than 100,000 wells, very few have failed to find at least a show of gas. Jim Gray of Canadian Hunter says: "It is almost impossible to drill a totally dry hole in Alberta."

From the "nuisance" gas well that the CPR drilled at Alderson in 1883, when it was looking for water to fill its steam locomotive tenders, to the giant reef discoveries of recent years, gas has been a vital part of Alberta history. It was providing clean, cheap fuel for houses and industry in Medicine Hat before Alberta became a province, prompting Rudyard Kipling to describe that city as "having all hell for a basement."

Gas has long been a symbol of clear skies. Many years ago spectators at old Mewata Stadium in Calgary were urged by a huge display board: "Look up! The cleanest sky in the world is above you!" The reason for that clean sky was the ingenuity of the gas processing industry.

Great sour gas fields have made Alberta the world's leading centre of research and development in the technology of H_2S removal and sulphur recovery. They have led to the creation of diversified industries. Several generations of research chemists and engineers have established worldwide reputations on them. They provide substantial wealth from sales across Canada and abroad. Dr. Jim Hyne of Alberta Sulphur Research noted in a recent paper at *Sulphur '84* that Canadian sulphur literally keeps millions of third world citizens alive through its conversion to fertilizer.

This book is a comprehensive survey of the growth of gas processing in Western Canada and its impact. The historical and technical research has been done with great care and accuracy. It covers the whole range of the industry from the earliest gas discovery to the most recent trends in export markets, from the first simple "baling wire" technology to the complex chemistry of sulphur and its strange behavior under varied temperatures. It traces the changes in public awareness from the Turner Valley days, when the odor of sulphur dioxide represented "the rich smell of greenbacks in your pocket" to the new era of almost total sulphur recovery and H_2S removal to maintain a super clean environment under the highest air quality requirements in the world.

Throughout the book the author has displayed the role of people in this fascinating segment of the petroleum industry. He has caught the risk-taking, free enterprise spirit among the pioneers, the blend of failure and success and the frantic search by the early wildcatters for a few more dollars to drill those last 125 feet to where they knew the payzone was; and the exuberant celebration that greeted each new discovery.

It was people with dedication who made the gas processing industry and its companion supply and service structure what they are today. They worked long hours under "impossible" conditions to make the industry more efficient and effective, and they have come out on top. They have challenged nature and won. Significantly, they have enjoyed every minute of it. The common recollection is: "It's been a lot of fun."

This is still a feature of the current scene. All the technological developments that come along faster than anyone can imagine require human ingenuity to create and apply. The more computers and automation change the way things are done, the more urgent is the need for competent people to understand why and where they should be applied, in the right place at the right time.

The ability to keep a cool head and a sense of humor is a big key to success, according to many of the incidents related in the book. One panel discussion at a quarterly meeting drew a packed audience on the trenchant subject: "How many men does it take to run an unattended gas plant?"

The book narrates many human interest incidents and accomplishments. "Canadianization" was achieved through mutual assistance and swapping of knowledge long before anyone thought of putting a name tag on the voluntary efforts of engineers and technicians. Training programs developed by trial and error. Some of the field learning incidents were purely hilarious. Awareness developed quickly of how wide a difference there could be between what the engineering staff in the office thought they were designing and what the field crews were really doing under the stress of rough, tough reality.

There is something for everyone in this book, from a vast fund of technical information to the learning derived from the university of the field. It can be read for education, history and pure enjoyment. Most readers should be stimulated to scan it from cover to cover. It is an epic tribute to the quarter century of work done by the two Associations (CGPA and CGPSA), their individual members, and the pioneers who laid the groundwork for an essential and growing industry.

Les Rowland, Senior Editor, *Oilweek*
January 21, 1985

ACKNOWLEDGEMENTS

A great many helping hands and minds cooperated on this project, providing assistance the author is pleased to acknowledge. I would like to thank both the Canadian Gas Processors Association and the Canadian Gas Processors Suppliers' Association for initiating this anniversary project and for supporting it to fruition with funds and workable organization. The idea of celebrating the Associations' silver anniversary in this fashion came from Don McEachern, a charter member and the second president of the CGPA. Shortly after he had sold the Associations on the idea, Don was called away to an overseas posting and his place was taken by Jim Belding and Earl Scott who served as co-chairmen on the joint committee charged with bringing this book into being. Chairmen Belding and Scott and all the members of their committee and its sub-committees tackled the new task of publishing with thoroughness, professionalism and gusto.

I would particularly like to thank the members of the editorial committee, with whom I worked closely. Bob Smith (chairman), Elmer Berlie and Kevin Milne were able to outline the history from their own considerable knowledge and experience and were never stuck for a source or contact when further direction was needed. Much of these gentlemen's Christmas season was spent in nightly editorial sessions. Their patience and attention to detail were greatly appreciated. Also contributing to the editorial process was Les Rowland. Mr. Rowland lent the project his considerable experience by giving the book a final reading. I would also like to thank the project's efficient treasurer and accountant, Richard Arnold. (One always like to thank the person who wrote the cheques.) In general, it can be said that members of the CGPSA and CGPA took the project to heart and pitched in generously.

I would like to acknowledge the financial support given to this project by Canada Works, a job creation program of Employment and Immigration Canada. Many companies also contributed financially and corporate generosity came too in the form of office space, photocopying, paper and typewriter ribbon. Dome Petroleum and Travis Chemicals gave the project's researchers and author a place to hang their hats and Amoco contributed a much needed word processing service.

Much of the information found here comes from personal interviews and a special thanks goes to the many industry personalities who took time off from work, or who came out of retirement for an hour, to talk to us.

Most of those interviews were conducted by research assistant John McDowell on a jam-packed schedule, with something less than crystal clear direction from the supervising author. I thank him for this as well as for timely editorial assistance. An apology must also go to all those in the industry who have played a significant role in its coming of age, who have tales to tell, who we were not able to reach.

I would like to thank all the individuals and companies who foraged in their photographic collections for the images that appear in this book. A photo acknowledgements page appears immediately before the index. My thanks as well to the Glenbow-Alberta Institute for the use of its photographic and print archives.

Statistics for the graphs presented in Appendix 2 were prepared for the project by the ERCB. The project thanks the Board's George Warne for agreeing to help us in this way. Esso's Jussi Alto was convinced by *Project 25* chairman Jack Willison, also of Esso, to apply his computer skills to the creation of the graphs. I would also like to acknowledge the work done by Christl Ganz at the APEGGA office in handling book orders.

Finally, the author would like to express a humble thanks to the many authors, past and present, technical and literary, who are quoted and relied upon for fact in these pages.

Fred Stenson
Feb. 1, 1985

Dingman #1.

THE ORIGINS OF AN INDUSTRY: FROM PERPETUAL FIRES TO HOME FIRES

1

If an Egyptian Pharaoh were to migrate across time and enter the home of an average middle class North American, it is doubtful he would want to return to his ancient throne. Heat and light at the flip of a switch, hot and cold water flowing from taps — and everyone's taps at that; it would make the Pharaoh's treasures seem less than splendid. One of the factors creating that gap, allowing our average amenities to dwarf the wealth of ages past, is the economical supply of clean-burning natural gas. This excellent fuel has powered and continues to power many of the advances that make 20th century life so enjoyable to live.

The calculated and widespread use of natural gas is relatively new, but man's first encounters with the substance are ancient. Unless trapped below the earth, natural gas will migrate up through porous layers to the surface. Gas seeps bubble in lakes and rivers, hiss out of crevices in stone. If by friction or lightning bolt the venting gas catches fire, it will burn until the seeping gas is choked off or exhausted.

These *perpetual fires* were man's introduction to gas. The significance attached to them was not surprisingly religious. One of the oracles of Ancient Greece spoke its prophecies from the everlasting fire at Delphi. The burning bush, the fiery furnace of Shadrach, Meshach and Abednego, the fire temples of Baku on the Caspian Sea — all have been connected to burning natural gas by those who seek natural explanations for mystical phenomena.

It took the pragmatic Chinese civilization to harness seeping natural gas and put it to use. As early as the Shu Han Dynasty (A.D. 222-263), the Chinese were using natural gas to light their temples. In 10th century Peking, natural gas was used for street lighting. Credit also goes to the Chinese for the first gas pipeline and the first industrial use of gas. They transported natural gas from source to lamp through lengths of bamboo, and they used the heating power of natural gas to extract salt from brine. Europe would not duplicate these feats for hundreds of years.

Modern uses of natural gas were heralded by the accidental discovery of artificial gas by Flemish chemist Jean van Helmont in 1609. Van Helmont found that coal, heated in a sealed crucible, "did belch forth a wild spirit or breath.".. He called his invention *gheest*, the Flemish word for ghost, and this is believed to be the origin of our word gas.

Van Helmont's coal gas, rather than natural gas, fueled various aspects of the Industrial Revolution and supplied light to European cities in the early 19th century. But it had to acquire its following slowly and in spite of ridicule from several famous people. No less a man than Napoleon scoffed at the idea of "flammable air". He called it "une grande folie". When a German by the name of Frederic Albert Winzer came to England in 1803 and took out a patent for the manufacture of gas (and changed his name to Winsor), author Sir Walter Scott found the whole thing desperately funny. "There is a madman", he wrote to a friend, "proposing to light London with, what do you think? Why, with smoke!.." The last laugh, as it happened, went to Winzer/Winsor who put down lead pipes and lit one side of Pall Mall with gas in 1807. Coal gas light came to Canada when a gas works was built in Montreal in 1836. Toronto acquired coal gas in 1841.

Natural gas has always had distinct advantages over the manufactured variety. There is no cost of conversion and natural gas has a greater heating value. Its use was prevented for a long time, however, by the lack of technology capable of digging down far enough to reach the natural product. The first natural gas utilized in North America came from a twenty-seven foot well in New York State. The year was 1821 and the gas was piped through hollow logs to Fredonia, N.Y., which promptly claimed for itself the title "best lit city in the world". But, clearly, the natural gas industry was not going to get far on twenty-seven foot* wells and log pipelines. Before natural gas could take its rightful place as an energy source, cable tool drilling and leak-proof pipelines had to be developed. Knowledge of underground geology had to be improved. On the consumer end, gas stoves and gas lights had to be invented of sufficient quality and safety to attract the public.

By the late 19th century, all this had come to pass. Robert Wilhelm von Bunsen had invented the blue flame gas burner and his student Carl Auer von Welsbach had invented the incandescent mantle. Samuel Clegg had invented that machine so dear to the hearts of all sellers of gas, the gas meter. Clegg was also the inventor of a gas stove which shut off its gas automatically when the flame was extinguished.

The art of cable tool drilling developed slowly in the field, with the chisel-edged bits smashing stone at ever increasing depths. In 1872, the

---

*Throughout this book, the units of measurement are imperial. This reflects the common practice in the industry in the period about which the book is written. For the convenience of those raised in the age of metric measures, an imperial to metric conversion chart is found in Appendix I.

first cast-iron pipeline was built in the United States. It covered the distance of 5.5 miles from Titusville to Newton in Pennsylvania.

ORIGINS OF THE GAS INDUSTRY IN CANADA

Credit for founding Canada's natural gas industry generally goes to Eugene Marius Coste who discovered gas in Essex County, Ontario, in 1889. But, natural gas had been found in Canada several times before Coste made his discovery. The difference between the earlier finds and Coste's was that Coste was *trying* to find natural gas at the time and knew what to do with it when he had it.

The gas discoveries that pre-dated Coste's Essex County well were generally accidental and botched in one way or another. In 1859, Dr. H. C. Tweedle found both gas and oil in the Dover fields near Moncton, New Brunswick, but water intruded before he could make any commercial use of his find. Sulphur gas was found near Port Colborne, Ontario, in 1866 when the object of the search was oil. Gas often came up in association with the oil found in the early Ontario play, but it was regarded as a nuisance to be flared before it got away and flared you.

Perhaps the oddest accidental find was made in the West in 1883. The CPR was beginning to operate its railway across the dry prairie country (even drier than usual in the 1882-86 period) and shortage of water for its steam locomotives had become a chronic problem. Crews were sent out to drill for water along the CPR right-of-way. Near a siding called Langevin*, west of Medicine Hat, they hammered down their first well. At 523' they still had not found water but, as the hole was going down easily, they continued. At 1120' they were interested to see gas coming out of the hole, flammable gas, but they kept drilling in spite of it. At 1155', another layer of gas was hit and this one caught fire. As reported by the *Calgary Herald*, January 16, 1884: "The frame building surrounding the engine (*derrick to you and me*) was in a few moments destroyed, and the men at work were in eminent (sic) peril of their lives." It seems the peril was also "imminent". Mr. Haines who was trapped in the derrick when the gas caught fire broke a leg jumping to safety.

Somehow the well was brought under control and a second well was drilled at Langevin using the gas from the first to fuel the cable tool drilling rig. Nearly all the wells drilled in this era were cable tool operations, a type of rig that featured a heavy, chisel-edged bit that was dropped repeatedly, smashing the rock at the bottom of the hole. The second CPR well at

*Langevin was later renamed Alderson.

Langevin was hammered down in this way and, not surprisingly given its closeness to the first well, struck gas at the identical depth of 1155'.

The Langevin gas was put to immediate use fuelling the cooking and heating facilities of the local CPR section house. In the long term, the two Langevin wells had a more profound effect. As pioneer geologist George M. Dawson put it in a paper delivered to the Royal Society of Canada in 1886, the two wells

> demonstrated the very important fact that a large supply of natural combustible gas exists in this district, at depths of 900 feet and over, in the sandy layers of the 'Lower Dark shales'. In consequence of the generally horizontal position and widespread uniformity in character of the rocks, it is probable that a similar supply will be met with over a great area of this part of the Northwest, and that it may become in the near future a factor of economic importance. The gas is doubtless derived from the decomposition of organic matter in the dark carbonaceous shales occurring in this section.

Had Eugene Marius Coste been present at the Society's session, this final remark by George M. Dawson could have triggered an argument. Coste was a staunch believer in the French theory that oil and gas did not originate organically, but were formed by volcanic activity, the petroleum migrating from its igneous source beds to the sedimentary reservoirs where it is traditionally found. Although we have no way of knowing how many people believed him, Coste's uncanny ability to find gas must have been compelling evidence for his theory. Promptly after his first success in Essex County, Coste drilled a second wildcat 200 miles east near Niagara Falls and struck gas again. In the winter of 1890-91, the gas from the second field was exported to Buffalo, New York, and later, in 1895, Essex gas was pipelined to Windsor and across the river to Detroit, Canada's first natural gas exports!

It was a common fallacy in those days to believe that natural gas fields were inexhaustible; the word crops up frequently in news reports of the day. The average person — the average reporter at least — seemed to view the earth as something like a huge beach ball, covered with a thin skin and filled with bountiful quantities of natural gas. Puncture that skin in the right place and the gas would flow forever. The fault in the fancy showed itself quickly to the people of southern Ontario when pressure in their *inexhaustible* Essex field began to drop off drastically after a few years. A loud (and now familiar) cry went up from the local consumers to "Stop Exports Immediately!" Their government began to grope around for a politic way of obeying. Finally the government revoked the licenses for pipelines crossing beneath rivers — a neat political move if there ever was one! While not expressly prohibiting exports, it did effectively block the watery border crossings to Buffalo and Detroit. It was too little too late in any case. By 1904, the Essex field was depleted.

ALL HELL FOR A BASEMENT

Meanwhile in the West, far from major population centres, interest in natural gas was slow to focus. For several years after the Langevin strikes, the sporadic search for petroleum was really a search for oil, concentrated mainly in the Waterton-Pincher Creek area. In 1886, frontiersman Kootenai Brown found oil seeping into a creek near Waterton, and enough hoopla was generated to produce a small boom and a short lived Oil City.

Kootenai Brown, whose 19th century trades included trading, buffalo running, Pony Express riding and gold prospecting, went into the oil business as that century drew to a close. He soaked up oil off Cameron Creek near Waterton Lakes and squeezed it out into bottles which he sold to farmers and ranchers as lubricant.

To get the natural gas industry off the ground in Western Canada, one more accidental find was required. The CPR was destiny's instrument once again. This time, the railway company was digging for coal along the South Saskatchewan River at Medicine Hat when it hit gas. The year was 1890, and the idea of a bountiful fuel supply right there beneath the streets of Medicine Hat was received enthusiastically by some village leaders. They approached the CPR to see if the company might be interested in deepening its Medicine Hat well. CPR president Sir William Van Horne had no such interest but he did lend the town his cable tool drilling rig on the understanding that the town would look after its own drilling costs. The result was a 650' well producing gas at 250 pounds per square inch. Strong water intrusion prevented their going any deeper.

An interesting aside to this appears in J. W. Morrow's 1923 "Early History of Medicine Hat". He notes that, in 1899, an enterprising Medicine Hat citizen by name of Charles Colter patented a gas burning furnace, and commenced piping gas from *his* well on Second Avenue to not only his house but to his neighbours' as well. The dates of these occurrences would seem to indicate that Colter was ahead of the town by several strides in the race to provide Medicine Hat with gas. When he undertook to cross the street with his wildcat pipeline, the town put a stop to it.

Records of what drilling took place at Medicine Hat over the next several years are sketchy. According to one estimate, there were seven wells in existence by 1901, four belonging to the town and three private (including Colter's). They were all drilled to the shallow gas horizon, known as Milk River sand (between 650 and 750' in depth).

In 1904, Medicine Hat finally managed the deeper well it had been planning since the first entreaties to William Van Horne in 1890. That year, the Main Street well was pushed down to 1010' and a large volume of gas was struck at a closed pressure of 500 pounds per square inch. This new gas horizon was larger in volume and stronger in pressure by far than the gas from the shallower sand. Important as well, the gas was not accompanied by free water.

Shortly after this discovery, the newly incorporated city of Medicine Hat acquired gas lights on its railway platforms and downtown street corners, making the headlines of Robert Ripley's "Believe it or Not" in the process. Ripley invited his readers to believe or not the fact that Medicine Hat's gas lights were left burning 24 hours a day, it being cheaper to burn the extra fuel than to hire a lamplighter.

Best-selling British author Rudyard Kipling made a contribution to the gas saga of Medicine Hat when he visited the town in 1907. The city went to elaborate lengths to entertain its celebrity, taking Kipling for a motor car ride, treating him to a community picnic, and, the *pièce de résistance*, a long gander at a roaring gas flare unleashed from the city's fiery bowels.

The idea of a city built atop this infernal power evidently created a second flame in the writer's imagination. Kipling declared Medicine Hat the city with *All Hell for a Basement*. The relationship between Kipling and the Hat didn't end there either. A few years later, some of the citizens of Medicine Hat were so angry about ridicule of their city's name that they launched a campaign to have it changed. The defenders of the name hit upon the idea of sending a letter to Rudyard Kipling. The author's reply was both lengthy and passionate. He listed a number of other bizarre names from the map of North America and then concluded: "To my mind the name Medicine Hat has an advantage over all the names I have quoted. It echoes, as you so justly put it, the old Cree and Blackfoot tradition of red mystery and romance that once filled the Prairies. Also it hints, I venture to think, at the magic that underlies the city in the shape of your natural gas." The movement to save the name worked. The name stuck and so did the tradition of lighting flares to fête dignitaries and to cheer up the general populace. If the civic principle of ancient Rome was to give people circuses, the principle of Medicine Hat was to give them flares.

THE RACE TO SUPPLY CALGARY

Medicine Hat's handy fuel supply became the envy of every young town in the West. Several of them punched down wells of their own to see if they might be similarly fortunate. Calgary, with its image of a budding metropolis, was perhaps the most determined to erase Medicine Hat's edge and destroy early any notion that city might have of becoming the number one centre for the area.

Calgary's first effort to find gas was a downtown well drilled in 1895. It was a dry hole. By 1903, the city seemed ready to accept its gasless fate in that it granted a franchise to civil engineer David Morris to manufacture artificial gas. Morris' enterprise, called the Calgary Gas Co., served 1800 customers through twenty-six miles of intra-city pipeline.

When it looked as if Calgary might have no natural gas in its vicinity, the city granted a manufactured gas franchise to David Morris.

In 1902, an entrepreneur by the name of Archibald Wayne Dingman from Ontario came to Calgary. Dingman was already a veteran of a number of business ventures and, looking over the prospects in Calgary, he decided that supplying the city with natural gas had to be among the best in that locale. He acquired a franchise from the city to do this in 1905 and, by the following year, his Calgary Natural Gas Co. drilled its first well. The location near Lott Creek on the Sarcee Indian Reserve was selected on the advice of D. B. Dowling of the Geological Survey of Canada. Dingman took the hole down to the then remarkable depth of 3400′, but any shows of gas were small.

Meanwhile, Eugene Coste, the already successful Eastern gas entrepreneur, brought his show to Western Canada. His goal was the same as Archibald Dingman's — and then some. Not content merely to supply Calgary with natural gas, Coste intended to bring gas to all the towns of southern Alberta. He came to these conclusions while drilling wells on contract for the CPR along the company's right-of-way. Working for Coste was an experienced team of cable tool drillers, W. R. "Frosty" Martin and A. P. "Tiny" Phillips. When Coste first approached Phillips about making the move West, he specified that they would be working in the Provinces of Saskatchewan and Alberta. Phillips had heard of neither and had to be shown their location on a map. This is probably more excusable than it sounds for the year was 1905 and both Provinces were brand new.

Coste's CPR drilling program turned up a number of commercial gas finds — at Dunmore, Cummings, Suffield, Brooks and Bassano. But the big find, the one that changed history, was the *Old Glory* well at Bow Island, drilled in 1908-09.

There is a legendary quality about most big strikes, and the story of *Old Glory* is a classic of its genre. It has the common themes of almost never getting started and of being stopped before the big pay was struck. When Frosty Martin arrived at the Bow Island site, the derrick was built and the pipe was on the ground ready to go. But, before they could start drilling, Eugene Coste announced that the rig was on the wrong site, not even on CPR land, and would have to be moved. Martin argued against this. Perhaps he had a superstition about dismantling a prepared site. Martin's account of it contained the statement: "I was able to reason with him (Coste), due to the fact we had all our equipment ready to go and our camp established, that it wouldn't take long to drill the well down to Medicine Hat sand. With plenty of misgivings, he reluctantly agreed."

Finally Martin and Phillips had the well underway. A common practice among these old-time drillers was to establish a "bank-roll", meaning they would report their progress to head office as being considerably less than it actually was. Then, if they ran into trouble, they would use some of that bank-roll while the problem was solved. According to Martin's agreement with Coste, *Old Glory* was to go down to Medicine Hat sand which they expected to hit around 1100′. In fact, Martin and Phillips hit this sand layer and found it unproductive when their reports back to Coste in Winnipeg were showing only 900′ of progress. Martin decided to use his bankroll to go deeper, hoping to hit Dakota sandstone. At 1700′, the well ran into trouble and the crew had to fish for tools. To use Martin's expression, he "reached the fishing job with (his) bankroll" and "was ordered by wire to abandon." That is, his reported progress caught up to his real progress, he had to admit to a lack of gas in the Medicine Hat layer, and Eugene Coste gave orders to stop drilling.

But Martin did not stop. According to his version of the story he

> waited a day or two and wrote a lot of alibis instead of wiring, that way gaining a few more days. After two or three more wires to abandon, we finally got through the fishing job . . . A few days later, we were down to 1909′. We had run into Dakota sandstone and the well began to produce eight million feet.

The entrepreneur and drilling crew at **Old Glory**: (l. to r.) W. R. "Frosty" Martin, H. Lloyd, Eugene Coste, J. Green and A. P. "Tiny" Phillips.

Tiny Phillips recalled that *Old Glory* came in on the daylight tour:

> It was spitting sand out of the hole after we drilled a few feet into the
> Dakota formation. There was a great jubilation that day for this was the
> first big producer in the Province of Alberta.

Thanks to this curious, almost formal ritual of deceit, and to the
amazing confidence of the Martin-Phillips drilling team, Eugene Coste
had the cornerstone of his Alberta distribution empire. Many steps remained to be taken, however, and Archibald Dingman for one was not
ready to concede.

Dingman had started a second well after his Sarcee Reserve failure on
the James Walker Estate near Calgary, in July of 1908. Problems of both the
financial and geological kind hampered his progress and, by the spring of
1909, after Old Glory had already been completed and its success pub-
licized, the Walker well was down only 1600' in slow going.

Dingman needed more money. He tried the City of Calgary first but
the rate-payers voted down giving him assistance. Then he went to the CPR
and, surprisingly — certainly to Eugene Coste's surprise — the CPR
kicked in $5000 to be paid in $1000 installments, payable on completion
of each 240' of drilling.

At 2900', the Walker well came in with a reported flow of between
half a million and a million cubic feet a day. Some at the CPR felt that the
remaining $4000 in the agreement with Dingman should be handed over
immediately. Others, including Eugene Coste, felt it should not be paid at
all. Before a decision was made on this, the CPR thought it should have its
own valuation of Dingman's well. Eugene Coste was given the job and he
handed it over to Frosty Martin. When Martin arrived, Pitot tube in hand,
to test the well, Dingman would not let him anywhere near it — the first
real sign of how much bad blood existed between Dingman and Coste.
Martin apparently snuck in later when Dingman was not around and tested
the well at 360,000 cubic feet a day, considerably less than what was being
reported.

At issue here was nothing less than the exclusive right to serve
Calgary with natural gas. Whoever succeeded in getting that right would
likely become a rich man. As rivals for the prize, Archibald Dingman and
Eugene Coste were not overly fond of one another. The CPR, meanwhile,
had its feet and money in both camps, a position that annoyed Coste no
end.

While Coste did his lobbying mostly in boardrooms, emphasizing
the lower than reported flow at the Walker well and predicting that the
reservoir was thin, small and of poor quality, Dingman used more public

means: the press and the age-old but always inspiring symbol of the natural gas flare.

In the summer of 1909, Dingman lured a reporter out to the Walker well. When later the reporter sat down to write about the experience, he described the evening this way:

> The city loomed black against a gorgeous mixture of cerise, gold, maroon and scarlet sky; the green fields stretched soothingly around and the mosquitoes softly insinuated.

(Dingman had indeed done a masterful job of scene-setting if he was able to limit the mosquitoes' activity to soft insinuation.)

> We had fed sumptuously of real cream, raspberries and cake served by a real Chinaman. We felt at peace with the world.

With the reporter lulled into this state of belly-full contentment, Archibald Dingman turned on the gas!

> The white sheet of gas flame sprang, quivered and leaped. From a soft muttering sound it turned to a deafening roar as the great flame sprang sixty feet in the air and struggled to get higher. A withering blast of heat swept out from the flame, forcing all living things back to the safety of a hundred feet distance.

Gas from A. W. Dingman's Walker Well lit this flare at the Calgary Brewing and Malting Company just before the gas was tied into the brewery's power plant; April 11, 1910.

After all that, Archibald Dingman told the reporter that his supply of gas was inexhaustible and the reporter believed him. In fact, the reporter said so twice in the remainder of the article.

Dingman was no fool. He knew that he had nothing as yet to compare with Coste's Bow Island reserves. He tried deepening the Walker well and when that did not improve the flow he moved on quickly to the Gleichen district to try a series of wells there.

Coste was having his own problems. He believed absolutely that he could build a pipeline 170 miles from Bow Island to Calgary and operate it profitably and successfully. But the CPR was not with him. The CPR board of directors did not believe, and could not be convinced, that gas could be transported over that distance. Finally, through a complicated set of agreements, Coste formed his own company, the Prairie Fuel Gas Company, and took over the CPR's producing wells.

To raise money for the Prairie Fuel Gas Company and for his pipeline, Coste took a trip to England. If anything, his luck with English investors was worse than his luck with the CPR. The problem, or so his English underwriters told him, was his company's name. The average English investor had no knowledge of either prairies or fuel gas and was not about to part with pounds sterling to invest in what he did not understand.

One can almost sense Coste's frustration in the bombastic title he came up with to remedy the problem. "If the so and so's can't figure out Prairie Fuel Gas Company," he seemed to be saying, "we'll give them the Canadian Western Natural Gas, Light, Heat and Power Company." Long and cumbersome as the new name was, it sold debentures. Soon Coste had all the backing he needed.

Back in Calgary, Pat Burns, a rancher and meat packing entrepreneur who had acquired Morris' artificial gas franchise for the city, agreed to deal that franchise to Eugene Coste. At that point, Archibald Dingman knew he was licked. His exploration wells at Gleichen had met with little success and he had little choice now but to follow Burns' lead and sell his Calgary gas franchise to Coste as well. With the gas, money and franchises in place, Coste was ready to bring his Bow Island gas to Calgary.

A PIPE SIXTEEN INCHES BY ONE HUNDRED AND SEVENTY MILES

Eugene Coste's 170 mile Bow Island to Calgary pipeline was one of the greatest industrial exploits of its time. Construction of the sixteen-inch mainline began on April 22, 1912, with two companies, T. J. Driscoll and J. G. Corcoran, starting from opposite ends. Steam tractors and horse teams towed wooden-wheeled wagons full of pipe from the railway sidings to the pipeline right-of-way. Steam driven trenching machines twice the height of a man carved the ditch, while the rest of the work — the lowering and coupling of the lengths of pipe — was done by hand.

Horse, steam and manpower combined to put the Bow Island to Calgary natural gas pipeline into the ground in 1912. Horse teams (above) hauled the pipe to the right-of-way; an elaborate steam-driven trencher (below) dug the hole.

The pipeline plan included tying in the towns of Lethbridge, Nanton and Okotoks by ten-inch lines off the main, but Lethbridge's cooperation in the scheme was by no means a sure thing. Lethbridge, a coal town situated on a vast supply of the stuff, had a natural predilection for fuelling with its own product. Coste argued that natural gas was still cheaper than Lethbridge coal, but, as writer Ed Gould has pointed out, the miners living in north Lethbridge were getting a discount on coal that brought it back down below the price of gas. With Coste's pipeline fast approaching, the citizens of Lethbridge had yet to put the matter to a vote.

Coste could see that logical argument was failing him — so he resorted to showmanship. Arriving at the Old Man River, eight miles north of Lethbridge, he invited the townspeople out to witness a flare-lighting ceremony. The sight of fire, a gigantic plume of it, leaping from the standpipe worked its ancient magic once again; three days later the ratepayers of Lethbridge voted to let the gas come in.

On July 17, 1912, another flare-lighting ceremony took place, this time in Calgary. The newspapers described the event as an unparalleled success, but eye-witness accounts hint at less than perfect execution. In the afternoon, an attempt to build extra pressure in the line caused a blowout in a slough near DeWinton. Fast work by the repair crew averted disaster and the line was pressured and ready in time for the ten o'clock show (at night, for maximum drama). Most estimates put the crowd that gathered for the flare-lighting at around 12,000, but the *Calgary News Telegram* one-upped its competitors with an estimate of 15,000. According to the *Telegram*, Scotchman's Hill took on the appearance of a vast ant hill.

Whitey Foster was manning the valve and "punctually at five to ten", Eugene Coste gave him the signal to turn on. P. D. Mellon, once a vice-president of Canadian Western, was there and related that Whitey "turned it on plenty, because coming out of the standpipe, there was first a tremendous amount of dust, then stones and great big boulders, two or three pairs of overalls, pieces of skids . . . almost everything came out."

Mrs. Coste had been delegated to light the flare with Roman candles, but was off the mark with the first few. The next couple were in the right place but the force of the gas blew them out. At last, with a blinding flash and a gigantic report, the flare caught.

The mighty sight and sound almost panicked the crowd. Coste quickly signalled Whitey to turn the flare down, but Whitey was so caught up in the exuberance of the moment he misunderstood and cranked the valve open another turn. With the flare pumping and roaring, the ground trembling, the crowd did panic, crashing into one another in the mostly futile attempt to escape. Eventually, the hilltop around the standpipe was

P. D. Mellon, driving Canadian Western's first company vehicle in 1912.

clear. From a more respectful distance, the crowd watched the rest of the show.

After such a spectacle, no one in the city could have reasonably been unaware of Calgary's entrance into the age of natural gas. As the *Herald* put it: "The natural product has supplanted the artificial." And no matter how humbly he behaved, the hero of the hour was Eugene Coste.

On the night of July 17, 1912, Calgarians watched a ceremonial flare-lighting on Scotchman's Hill.

EUGENE MARIUS COSTE

It is always interesting to locate a moment in history when the fate of a region was suddenly changed. In the history of Canada's natural gas industry, one such moment occurred when Napoleon Coste of Marseilles, France, jumped ship at Amherstburg, Ontario. Without that moment, gas entrepreneur Eugene Coste would not have been born a Canadian in Essex County in 1859, and probably would not have found gas in Essex County in 1889. After his years of study at the Académie de Paris, the École Polytechnique in Paris and l'École Nationale Supérieure des Mines de Paris, Coste made his first commercial gas find only a few miles from his Canadian birthplace.

In an industry in which the gift of being able to locate the product is rare, Coste was adept at both finding gas *and* building the apparatus necessary to market it. He was at home in the boardrooms of Canada's most powerful companies and on the well sites where his wealth originated.

Driller Tiny Phillips, who worked for Coste in the early years, described him as having the "common touch". "He (Coste) would pay an inspection visit to a drill crew," Phillips said, "and if an overnight stay was required and no cots were available, he would roll up in a blanket on the floor of the tent." Phillips and his partner Frosty Martin found out about Coste's temper and honesty the first time they hired on with him to drill a well. It was in Ontario and, when Coste came to look at their cable tool rig, he declared it unfit to drill the hole he needed. Phillips and Martin came back at him hotly, arguing that this rig was what made their livings for them and had been doing for some time. Right then, Coste made his deal with them; he admired their spirit.

Coste had another touch that working men like in a boss and that was the *golden* one. According to Tiny Phillips, "every project he touched made money." It's hard to argue with that assessment given that Coste originated both Canadian Western Natural Gas and its sister company Northwestern Utilities, and that one of his companies was part of the nucleus around which Union Gas of Canada was formed.

Eugene Coste.

The Coste story, like many a good story, ends in a mystery. In 1921, Coste suddenly gave up his seat on Canadian Western's board of directors, sold his interest in the company and moved back East. John Schmidt, from whose research paper many of the above facts are taken, says that the Costes left "for a reason that remains conveniently forgotten by those Calgarians who should know."

THE DINGMAN BOOM

Somewhere in the crowd the night the flare was lit in Calgary with Bow Island gas, A. W. Dingman was probably standing — and probably feeling somewhat bitter about the way things had turned out. A bit more luck and it could have been he rather than Coste receiving the cheers of the crowd and the kudos of the press the next day. But A. W. Dingman was not the kind of man to brood long about failure. In his one known attempt at poetry, he shows himself to be an early advocate of the power of positive thinking:

> *If you think you'll lose you're lost*
> *For out in the world you find*
> *Success begins with a fellow's will*
> *It's all in the state of the mind.*

Dingman quickly turned his back on the natural gas business and set about looking for oil in a place that would soon be known to the world as Turner Valley.

A. W. Dingman with his family in Ontario in the 1890's. Before coming West, he was involved in several ventures including the manufacture of soap.

A. W. Dingman got involved with Turner Valley through William Stewart Herron, a former oilman and hardrock miner from Ontario who had lately taken up ranching near Okotoks. One day while hauling coal, Herron noticed a gas seep along the banks of the Sheep River. By placing a barrel over the seep, he was able to catch a sample which he sent to the University of California for analysis.

The seep had been noticed once before, in the late 1880's, by Negro cowboy John Ware. Ware had also had the gas analysed by a Calgary doctor who wrote it off as a worthless accumulation of coal gas.

Herron's analysis was more promising. It showed that the gas was *wet*; that is, contained some hydrocarbons heavier than methane. It was not coal gas or marsh gas at all, but the kind of gas found in a reservoir, with or without oil. Herron sank everything he had into the purchase of surface and mineral rights in the valley then went looking for partners.

Herron approached both A. W. Dingman and Eugene Coste, but neither of them was very interested in a well on the Sheep River. Coste had his Bow Island field and pipeline to worry about and, in any case, did not believe that gas could accumulate so close to the foothills. Dingman was in the process of severing relations with the Calgary Natural Gas Company and would not take on anything new until that break was complete.

Herron did not give up. A while later he invited A. W. Dingman and driller William Elder out for a demonstration of his find. Arriving at the gas seeps, Herron struck a match to one of them and, pulling out a pan, fried eggs for his company over the blue flame. The gimmick worked. Before long a new company, Calgary Petroleum Products, was formed for the wildcat exploration of Herron's Sheep River leases.

From the moment Calgary Petroleum Products #1 spudded in January of 1913, there was wild speculation about it. As the drillers made hole, the newspapers made report after premature report of the well's fabulous success. Small shows of natural gas and condensate, enough to fuel the boilers, had the *Calgary News Telegram* of July 13, 1913, reporting that local oil men were "generally agreed that oil will be struck inside 30 days."

By October 9, 1913, the *Calgary Herald* was announcing that "a first class quality of oil has been struck . . . . at 1562' and although no gusher has been brought in, samples are now in the city." On November 25, 1913, A. W. Dingman wrote a letter back to the *Herald* protesting the exaggerated accounts.

All in all, the city was well primed when Calgary Petroleum Products #1 really did blow in on May 14, 1914. The well produced four million cubic feet of gas a day, saturated with a pale light-gravity oil. In Calgary, a profusion of companies came into being overnight. People lined up every-

The Dingman wet gas strike at Turner Valley in 1914 created a stock buying frenzy in the young city of Calgary.

where to buy the garish, important-looking share certificates. The take was so great that cash registers could not hold it all. Clothes hampers were put to work to catch the excess flow of funds.

Satirist, Bob Edwards had a few things to say about all this in his *Calgary Eye Opener*. Before the strike, he had written: "The trouble with this oil situation at this formulative stage is that you are never quite sure whether the man you meet on the street is a multi-millionaire or just an ordinary, common millionaire." After the Dingman strike, in the May 23, 1914 issue of the *Eye Opener,* Edwards drew his readers' attention to "the beautiful raft of oil ads in this issue."

> Of one thing you can be sure, every oil ad you see in this paper is that of a good sound company. The men behind each company advertised here are responsible Calgary businessmen, well known to everybody. No wildcatters are allowed to wander in these columns.

It was Edwards' way of warning the unwary, and perhaps of apologizing for making advertising money off the general fraud. But the irony was lost on a populace almost desperate to be bilked. People practically begged to be sold the bogus shares and, after a very short while, most had become nothing more than expensive wallpaper.

Some legitimate companies did drill legitimate wells into the Dingman horizon, but the results were never spectacular enough to outweigh the negative impact of so many paper companies disappearing into the night. The outbreak of World War One also had a dampening effect. During the War, the natural gasoline or *naphtha* at Turner Valley was stripped from the flow in wellhead separators and rudimentary absorption plants (of which we will hear more later). As for the natural gas, some of it was tapped to run boilers or to fuel the drilling of more wells, while the majority went to flare. This continued until a drastic loss in pressure in the Bow Island field brought Canadian Western to Turner Valley in search of gas to bolster the supply to Calgary. A pipeline was built from the Valley to connect with the Canadian Western mainline at Okotoks. On December 31, 1921, Turner Valley gas was sent to Calgary for the first time.

EDMONTON'S GAS DILEMMA

Rivalry between towns is a feature of most frontiers. Each town senses that it could become a major centre, or, given a few unlucky circumstances, a ghost town. The rivalry between Calgary and Edmonton was particularly intense and acquired a bitter edge in 1905 when Alberta became a province. Edmonton was not only named capital city of Alberta, but was given the province's only university as well. One of the delights of Calgary's 1912 acquisition of natural gas was knowing that Edmonton did not have gas and was not apt to get any in the near future.

Initially, Edmonton was able to pretend some indifference to this fate because, like Lethbridge, it was built atop a goodly supply of coal. Edmonton businessmen were worried enough, though, to create an Industrial Development Association dedicated to supplying Edmonton with gas. The Association first considered Pelican Rapids, far to the north on the Athabasca River. A gas well had been drilled there in the 1890's by the Geological Survey of Canada, and had been burning out of control ever since (a perpetual fire aided into existence by man). For Edmonton's purposes, Pelican Rapids was finally judged to be too far away across too rugged a terrain.

Another problem for the Association, beyond a point of supply, was the mood of the Edmonton rate-payers. For years, whenever they were polled as to their interest in natural gas, they responded favourably. But, when any *specific* scheme was put to them for finding and delivering that gas, they promptly voted it down. So perplexing was the problem that the city hired a Glaswegian gas expert, James Brodie, to come and make a study of it. After extensively looking into the matter, Brodie told the city that, yes, its people *did* favour gas in theory, but would not vote for it in fact. Amen. Brodie drew his pay and went home.

The Industrial Development Association's faith in consultants may have been shaken, but evidently was not toppled for they turned around in 1914 and invited two English ones, Clapp and Huntley, to come to Edmonton and help the city choose an area where a supply of gas might be found. Clapp and Huntley recommended the drilling of a well near the village of Viking, southeast of Edmonton about eighty miles.

The Viking well was a great success, blowing in at over nine million cubic feet a day. Ed Gould has unearthed the fact that the occasion's Paul Revere was driller C. M. Flickinger. By motorcycle and "at lightning speed", Flickinger brought the good news to Edmonton.

In the excitement that followed, the Edmonton voters finally approved the granting of a gas franchise to the Northern Alberta Natural Gas Development Company, among whose prominent investors were Eugene Coste and future Prime Minister R. B. Bennett. Plans were rapidly made for developing the Viking field and piping its gas to Edmonton. But any Edmontonian possessed of the notion that he would soon be burning natural gas in his home was many years mistaken. For a variety of complicated reasons, having to do with World War One and the escalating price of steel, the company found it more profitable to resell its pipe than to put it in the ground. It was 1923 before a new company, Northwestern Utilities, took over the Viking field assets and finally installed the seventy-eight mile pipeline to Edmonton.

Among those who contributed to the rapid completion of the Viking-Edmonton pipeline was a man named Guy S. Connors who arrived from Idaho with a team of horses just in time to be hired. It was close to the

With promotions like this one in 1923, Northwestern Utilities finally sold Edmontonians on the idea of natural gas.

beginning of an incredible career in that business that would earn Connors the title *Dean of Pipeliners*. When Guy Connors finally retired from the Williams Bros. Corporation in Tulsa over forty years later, he had built more miles of pipeline world-wide than any other pipeliner.

By 1923, Edmonton had gas, Calgary had gas, Lethbridge had gas, Medicine Hat had gas; and an ever increasing number of smaller Alberta communities had gas as well. Demand and supply were fairly comfortably in balance. Meanwhile in Eastern Canada, where seemingly *inexhaustible* fields had declined alarmingly, there was a deep-rooted fear that natural gas was not long for this world. The April 1, 1921, *Canadian Gas Journal* asked the question: "If natural gas is giving out, as generally believed, what is the fuel of the future?" Professor D. J. Demorest of Ohio State University was urging cities to accept the inevitable and prepare for a return to artificial gas made from coal.

Soon, in Turner Valley, there were to be events that would shake such a certainty. An almost crazy situation was about to develop in which one end of the country carefully hoarded its declining reserves while the other blew natural gas sky high because it had nowhere to sell it. An era of new discovery and tremendous waste was at hand.

The Northwestern Utilities pipeline was put beneath Edmonton's McDougall Avenue in late summer, 1923.

GAS AT LLOYDMINSTER

In 1934, the town of Lloydminster, which sits directly on the Saskatchewan-Alberta border, and is incorporated in both provinces, became the first community in Saskatchewan to achieve a supply of natural gas. In a 1955 issue of the *Western Oil Examiner*, Harold Spaetgens of Husky Oil took the history of natural gas at Lloydminster even farther back than that, tracing it to a water well on the William Garton farm south of Lloydminster which turned itself into a gas well in 1926. Local businessmen and farmers kept up an obstinate search for oil and gas in the area right into the Depression years. They formed the Lloydminster Gas Company in 1933 and drilled a well on a lease filed by O. C. Yates that year. The site of the well was allegedly the same as that where the first Barr Colonist tent was pitched in 1903. Another symptom of the Depression, the drilling crew which made the Lloydminster #1 hole took company stock in lieu of wages.

That turned out to be a fair deal when the well hit gas of sufficient pressure to blow the bailer out of the bottom of the 1974' well and through a fourteen-inch timber at the top of the derrick. The first test showed a flow of over sixteen million cubic feet of gas per day. In May of 1934, the company obtained a franchise to supply the town of Lloydminster with gas. It went on stream in September of that year, serving 183 customers.

The Barr Colonists themselves incorporated The Colony Oil and Gas Company in 1935 under the leadership of R. L. Shaw. Their #1 well came in on the outskirts of town at a magnificent 42.75 million cubic feet of gas per day. For a time, it enjoyed the status of largest natural gas well in the British Empire. A black, heavy crude oil was later found below the gas in the Colony sandstone.

Royalite's 1921 compressor station and absorption plant in Turner Valley.

THE ORIGINS OF GAS PROCESSING: OIL ABSORPTION AND SCRUBBING WITH SODA ASH

2

If you define gas processing as extraction of by-products from a natural gas stream, Canadian processing got its start in Turner Valley in 1914. If you define it as purification for consumer use, the first step was the Port Alma, Ontario, purification plant built in 1924.

In world terms, the processing of natural gas may have begun in the United States in 1903 in an attempt to prevent liquids carried in a small natural gas pipeline from hanging up in the low spots and cutting off the flow. According to Gibbs and Vervalin in a 1959 *Petroleum Refiner* article, this problem at a small Sisterville, West Virginia, operation caused the owners to experiment and find that the liquids would condense out of the gas if the gas was cooled. Their *plant* for this purpose consisted of a system of coils in an old boiler full of water.

In 1905, William Mayburg, a retired man of the cloth from New York, used a Bessemer engine to compress a *wet* natural gas* stream and thus invented the compression method of getting the gas to surrender its liquids.

As the *horseless carriage* gained popularity, a new reason came into existence for processing the gas for liquids. Formerly a nuisance which had to be burned, the extracted liquid, or *casinghead gasoline*, was blended with heavier hydrocarbons to make a usable automobile fuel. Increases in the popularity of autos continued to translate into greater value for casinghead gasoline until, finally, it eclipsed in price the natural gas from which it was chilled or squeezed.

As for a definition of natural or casinghead gasoline, it was anything that would stay in a tank car or barrel long enough to be shipped and burned. Specifications had it none. Some refiners balked at taking this undependable substance, but the more the supply of fuel fell behind demand, the more volatile the mixtures the market was willing to accept.

---

* *Wet* and *dry* are the words the industry uses to describe natural gas containing or not containing quantities of liquid hydrocarbons.

In the United States, this led to tragic consequences: a tank car explosion in Ardmore, Oklahoma, in 1915, that killed 43 and injured 500. The first association of gas processors in the United States came together in an attempt to establish specifications for casinghead gasoline and to erase the stigma that marked producers of that commodity after the Ardmore incident.

This was the state of the processing industry when Dingman #1 blew in at Turner Valley, southwest of Calgary, Alberta, in 1914. Natural gas streamed from the well at four million cubic feet per day, dripping with casinghead gasoline, or *naphtha*.* According to a *Calgary Herald* report, the directors of Calgary Petroleum Products, the company behind the find, raced to Turner Valley in their cars and, upon arrival, two of them emptied their gas tanks and filled up with "oil directly from the well". More likely, they filled up with naphtha from a make-shift separator. The article went on to say that the directors "returned to the city, a distance of 41 miles,

A. W. Dingman stands with his hand on a pipe delivering naphtha from Dingman #1. In the crowd of onlookers directly behind Dingman are two more distinguished oil and gas explorers: W. S. Herron (on the far left) and R. A. Brown Sr. (fifth from the left with a white overcoat over his arm).

*These two terms were often used interchangeably, but in the pioneer period of United States processing, "naphtha" described the heavier, non-volatile ends found in natural gasoline.

finding to their amazement that the power generated was at least 25% greater than that obtained from the gasoline on sale in the city."

To enhance naphtha recovery, Calgary Petroleum Products brought in a compressor. Although it was the first compressor used in Canada for the purpose of recovering natural gasoline, it does not represent a particularly dramatic milestone in that literally hundreds of such compressor plants already operated in the U.S. More amazing is the fact that Calgary Petroleum Products supplemented the compression process with an absorption plant, also built in 1914. This plant was a Canadian debut and had few predecessors anywhere in the world. The patent owner, Hope Natural Gas, a Standard Oil Co. (New Jersey) subsidiary, built the first absorption plant at Hastings, West Virginia, only one year earlier in 1913.

The Calgary Petroleum Products absorption plant was built by an American named Ed Fryer. It operated off and on from 1914 to 1920. The $70,000 plant* represented such a large investment for the small company that it kept C.P.P. constantly on the edge of bankruptcy. The directors of the company wanted to get financial help from Britain, and while they sought support in that direction, they had to fend off the overtures of Imperial Oil.

Imperial was one of the oldest oil companies on the continent. It had been created in 1880 in southern Ontario, with head offices in London, Ontario. By 1893, it was producing and refining oil, had twenty-three branch offices across Canada and sported the slogan *Everywhere in Canada*. By 1899, it was still everywhere in Canada, but was owned in the United States. John D. Rockefeller had translated a minority interest into control by consolidating all the Standard Oil affiliates in Canada under the Imperial Oil banner. Imperial started exploring Western Canada in 1914 and, before the end of the decade, it had spread its field parties from the Arctic to the 49th Parallel with notable discoveries in the Peace River country and at remote, northerly Norman Wells. Imperial expressed its interest in Turner Valley by purchasing a minority interest in Calgary Petroleum Products and by urging the other shareholders to let Imperial take over majority control. In the early years, the shareholders resisted.

Tommy Grisdale, who worked at the Ford garage in Okotoks before starting a long career at the Turner Valley gas plant, remembered one form of stock promotion used by Calgary Petroleum Products' Archibald Dingman. Tommy often had the job of picking up Mr. Dingman and a party of guests at the Okotoks train station and driving them down to the absorp-

---

*The cost seems high by the standards of the day. The cost of a compression plant in the U.S. in 1922 was around $20,000. Absorption plants cost less.

tion plant at Dingman #1. The party came equipped with picnic hampers and, after a feast on the banks of the Sheep River, Dingman would lead a procession through his absorption plant, just in case anyone was interested in investing.

Then, on October 20, 1921, disaster struck. One of the two CPR locomotive compressors at Dingman's plant blew up and started a fire that destroyed the absorption plant and Calgary Petroleum Products with it. The company could not begin to sustain the $70 thousand loss and was forced to welcome Imperial refinancing. Out of the ashes of the absorption plant rose a brand new company, Royalite Oil Company Ltd., a wholly-owned subsidiary of Imperial Oil.

Royalite was a busy company during its first year of existence. In one of his first acts as Royalite manager, John H. Macleod hired Sam G. Coultis away from the Alberta Southern Refining Company to be Royalite's first field employee, in charge of natural gas and naphtha production. Coultis, in turn, hired another Alberta Southern employee, John Gallagher, to assist him. Gallagher, a native of County Mayo, Ireland, was an expert in the valuable art of firing steam boilers. Together, they proceeded to rebuild the destroyed absorption plant. When interviewed for this book "Jack" Gallagher had just turned ninety-five. He remembered both the new absorption plant and the old one clearly. The first absorption plant had a

Jack Gallagher at his home in Black Diamond shortly after his ninety-fifth birthday.

horizontal absorber, a long pipe through which the raw gas was fed. "Every couple of feet" along the pipe were lean oil sprays. As the oil spray hit the gas, the gas liquids would be partially absorbed. The rich oil was then heated by steam and fed to a still where it was stripped of its natural gasoline and fed back to the sprays. The 1921 absorption plant, designed by Sam Coultis, represented a step up in technology in that absorption oil was sprayed into the gas in both horizontal and vertical absorbers.

Still in his first year of employment with Royalite, Sam Coultis received orders to build a compressor station. In 1921, Royalite signed an agreement with Canadian Western Natural Gas that would see Turner Valley gas go to Calgary to make up for declining production in the Bow Island field. Royalite built the compressor station and supplied the gas (pressure not to exceed 100 pounds). Canadian Western was responsible for building a pipeline, not less than six inches in diameter, from the absorption plant to the sixteen inch mainline near Okotoks, and a measuring station "not further than one mile from Royalite's absorption plant."

The order to build the compressor plant came in November of 1921 and it had to be completed by December 31, the day the agreement with Canadian Western came into effect. The first two months of winter were unusually cold that year and Sam Coultis remembered pouring the foundations for the compressor plant on a -36 degree F day. Six 80-horsepower Clark gas engines supplied power to the compressors. In spite of the weather, Royalite met the deadline and turned gas from the Royalite #1, 2 and 3 wells (formerly Dingman #1, 2 and 3) into the line on New Year's Eve.

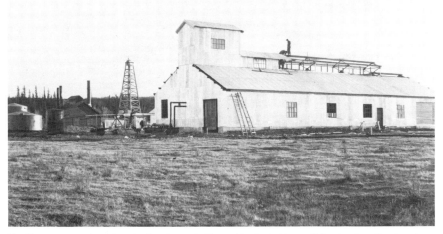

The first gas processing plant in Canada was built on this site in Turner Valley by Canadian Petroleum Products in 1914. In the above photo, the plant is being re-built by Royalite Oil Company Ltd. in 1921.

SKUNK OIL

For those who lived in Turner Valley and owned cars, going to the service station was regarded as a needless extravagance. The far more common practice was to fill up with naphtha at your local well. Needless to say, the gasoline was not to any specification and it could be so volatile it would turn to vapour in the engine carburetor causing sputters, coughs and the crowning glory: vapour lock. Talking to Turner Valley old-timers, the usual description for this casinghead gasoline is that is was "wild stuff". John Gallagher recalled that you could lose half a barrel to atmosphere just by trying to measure it with a stick.

Providing you could keep it in your tank long enough to burn it, casinghead gasoline was very cheap, a factor that accounts for its popularity especially in the Hungry Thirties. In fact, for some who weren't too particular, natural gasoline was free. Tommy Grisdale recalls an occasion when a roughneck at the South End was busily filling up his car with free naphtha when who should happen along but Sam Coultis, the Royalite field superintendent. The roughneck thought he would outwit Sam by quickly shifting round and pouring the naphtha into his radiator. As Sam walked by, he said quietly, "Son, I think you're pouring it in the wrong end."

Calgary gas stations of the 1930's often had a buyer-beware sign that read "Turner Valley gas".

Because of its hydrogen sulphide and mercaptans* content, Turner Valley gasoline acquired another nickname: *skunk oil*. Roy Flieger of the Valley remembered that when you drove in at a Calgary filling station, the pump jockey would pull off your gas cap and say: "Whew! Turner Valley, eh?"

*Mercaptans are sulphur compounds which have a strong, unpleasant odour.

ROYALITE #4

Turner Valley was by no means booming as the calendar flipped over from 1921 to 1922. The excitement that followed the Dingman strike of 1914 had cooled long ago and a post-war economic recession gripped the country. Royalite, however, with its commitment to Canadian Western, went ahead with exploration. In September of 1922, it began drilling Royalite #4 in Turner Valley, at a location recommended by Royalite's first geologist, George Simmons. The drilling superintendent was Bill Applegate.

A year later, at 2890', the #4 well struck a large flow of gas and flowed 7 million cubic feet a day from the Lower Cretaceous sands. Royalite must have been short of gas for its pipeline agreement because it promptly tied #4's production into the Calgary line. But, by the following spring of 1924, production from the new well had declined so badly that Royalite decided to deepen it.

At 3450', the bit chewed into Paleozoic limestone and the glimmers of optimism for #4 died. Everywhere else in Alberta the limestone had proven dry. Royalite management wanted to abandon, but Sam Coultis spoke out against it. Who else, he argued, was going to test the limestone interval at Turner Valley if Royalite didn't?

The driller put the well down another 280 fruitless feet before orders again came to stop. This time the driller on tour decided they might as well keep going until the shift finished at least. On that day, October 14, 1924, a rush of gas greeted the bit at the 3470' mark. The downhole tools blew upward and tangled with the cable. Even with that much junk in the hole, the well flowed 21 million cubic feet and 600 barrels of naphtha a day.

On October 18, 1924, Royalite tried to close #4. The crew tightened down the valve and the gauge showed a rise in pressure of 100 pounds per minute. After fifteen minutes, the casing started to rise. It grew out of the ground all the way to the crown block and then began to sag. Downhole, at 1194', the six and eight-inch casings had parted company.

The well was out of control again and, to make matters worse, a stone blew out of the hole, hit the rig with a spark that set the well on fire. A pair of wild well experts were finally summoned from Oklahoma and they extinguished the blaze by first blasting out the flame with dynamite, then dousing the area with steam from a battery of boilers.

This event had a dramatic and long-lasting effect on all those who watched or heard about the extraordinary power of Royalite #4. It accounted for much of the waste of natural gas for which Turner Valley is still famous. When asked why they would not close their wells, operators would often cite the explosive beginnings at #4. They simply didn't believe that wells could be closed safely against that kind of pressure.

The discovery of wet gas at Turner Valley, in limestone of Devonian age, was an event of tremendous importance to Western Canada. In a sense, it was like the discovery of a new continent suitable for colonization. Suddenly, a vast new territory existed for oil and gas men to move into with their rigs — and what discoveries they would make along that new horizon!

THE FIRST SCRUBBING PLANTS: PORT ALMA AND TURNER VALLEY

The fly in the ointment flowing from Royalite #4 was hydrogen sulphide (H_2S), a gas several times more poisonous than carbon monoxide. The shallower Dingman wells had been *sweet* but the deeper #4 well had penetrated the Mississippian limestone and was *sour*.* At 640 grains of hydrogen sulphide per one hundred cubic feet of gas, the H_2S content could not be ignored. People in the gas industry did not understand H_2S as completely as we do today, but they did know from observed accidents that it was nothing to fool with. Canadian Western told Royalite that before it could market the new gas, the rotten egg smell of H_2S would have to go.

In setting out to conquer the problem, Royalite could look to one important Canadian precedent. In southern Ontario, gas from the Tilbury field also contained H_2S — in tiny but obnoxious quantities. As early as 1913, consumers of Tilbury gas had bitterly complained about it. As of the early '20's, the only gas purification technique in existence was that discovered by the Koppers Co. of Pittsburgh for cleaning up coal gas. Their process (known as the Seaboard Process) was widely used by manufactured gas companies, but had never been attempted with natural gas. The Union Gas Company of Toronto decided to give the Koppers process a try on the H_2S in Tilbury, Ontario, gas. By constructing the successful purification plant at Port Alma, Ontario, in 1924, Union Gas established itself as the first company to use the Koppers or Seaboard Process on natural gas, also the first to purify gas at high pressure.

Just months later, Sam Coultis designed and built his gas "scrubbing" or sweetening plant in Turner Valley, employing the same Seaboard process to remove H_2S from the sour Royalite #4 gas. The plant consisted of a steel tower containing a grid of Redwood timbers. To the bottom of this tower he led a raw gas stream; to the top, an aqueous soda ash solution. As the two

---

* *Sweet* and *sour* are the industry's code words for hydrogen sulphide content of a gas mixture. "Sweet gas" doesn't contain any H_2S, whereas "sour gas" contains a significant amount of the compound.

Construction of the Turner Valley Royalite scrubbing plant in 1925.

streams contacted in the tower, the sodium carbonate and the H_2S in the gas combined in a simple, reversible chemical reaction.

$$(Na_2CO_3 + H_2S \rightleftharpoons NaHCO_3 + NaHS)$$

The sweetened gas went off overhead and the reacted solution was drawn off the bottom and fed to a reactivating tower where it passed downward counter to a current of air. This regenerated the soda ash solution and liberated the H_2S. Interviewed in his nineties, Sam Coultis was still a bit cagey when asked about the fate of the freed H_2S. "I've got to be careful there," he said. Then after a considerable pause, he fessed up: "Those tall smoke stacks that used to be there; they got a lot of it."

This was a definite problem with the Seaboard process. The strong current of air would kick the hydrogen sulphide up into the atmosphere, but, being heavier than air, it would not stay there. For people living in the Valley, H₂S became a fact of life. People who lived in the Valley in the early years claimed that the exposure to hydrogen sulphide made the people immune to medical anaesthesia. "In fact, it was impossible to knock some people out and the doctors admitted this themselves," said one old-time driller. "They said they give some of those fellows enough chloroform to kill them and yet they couldn't knock them out."*

More scrubbing units were added as the Calgary demand for gas increased: two more actifiers†, another stack and solution pumps. By 1928, the plant had a capacity of 60 million cubic feet of gas per day. In 1935, Royalite further modernized the plant, trading in the wooden internals of the scrubbing towers for steel bubble cap trays. This increased capacity to 75 million cubic feet per day.

Royalite finally laid the Seaboard process at Turner Valley to rest in 1951, and a year after that a sulphur plant was added to the sweetening plant which ended for good the practice of venting extracted H₂S into the Turner Valley atmosphere. Lest we overly malign the Turner Valley Royalite plant, it should be added that it held a reputation for incredible reliability. In 1954, the current plant superintendent Bud Pearson was able to say that Turner Valley Royalite had not failed in its delivery of gas to Canadian Western in twenty years.

The crew at the Royalite absorption, compression and scrubbing plant; ca. 1926.

---

*Modern evidence contradicts this. It is more likely that the more H₂S one is exposed to, the less one can tolerate.

†Today, the device in which gas and chemical solution are brought together is called an absorber or contactor.

SAMUEL G. COULTIS

So many of the pioneering ventures in the Canadian oil and gas industry begin with or contain the name Sam Coultis, he has almost become a legend, a Paul Bunyan. The difference is that Coultis did exist and did accomplish all the things ascribed to him.

Sam Coultis was born in Forest, Ontario, in 1887, and he died in Calgary, Alberta, in 1983. Considering the incredible length of his life, it's hard to believe that he came West because of delicate health, but so he claimed. After graduating from Ann Arbor, Michigan, as a chemical engineer, he found himself with a month-long racking cough. When a local physician met him on the main street of his home town and heard about his plan to move West, he couldn't understand why. "All right", Coultis said to the good doctor, "no doubt you studied bacteriology. Would you know of a better culture medium to grow bacteria on than my irriated lungs? In other words," he added, "I'm going to beat the bug!"

In Calgary, in 1913, Sam got a job as the city chemist, which involved health department work, police department work and materials testing for city construction. In an interview with Tom Kirkham, Coultis pronounced himself quite proud of "that old

Sam Coultis in 1944.

Centre Street Bridge". He'd tested the concrete and "turned down plenty of it". His work also involved giving expert evidence in court cases. In one of these he was asked to comment on the possible use of a mysterious powder found among the effects of an arrested ne'er-do-well. Betraying a knowledge of things beyond chemistry, Coultis testified that, given the powder had a mercury base, and given that a set of dice had also been found among the man's things, it was possible, just possible, that the man had been drilling pin holes in the dice and siphoning in the heavier powder to weight them.

Sam Coultis went to Turner Valley during the Dingman boom and applied his knowledge of chemistry to the building of an oil refinery for the Alberta Southern Refining Company. In George de Mille's excellent history OIL IN WESTERN CANADA, Coultis' refinery is described as the best one out there at the time. It produced gasoline, kerosene and two kinds of distillate and paid three dividends of 10% before it closed in 1926.

When Royalite sprang into being out of the ashes of Calgary Petroleum Products in 1921, it made Sam Coultis its first employee. Sam Coultis built Royalite's absorption plant, including the first vertical absorbers in Canada; he built a milestone compressor plant for boosting Turner Valley gas to Calgary; he built the second scrubbing (sweetening) plant in Canada in 1925 to take the hydrogen sulphide out of Royalite #4 gas. By his own account, he had worked in "drilling, production, pipelines and plants of all descriptions", pipelines being his favourite.

In 1938, Sam Coultis became president of Valley Pipe Line, a public utility gathering oil from the field batteries of all Turner Valley producers and transporting it to Calgary. In 1949, when Imperial sold Royalite they asked Coultis to move to Edmonton as vice-president and general manager of the Imperial Pipe Line Company. He started work on the Interprovincial pipeline system to Sarnia and also built a system of laterals gathering oil from the Leduc field. In 1942, he was president of the Association of Professional Engineers of Alberta.*

When he finally called it a day, Sam Coultis had forty-two years of oil and gas industry experience under his belt.

*This organization is now known as the Association of Professional Engineers, Geologists and Geophysicists of Alberta (APEGGA).

HELL'S HALF ACRE

In 1924, Royalite #4 touched off the second boom in Turner Valley. A number of companies began drilling the limestone reservoir Royalite had discovered, still in pursuit of the naphtha or natural gasoline the gas contained. This they sold for blending in automobile fuel. The gas itself was nothing to them but the means by which the naphtha was recovered. Royalite's exclusive contract with Canadian Western ensured that this attitude would not change. Unable to sell to Canadian Western, the only gas customer in the area, all the companies except Royalite saw themselves as having no option but to send the stripped gas to flare. In the summer season, even Royalite had more gas than Calgary could use and they also flared the excess.

Before constructing its sweetening plant, Royalite flared all its gas in a gully southeast of the #4 well, near a rock cut along the Sheep River. The

Hell's Half Acre.

other companies drilling in the area used the same gully for their flares and some wit whose name is lost to history dubbed the garden of flames *Hell's Half Acre*. Hell's Half Acre became Alberta legend. At its peak, it eliminated the need for street lighting in Calgary. Its light could be seen as a pink glow on the horizon as far away as Lethbridge and Pincher Creek. Locals read the newspaper by its night light while others went on midnight rabbit hunts. Wildlife came in close to the flares to feast off the unnatural lushness nurtured by the heat and light.

In the season of bird migration, ducks and geese which flew into the glow at night seemed to become mesmerized. They flew round and round the flares as if locked in by the light. Only when dawn came were the birds able to break the spell and continue on their way. Occasionally a duck would strike the cold air and suddenly plummet, its wings frozen. Tommy Grisdale remembers picking up these pathetic birds and taking them into the plant buildings. He would thaw them out, dry them off and turn them loose, apparently restored to health.

When the Depression struck, processions of jobless men came to the Valley, most looking for work, but some to live in the year round warmth of the flares. Those with jobs passed the hobos curled up on the warm dry ground when they went to work on winter mornings.

The Turner Valley boom of 1924 did not last long. The wells that followed Royalite #4 were not as productive and interest waned. The brokerage firm Solloway and Mills managed to whip up interest with clever stock promotions after 1927, and a big wet gas strike in 1929 by Home Oil in the northern part of the field opened things up again. The first three Home wells dripped with naphtha. Number one and number three were rated at 800 barrels a day. The find is often credited for softening the blow of the October, 1929, stock market crash. Turner Valley was hit hard by the Depression, but it did not totally die. Royalite in particular continued to drill throughout the *Hungry Thirties*.

A NEW GENERATION OF PROCESSING PLANTS

For a long time at Turner Valley, no one duplicated Calgary Petroleum Products' (then Royalite's) experiment with gas liquids extraction by oil absorption. In fact, Royalite itself closed the old absorption plant in 1927. To strip the naphtha, some companies used drips and Smith Separators while others had small compressors squeezing the liquids out of the gas. Absorption plants were well established in the United States, but no one in the Valley seemed to think his operation warranted such a big investment.

In 1933, Royalite changed that. The company built a modern plant, employing the lean oil absorption process to recover natural gasoline from the gas leaving the separator. The new plant operated on the same principle used in the 1914 and 1921 plants, but had more sophisticated equipment.

Charlie "High Pressure" Ward, a fast moving Oklahoman who earned his nickname by cranking up the pressure on a well so high the separator exploded, supervised the construction of the 1933 version of Turner Valley Royalite. True to his nickname, Ward's Turner Valley plant could indeed handle high pressure gas.

The wet gas entered the vertical absorption towers at the bottom. It was contacted in a series of steel cups or bubble caps with a stream of lean oil flowing in the opposite direction. A special lean oil was concocted for this purpose at Imperial's Calgary refinery. The improved contact in the absorption towers and the special oil resulted in a much higher percentage of natural gasoline recovery.

This absorption plant was successful, so successful it made other producers in the Valley wonder if they had not made a mistake by not going to absorption plants themselves. Suddenly, absorption plants were the order of the day. Royalite constructed a second one in the south end of the field (which the company later dismantled and moved in with the #1 plant at Turner Valley). In 1934, A. H. Mayland, a rancher, meatpacker and oilman, purchased a used absorption plant in the United States and had it installed near Hartell under the company name Gas and Oil Products Limited. (It was sometimes called the Mercury plant after one of the wells whose gas it processed.) In 1936, south of Hartell, British American Oil Ltd. built another absorption plant a mile east of Little New York (now known as Longview). This plant, also second-hand, came from Coutts,

B.A. Longview was built in 1936, one of three absorption plants in Canada — all located in Turner Valley.

Montana. David Evans and Morris Stevens worked on the plant's reconstruction at Longview, and George Lambert was the first superintendent.

An aura of mystique surrounded this new generation of processing plants, a product of their size, perhaps, and the fact that almost no one really understood how they worked. But no matter how sophisticated they seemed, and mysterious, the product of this mature-looking generation of plants was still plain old natural gasoline for blending as motor fuel. What's more, because of Royalite's exclusive contract with Canadian Western (still in effect during the '30's), B. A. Longview and Gas and Oil Limited at Hartell had to flare all the stripped gas they could not use to fuel boilers and heat bunkhouses.

The big change at Turner Valley during the 1930's came not so much from the processing plants as from the wildcat drillers. After twenty-two years of wet gas production, the gas and oil community of Turner Valley suddenly had to come to grips with the fact that the Valley was more than a wet gas field. It was an oil field as well, and the biggest one in the British Empire.

The first tip-off for those wise enough to see it came from the Model wells in the north end of the field in the early 30's. Gas from these wells came to the surface discoloured. The reason for the discoloration was oil. Few took notice, except the purchasers of the naphtha who promptly penalized Model in price for its funny-coloured, oil-stained product.

One other person to take a hint from all this was R. A. Brown of Calgary. By day, R. A. Brown was superintendent of the City of Calgary Electric and Street Railway Department, but by moonlight he was a Turner Valley wildcatter. The oil in the naphtha at the Model wells and other omens had convinced Brown that the Turner Valley reservoir contained a liquid phase, an oil column downdip from the wet gas cap. He went to the unexplored West Flank of Turner Valley and started putting down a deep well. Money ran out several times and drilling had to be stopped while Brown found more backing. But finally, in 1936, R. A. Brown's Turner Valley Royalties #1 reached down far enough in the Mississippian lime- stone to pierce the oil column. The well blew in at 6828', twelve years after the discovery of the gas cap above the oil.

Floyd Beach (who later became well known as an oil and gas historian and writer) was testing wells for the government at this time and he recalled going out to the new strike with Vern Taylor, a government geologist. "It didn't make the noise that we usually heard at the gas wells," Beach said in a 1956 interview. "There wasn't a large flow of gas and we could see the oil dripping from it as it drifted in the breeze."

Oil was indeed in the wind. The R. A. Brown discovery of the oil column in the limestone touched off Turner Valley's most explosive and final boom. The sight of 800 barrels of oil accumulating each day in the Turner Valley Royalties #1 separator whetted an appetite for drilling and the field was extended in every direction. A. H. Mayland responded to the strike by building a refinery to go along with his gasoline plant at Hartell, a few miles north of the discovery well.

But, in amongst all this excitement, certain nasty facts were coming home to roost. The 116 producing wells drilled into the Turner Valley gas cap over the past two decades, flowing open and flaring gas, represented not only lost energy but lost pressure. The pressure of the gas cap is the natural drive that pushes the oil out of its reservoir rock. Reduce that pressure and recovery of oil is reduced right along with it. That conclusion was occurring to many, along with the strong conviction that the remaining gas cap at Turner Valley must not be squandered. If primary oil recovery was going to do more than scratch the surface of the great Turner Valley reservoir, the remaining gas cap was precious indeed. This realization was the stimulus behind the creation of the Petroleum and Natural Gas Conservation Board by the Alberta Government in 1938. Another dramatic development, however, was going to make it difficult to put conservation into practice during the next several years. That development was the Declaration of War by Britain and her allies on Nazi Germany in September of 1939.

LIFE IN THE VALLEY

People who lived in Turner Valley during its heyday tend to be fiercely loyal. They have good things to say about the companies they worked for, even better about the people they worked and neighboured with. The consensus seems to be that it was a wide-open, friendly kind of place where you could usually make a good dollar, where no one tried to get too far above anyone else, and where not too many laws got in the way of a good time. The rules of work were simple: you got there on time and worked hard or you didn't have a job the next day. If you were educated, you soon

Little Chicago — one of the shack towns that sprang up in the boom times and disappeared when the rigs moved on.

found out that no one believed anything you learned at school and insisted on teaching you all over again.

Shack towns sprang up and died just as quickly when the focus of activity shifted from one strike to the next. *Dogtown, Poverty Flats, Naptha, Cuffling Flats, Mercury, Little New York, Calmont, Little Chicago, Whisky Row*: each had its blaze of glory and most vanished back into the pasture from whence they came.

Where did these imaginative names come from? *Little Chicago* (later known as Royalties) got its name from the local bread man, Rex Warman. Owing to his high prices and a scar that ran along his upper lip, the locals nicknamed him *Little Al Capone*. What better name for his base of operations, then, than *Little Chicago*? As for *Little New York*, well, it got its name from being just over the hill from *Little Chicago*.

Rex Warman's store and bread truck in Little Chicago. Warman's nickname was Little Al Capone and the town was named in his honour.

As might be expected, the villages associated with the gas plants were the most stable and longest lasting. Turner Valley and Black Diamond flanked the Turner Valley Royalite plant (later known as the Madison Natural Gas plant) and there they remain. Longview (formerly Little New York) was the business and bedroom community for the B. A. Longview processing plant. Longview managed to outlive its plant, but the hamlet of Hartell became little more than a post office and general store after the nearby Mercury plant (then owned by Anglo American Exploration Ltd.) closed down in 1961.

A little shack with a great big car out front was a common sight in Turner Valley. The apparent symbol of improvidence may have been quite practical. For one thing, with the centre of employment shifting frequently, a person wanted to be able to take his home from place to place rather than be constantly rebuilding. Mobile homes on wheels had yet to be invented so the best compromise was to have a house small enough that you could put it on skids and move it where you needed to go. Work in the Valley would dry up entirely from time to time, in which case you didn't want to have a lot of money tied up in a house. You were better off investing in your car. "Knock on the front door and go round to the back," was the rule at most of these Turner Valley homes.

This passion for mobility also extended to the gambling casinos and houses of prostitution, the latter colloquially referred to as the *cathouse*. The Turner Valley cathouse, a skid-mounted mobile home, started out in the north end in the '20's, moved to *Little Chicago* in the '30's and, when the reservoir and the men's pocketbooks both showed signs of depletion, it left the Valley entirely. The ladies went to Calgary where they consolidated with Pearl Miller's legendary enterprise. (One wonders how often in Turner Valley history a man wound up in the *doghouse* for being in the cathouse when he claimed to be in the doghouse.)

Another way to get into the domestic doghouse was to be too often at *Pete Crowe's* house, Turner Valley's travelling gambling casino. Mr. Crowe must have done a good business for the game was poker and he took a percentage off every pot.

Beer parlours tend to be more stable enterprises. The two in Black Diamond and the one in Little New York, were supplemented by bootleggers as needed. The beer parlours stayed open from 8 a.m. until 10 p.m. so that everybody, no matter what shift they worked, could get a drink.

Colorful characters abounded, although most plant personnel will argue that the really rambunctious types were from the rigs. To quote Sam Coultis: "Some of them were bad actors, but probably they were not my men." R. K. "Bob" Graves, who worked at B. A. Longview, remembers one problem character who would invariably get on the fight at dances after he'd had something to drink — which is to say, usually. The real problem was that the fellow was not only obnoxious, he was tough. The solution, one worthy of Solomon, came in the form of the fellow's brother who lived in a nearby town, and had similar size and tendencies. He received an invitation to the next dance. When the inevitable unpleasantness began, everyone conspired to pair the brothers off. As they beat one another senseless, the dancing and merriment went on undisturbed.

Big Jim Tardiff, another Turner Valley strongman, a rig builder, won a nomination for THE GUINNESS BOOK OF WORLD RECORDS. He is believed to be the only man in history to singlehandedly throw a piano out a second storey window. He accomplished the feat in an Edmonton hotel.

Turner Valley shared with the nation an obsession with hockey. Technically, the Turner Valley team was amateur, but a good player received a guarantee of work, usually with Royalite. Turner Valley's first team, the *Imperials*, was formed in the late '20's. One of its players, enticed all the way from the junior leagues of Ontario, was Bill Sage. Sage played only three games for the Imperials before the team had to fold. The Depression had left everyone so short of cash the once tremendously popular hockey team could not fill the seats of the Okotoks arena. Sage had little choice but to pursue a career in the gas industry (a career spanning four decades and culminating in the position of Imperial engineering coordinator for all Western Canada).

Like everything else in the Valley, Turner Valley's hockey had a rough

Turner Valley's semi-pro hockey team came back to life in 1938 as "The Oilers", with coach E. R. Piper at the helm. Piper had recently coached the Trail Smoke Eaters to a world championship. The president of the Oilers was R. E. Trammell, Royalite's area superintendent after Sam Coultis. Among the club directors were R. A. Brown, Ralph Will and two generations of W. S. Herrons.

and ready quality. Calgary old-timer Ned Palmer, who played for Calgary's Altoma Athletic Club in a league with the Turner Valley Imperials,* remembers getting in the biggest brawl of his lengthy hockey career right in the Okotoks arena against Turner Valley. Palmer, a speedy winger, had been illegally decked umpteen times while going around an Imperials defenceman. Finally, fed up, Palmer dropped his gloves and the next thing he knew, he was at the bottom of a dog pile consisting of the entire opposing team, his team, and any number of spirited fans. In this day and age of hockey violence, we often hear of bench-clearing brawls, but perhaps those who complain should be applauding the fact that bleacher-clearing brawls are a thing of the past.

The Depression meant hard times in the Valley: an endless line of men, passing through, sleeping under the flares, hoping for jobs that were not there. When naphtha could fetch only pennies per gallon, companies stopped drilling and laid off their men. On behalf of Royalite, Sandy McNab killed beef and took it round to the families whose earners were out of work.

But, out of the Depression and out of Turner Valley, came a new generation who lived and breathed (literally) the oil and gas business from childhood on. A high percentage of these people would go on to work in the industry as it spread out across Western Canada, carrying a lot of Turner Valley know-how with them. They became the cornerstone of the oil and the gas processing industry in Canada.

For example, Ralph Archibald, well-known in gas industry safety, grew up in a shack town at Turner Valley. As a boy he made his way up to Society Heights (known also as Snob Hill) where he cut Sam Coultis' lawn for *two bits*. It was only the beginning of his entrepreneurial exploits. He collected beer bottles (10¢/dozen), rented out his Shetland pony (10¢/ride); and, with a friend, crawled under the boardwalk regularly from the bank corner to Buck's pool hall looking for dropped change. As soon as he was old enough, Archibald made his money from the oil and gas business. Eventually, he found himself in charge of gas plant safety for Shell.

Another youngster from the Valley, Gordon Barnes, remembers how the wartime manpower shortage translated into lucrative jobs for high school kids. A bus would stop outside the school to pick up boys and take them out for a shift on the rigs. Gordon Barnes preferred to spend his evenings operating the gas plant and refinery at Hartell. His hero in those days was plant superintendent Ken Carr, and his life's goal was to one day be

---

*This version of the Imperials was an amateur team.

a plant superintendent himself. Gordon Barnes achieved that dream in 1956 when he became superintendent at the B.A. processing plant at Nevis.

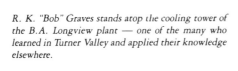

R. K. "Bob" Graves stands atop the cooling tower of the B.A. Longview plant — one of the many who learned in Turner Valley and applied their knowledge elsewhere.

Turner Valley was truly the crucible in which the modern Canadian gas processing industry brewed itself to life. Jim Harvie, who worked in early Turner Valley and whose father was a pioneer in conservation recalls an expression that seems to sum it all up: "They used to say, if you haven't come from Turner Valley, you haven't really learned."

EARLY CONSERVATION AND WORLD WAR II: A TWO-FOLD STIMULUS

3

Conservation is often looked upon as a threat, an obstacle; something that prevents industrialists from getting on with the job. Even among those who favour it, conservation is still seen as preventative medicine — the staving off of undesirable events. Among those in the Canadian gas processing industry, the word conservation has, or should have, a different connotation. In Canada, the move to conserve petroleum products, both gas and oil, has been a fundamental drive pushing the gas processing industry into existence. Later, conservation would stimulate the industry's technological progress and propel it toward international prominence.

Gas conservation in Canada was first enforced in Ontario. Operators in the Tilbury field believed in the costly fiction that, before a well would flow oil, it was necessary to get rid of the gas. They flared off the gas cap as fast as they could until the Ontario government stepped in and taxed the practice to a halt.

When the Alberta fields first went into production, there was little conservation, partly because of another fiction that the reservoirs were inexhaustible. In 1919, as part of a commission on power conservation in Alberta, Mr. James White spoke out strongly against this notion:

> It cannot be too often stated, nor too strongly stated, that a reservoir of this enormously valuable resource, once exhausted, can never be re-placed. It is exceedingly difficult, in fact, almost impossible to convince the 'man in the street' that the life of a gas well is limited to a few years at most, no matter what the initial capacity of the well may be. The recent decrease in the flow from the famous Bow Island gas field, which supplies Calgary, Lethbridge, Macleod and intermediate towns, emphasizes the foregoing in the most forcible manner.

The depletion of the Bow Island field led to reliance by Canadian Western Natural Gas on the Turner Valley field. This new contract with Canadian Western in turn caused Royalite to continue exploration and to discover the great limestone reservoir at Turner Valley with its #4 well. The disastrous attempts to close Royalite #4 in 1924 (the lifting and separation of its casing string) brought on a conservationist's nightmare. The Turner Valley operators accepted that their wells could not be safely closed; they let them flow wide open or nearly so and billions of cubic feet of natural gas went up in flames.

The flare from Royalite #4.

At this time, the 1920's, the federal government had jurisdiction over Alberta's oil and gas. The resources were administered by the Department of the Interior, largely through a Calgary office. When Royalite #4 blew in, that office was rapidly expanded. Grant Spratt ran the geological department, assisted by R. M. S. Owen. Charles Ross was supervisory engineer with a staff of engineers including C. W. Dingman, Floyd Beach, Colonel Steel, T. G. Madgwick and William Calder. Vern Taylor was the Department's representative in the Turner Valley field, a job that would later be taken over by D. P. "Red" Goodall.

During the 1920's, the men of the Department urged Alberta operators to observe proper drilling and casing practices. They were well aware of the damage done to production by allowing water to intrude into the petroleum producing strata. They also asked that the operators collect cutting samples and keep production records that the government could analyze. Department engineer William Calder investigated poorly cased wells in the city of Medicine Hat in 1926 and wrote a stinging report about the waste and possible danger from so many leaking wells within a city. Some of the worst wells were repaired or abandoned as a result, but Elmer

Berlie remembers combatting the same problem at Medicine Hat on behalf of the Petroleum and Natural Gas Conservation Board in 1956. Berlie roused the ire of the Hat's legendary mayor Harry Veiner, by telling him that Medicine Hat wells produced more gas when they were shut in for the summer than they did when producing in the winter time.

Part of Floyd Beach's responsibilities with the Department was to initiate a system of monthly production records. He devised a form for operators to fill out, one section of which dealt with the amount of gas produced and wasted. When one Turner Valley operator spied the blank marked "Waste", he turned on Beach. "You want me to make a criminal of myself, do you?"

Floyd Beach worked with the oil and gas industry for the federal government, the Alberta government and the Alberta Conservation Board. He was also one of the first to write about the history of that industry.

Anyone with eyes could tell that there was staggering waste at Turner Valley, but no one could seem to stop it at first. The Department of the Interior had certainly come to the conclusion that the waste was a grievous problem and even suspected it might be able to control the waste if it took place on Crown land. Private land was another story. The Department felt certain it had no legal jurisdiction over wells drilled there.

The prospects for voluntary conservation were equally bleak. Of all the operators in Turner Valley, only Royalite had a market for its residue gas. The exclusivity of Royalite's contract with Canadian Western, the only gas customer, left the other operators in no mood to conserve. As Floyd Beach put it:

> The owners of such wells with some right said, 'If you don't give us the right to sell our gas, you shouldn't make us preserve the gas for Royalite to draw through its wells.

The most significant act of conservation during this period of federal administration was undertaken by Canadian Western Natural Gas. On May 3, 1930, the utility company received Dominion approval to take Royalite's summer surplus of gas (which would otherwise be flared) and inject it into the depleted Bow Island reservoir. This meant sending the gas back down the mainline from Okotoks to Bow Island where compressors, the first in Alberta used for this purpose, supplied the pressure for reinjection. Bow Island, being of medium size, proved to be an excellent storage reservoir. It repressured rapidly, rising from 246 pounds per square inch in 1930 to 478 pounds by 1935. It provided Canadian Western with a valuable peak load and emergency supply of gas for its system.

The Bow Island repressuring plant, under construction in June of 1930; the first attempt to conserve excess Turner Valley natural gas.

ALBERTA TAKES CONTROL OF ITS RESOURCES

In 1930, Alberta's Premier Brownlee brought a piece of paper home from Ottawa that was to change the fate of the Province from that day forward. That paper confirmed the transfer of control over the Province's natural resources from the federal to the provincial level of government.

The transition was smooth and peaceful with the new Petroleum and Natural Gas Division of Alberta's Department of Lands and Mines picking up the reins as they were surrendered by the Department of the Interior. John Harvie, Deputy Minister with the federal department, oversaw the transfer and was duly thanked by William Calder who was the first director of the provincial Petroleum and Natural Gas Division.

William Calder (right) and associates John Harvie (centre) and Charlie Rankin at the Bassano Dam in 1933.

The big difference between federal and provincial control of resources was that the Province now controlled the mineral rights of over 80% of provincial land. Also, under the authority of the Oil and Gas Wells Act, the provincial government was able, for the first time, to regulate drilling and production on freehold land. This jurisdiction had yet to be tested in the courts, however, and provincial conservation actions between 1930-38 were, as we shall see, hampered by challenges to provincial authority.

The first excuse to move on Turner Valley gas waste came in 1931 when the City of Calgary applied to the Board of Public Utility Commissioners for a reduction in the rate paid for gas. Part of the hearing process was an estimate of the quantity of gas waste in the Valley between 1924 and 1931. For the first time, the problem had numbers attached to it, and shockingly large numbers as it turned out. The provincial and local governments were alarmed to hear that from 236 to 260 billion cubic feet of Turner Valley gas was already destroyed, and that this quantity represented from one-third to one-half of the total reserves of the field known at that time.

Shortly thereafter, the Alberta Provincial Government created a special advisory committee to look into the matter. This committee struck a technical subcommittee to work out a way of conserving the gas that would be regarded as fair by industry and government alike. The subcommittee consisted of F. P. Fisher of Mt. Vernon, Ohio, S. J. Davies, representing the independent producers, and R. O. Armstrong, representing Imperial who, through Royalite, had the largest interest in the field.

It became obvious to the committee that a reservoir pressure survey and flow measurements were needed before controls could sensibly be applied. But pressure testing meant closing the wells for the period of the test and this, of course, ran counter to the conventional wisdom that Turner Valley wells could not be safely closed. The conventional wisdom was looking a bit tarnished at this stage because Royalite had already closed a few of its wells with no dramatic results. Bill Sage, as a youngster with Royalite, helped in the first closure of a Turner Valley high-pressure well. He recalls that Charlie "High Pressure" Ward was the man in charge and that the well was closed by means of a bolted head.

Still, there was enough nervousness about these pressure tests, and resistance to them, that temporary legislation had to be passed in the spring of 1932 (the Turner Valley Gas Conservation Act) and a board created (the Turner Valley Gas Conservation Board) before the survey could be completed. When all was said and done, the technical subcommittee recommended that the field be unitized, and that production be cut from 500 to 100 million cubic feet per day.

Unitization implied cooperation between the producers and an agreement on who the operator would be, none of which seemed likely at Turner Valley. Royalite, being by far the largest producer, was the logical choice to operate the field under a unitization agreement, but many of the smaller producers feared that they would lose control and that Royalite would look after its interests first. Given these problems, a compromise recommendation was made whereby everyone would continue to operate independently

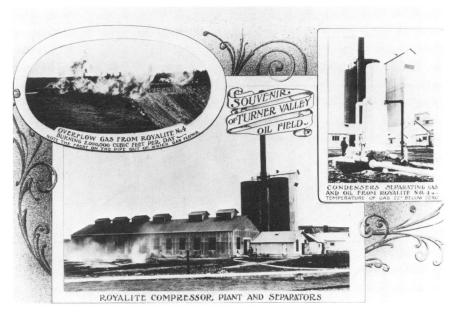

Turner Valley's waste of natural gas was a tourist attraction. To commemorate their visit to Hell's Half Acre, tourists picked up souvenir postcards like this one.

but would voluntarily adhere to a royalty-sharing and production-rating scheme.

William Calder, in a 1935 report, described the fate of these recommendations:

> When initiating the tests, the government hoped that operators, once they had definite and unbiased data, would appreciate the vital necessity of introducing efficient development of all wells under a unitization scheme, and thus assure for all participants an equal share in any benefits that might accrue in the event of a market being developed for the excess gas wasted. These worthy efforts were not appreciated by those who would have principally benefited, and considerable adverse publicity was circulated, misconstruing the efforts and insinuating that the endeavors of the government were confiscatory.

In any case, full agreement was never reached and the proposal had to be scrapped. With the completion of the reservoir pressure survey, the government honoured its promise to rescind the Turner Valley Gas Conservation Act and the Board was disbanded as well.

All of the above sounds negative, but in fact these first efforts to understand the Turner Valley reservoir and control its waste did produce a measure of conservation. After the tests, the Alberta Government ordered the producers to cut back their flow by 40% and this reduced the waste of gas by 50% to 250 million cubic feet a day. Aiding compliance with these orders was the discovery that the naphtha recovery at the lower level of flow was at least 20% more efficient.

Another finding made during the period of testing was that the pressure of the Turner Valley reservoir had declined to the point where, in William Calder's words, it was no longer "extraordinary". In fact, the waste of gas was reducing the pressure by 0.75 to 1.25 pounds every day. The 1200 to 1300 pounds of pressure still encountered during the closed pressure tests was easily within the capacity of high-pressure casings and modern control heads. Turner Valley could be shut-in with no explosions, no asphyxiations and no casings rising out of the ground.

The testing also confirmed that a field separator was not an ideal or sufficient means for extracting hydrocarbon liquids from the gas. From 0.05 to 0.25 gallons of naphtha per 1000 cubic feet of gas were getting past the separator and going to flare. This knowledge stimulated the rebirth of oil absorption processing in Turner Valley. The 1933 Royalite plant at the town of Turner Valley, Royalite's #2 plant in the south end, the 1934 Gas and Oil Products plant at Hartell and the 1936 British American plant at Longview were all attempts to harvest the naphtha that had previously been escaping in the separator flare gas.

CONSERVING OIL BY CONSERVING GAS

Can a reduction in waste from 500 million cubic feet of natural gas per day to 250 million cubic feet per day be considered conservation? Perhaps not in modern terms, but in the slightly bizarre context of early 1930's Turner Valley, it was conservation of a kind, and might have been considered sufficient conservation for several years to come if not for the discovery of the Turner Valley oil reservoir.

With the flow of oil from R. A. Brown's 1936 Turner Valley Royalties #1 well came the realization that much of the oil in the new-found reservoir could never be recovered because of the stupendous waste of gas that had preceded it. Understanding of reservoir mechanics had made a lot of headway since the Tilbury days and, far from believing that waste of the gas cap made way for oil, people in the industry now understood that the gas was nature's way of driving the oil from the reservoir rock and raising it to the surface of the earth. The need and right to conserve gas for its own sake had always been controversial, but now that the issue was *oil* conservation *through* gas conservation, government and industry alike saw the need to prevent further waste of the precious Turner Valley gas cap. What is more, they both favoured legislation over voluntary agreement as a means of effecting it. So it was that Nathan Eldon Tanner, Alberta's Social Credit Minister of Lands and Mines, introduced legislation in 1938 calling for the creation of a Petroleum and Natural Gas Conservation Board.

The Petroleum and Natural Gas Conservation Board consisted originally of three members backed by a small support staff. In search of a suitable chairman for the new board, Tanner contacted his ministry's U.S. counterpart, the Bureau of Mines. That Bureau recommended W. F. Knode.

Bill Knode already enjoyed wide experience in this relatively new field of petroleum conservation. In the 1920's, his job had been to encourage consent for voluntary conservation among Texas producers. For three years in the early 1930's, he had been chief petroleum engineer for the Texas Railroad Commission. When Tanner approached him, Knode was running a consulting business out of Corpus Christi, Texas.

Knode accepted the Alberta Board chairmanship and moved to Calgary. His deputy on the Board was C. W. "Charlie" Dingman, A. W. Dingman's nephew and a former inspector of oil fields for the Department of the Interior. The third Board member was F. G. Cottle, an accountant. Many members of the support staff, like Floyd Beach and Red Goodall, transferred over to the Board from the Province's Petroleum Division.

Probably to the Board's credit, it did not opt for sudden, indiscriminate action that would have halted the waste at the cost of all good will from industry. As Knode put it, "We had to find equitable ways of sharing the benefits of conservation. You couldn't ask the gas cap producer to suddenly shut-in his production and lose all his revenues so that the oil column producer might achieve greater oil recovery".

At the same time, Knode was very aware of the magnitude of the problem. A 1939 *Maclean's* magazine article claimed that 35,000 cubic feet of Turner Valley gas was being used to raise every barrel of oil. At 1939 prices that translated into a ridiculous situation where $10 worth of gas was wasted to produce each $1.20 worth of oil. The article quoted Knode as saying: "This is a crazy set up. If you let all this gas get away, how are you going to raise your oil? And if you can't raise your oil, where will you be?"

In September, 1938, the Conservation Board issued its first order with respect to gas cap conservation. It prohibited production from any gas well not connected to a market. As the only market for Turner Valley natural gas was Canadian Western, this meant that only gas cap wells hooked into Royalite's absorption and scrubbing plants would be allowed to continue operating. The rule would have necessitated the shutting down of both the Longview and Hartell plants except for the fact that it did not apply to oil wells which were allowed to continue producing and flaring their solution gas. The Longview and Hartell plants were able to stay in business by collecting solution gas from the oil wells. They processed the solution gas for its natural gasoline and then injected the residue gas into the gas cap. This allowed them to process an equivalent amount of gas cap gas for its naphtha content.

The Conservation Board's way of controlling oil well production was somewhat like the Petroleum Division's before it. The Board's system of prorationing to market demand allowed each well a daily volume of production based equally on potential, acreage, bottomhole pressure and gas-oil ratio. The gas associated with the oil was protected by such a scheme as well in that waste of solution gas would adversely affect both pressure and gas-oil ratio, resulting in a lower production allowable for oil.

ALBERTA ENERGY RESOURCES CONSERVATION BOARD CHAIRMEN

W. F. Knode (1938-1940).

R. E. Allen (1940-1941).

J. J. Frawley (1942-1943).

Dr. E. H. Boomer (1943-1945).

A. G. Bailey (1945-47).

I. N. McKinnon (1948-1959).

D. P. Goodall (1959-1962).

Dr. George Govier (1962-1978).

Vern Millard (1978-

WORLD WAR II

With all due respect to American fighting men, it has been said that the United States' greatest contribution to World War II was the ocean of petroleum products it was able to supply. Certainly, if that supply had ever flagged, the war would have taken a sharp turn for the worse. Canada played a similar role in the Allied war effort and played it earlier due to the country's simultaneous declaration of war with Britain against Germany. Turner Valley, Canada's only large oil field, was produced to the limit to meet wartime demand and the overproduction, compounding earlier mistakes, certainly shortened the life of the field.

In February, 1940, Stanley J. Davies released a "Memo on Utilization of Alberta Petroleum Resources During the War". Davies had worked in the Turner Valley fields for over a decade and he certainly knew his subject. His memo provides an interesting outline of what producers *wished* to see happen over the war period.

First, Davies addressed the subject of oil. How much should the field produce for the war effort? It was possible to get 28,000 barrels of oil a day out of the reservoir, but at that rate, bottomhole pressure fell and the gas-oil ratio shot up. That rate of production, in other words, could not be sustained. It promised to be a long war and Davies seemed to recommend going along with industry's and the Conservation Board's mutual opinion that the efficient rate of production for the Valley was 18,000 to 20,000 barrels of oil per day.

In fact, by 1941, the Oil Controller for Canada was calling for 25,000 barrels per day from Turner Valley as a war measure. The Conservation Board increased the allowables even though it made poor conservation sense. The new allowables consisted of a "conservation legal allowable" plus an "extra war emergency allowable". When the bottomhole pressure and gas-oil ratio went to pot, the Board tried to lower the conservation legal allowable, but the Oil Controller insisted that the total field output be even higher: 26,000 barrels per day.

This situation brought Dr. George G. Brown of the University of Michigan to Calgary in 1941. A chemical engineer, Dr. Brown had earned an enormous reputation in the United States. During the 1920's, he had participated with the Natural Gasoline Association of America in studies to determine the best fuel blends for contemporary automobile engines. Brown was retained by the Alberta Conservation Board to study Turner Valley and to recommend an equitable and efficient producing rate for the field.

What Dr. Brown suggested was a maximum withdrawal of reservoir fluid per acre per day, applying to all wells including those on the gas cap. The actual number of barrels suggested by Brown was twenty-five, but the more important thing was the way the plan focussed on well-spacing. It so penalized cluttered wells that it effectively enforced a 40-acre well spacing minimum. Both the Conservation Board and the industry accepted the *Brown Plan* and, by 1943, Dr. Brown was back in the United States helping to set standards for the sampling of high-pressure two-phase streams.

Dr. George Granger Brown, author of the Turner Valley Brown Plan.

The one thing the Brown Plan did not do — or set out to do — was control the waste of gas after it left the reservoir. In fact, no plan was in effect for this wastage and much of the produced gas still went to the flare stack as residue gas from absorption plants.

S. J. Davies' 1940 memo had quite a lot to say about this waste:

> At the present time, all natural gasoline plants in Turner Valley waste most of the propane, butane and iso-butane fractions of the natural gasoline produced.

The situation was unacceptable because these hydrocarbon compounds:

> form the raw material from which polymerized gasoline may be manufactured. This product from a polymerization plant is the base of aviation gasoline of the highest quality. *This is an essential war material which is not now made in Turner Valley, and the raw material from which it is manufactured is at present being wasted.*

Mr. Davies concluded that the Turner Valley absorption plants should make the changes necessary to capture and separate these light fractions and that polymerization plants should be erected in the Valley to process them into aviation fuel constituents.

Much of this came to pass. As a high school student, Gordon Barnes was pressed into the workforce by the manpower shortage. He worked evenings, weekends and holidays at the Gas and Oil Limited refinery and gas plant at Hartell. Barnes remembers that the plant was adapted to fractionate extracted liquids into propane, normal butane and iso-butane, "very high technology in those days". He also remembers that side oil from the combination tower and overhead gases were run through a U.O.P. Polymerization unit. Once again, we see the penchant for self-sufficiency that characterized this A. H. Mayland-owned and Ken Carr-run facility.

The Royalite absorption plants also added butane splitters to extract iso-butane, but their product was not polymerized in the Valley. Royalite sent the iso-butane to an Allied War Supplies Corporation alkylation plant in Calgary. The alkylation plant was situated adjacent to Imperial's Calgary refinery. After it had polymerized the iso-butane to create alkylate, the refinery blended the product in aviation fuel. Three hundred barrels of iso-butane went to the polymerization plant every day and, to supply that amount, the Turner Valley absorption plants had to process 88 million cubic feet of gas per day.

The aviation fuel produced after all this processing and refining did not go far. Southern Alberta was one of the sites of the British Commonwealth Air Training Plan. Young men from all over the Commonwealth came to training centres in small-town southern Alberta to train as pilots

Tiger Moths used in the Commonwealth Air Training Plan in Alberta during World War II.

and air crew for the war in Europe and most of the aviation fuel made in Alberta burned in the air over Alberta.

The Allied War Supplies Corporation had a second project in the Calgary area, an ammonia plant built in 1941 to supply fixed nitrogen for explosives. It was the only ammonia plant in the world running on natural gas at that time. It worked its way up from a four million cubic feet a day natural gas demand to a peak of nine million.

The gas for the ammonia plant came from the Royalite scrubbing plant in Turner Valley and it was not long until that plant could no longer keep up. The number of airports and barracks built for the Commonwealth Air Training Scheme had also jacked up the demand on the Royalite plant so that the ammonia plant was more of a final straw than a singular cause. To increase capacity, the scrubbing plant added a Girbotol unit to its existing Seaboard facilities. It was the first time that the Girbotol process (a Girdler Corporation patent invented by R. R. Bottoms) had been installed in a Canadian plant and it brought a new word to the vocabulary of Canadian gas processing: monoethanolamine. The Girbotol unit scrubbed the H_2S out of the gas with an aqueous solution of monoethanolamine. This substance was to dominate Canadian gas sweetening for most of the next two decades, but people gave up trying to pronounce it long before that. Monoethanolamine soon became M.E.A. The Seaboard and Girbotol units together gave the Royalite scrubbing plant a capacity of 100 million cubic feet of gas per day.

EXCLUSIVE CONTRACTS COME TO AN END

The demand for natural gas brought on by the war did not exceed the efficient capacity of *all* Turner Valley's wells. It certainly did exceed the efficient capacity (and the maximum legal allowables) of *Royalite's* Turner Valley wells. A situation developed where Royalite over-produced its wells and the Conservation Board ignored the violation of its own orders while, elsewhere in the Valley, the non-Royalite absorption plants flared their residue gas for lack of a market. Neither the cause of war nor the cause of conservation was being well served and it seemed that the time had come to give the exclusive contract between Royalite and Canadian Western a test.

Model Oils took the first step in 1943. Through its counsel D. P. McDonald, Model applied to the Supreme Court for a Mandamus Order directing the Conservation Board to enforce its own rule with respect to Royalite. That is, Model wanted to see the Conservation Board forced to shut in the Royalite wells for exceeding their legal allowables. Chief Justice W. C. Ives decided to hear the motion and, at the hearing, the Board admitted that it was not enforcing its own orders so as to meet the extra demands brought on by the war. The Mandamus Order was issued, Royalite was forced to close down its offending wells, and the Board changed its legal allowables so that the war plants could continue producing.

Long before finalization of the court case, however, the Conservation Board sought a solution to the contradictory and wasteful situation. The Board engaged Dr. Thomas R. Weymouth to work out a more sensible plan of gas conservation for Turner Valley.

Dr. Weymouth's plan, which was generally agreed to by industry, called for the field to be divided into three parts. The south part would be gathered by British American, the Hartell area by Gas and Oil Products, and the north and central areas by Royalite. Royalite's #2 absorption plant was to be moved and consolidated with #1 on the Sheep River near the town of Turner Valley. All the residue gas from the Hartell and Longview plants was to be piped to the Royalite plant for sweetening. If all of this gas could not be sold, the surplus would be injected into the reservoir. The iso-butane still sorely needed for aviation fuel was to go on being produced as before.

A new piece of legislation had to be passed which, among other things, rendered null and void the old exclusive contracts that had ruled the world of natural gas distribution since the beginnings of the industry in Alberta. The Natural Gas Utilities Act, passed in 1944, created a separate board, the Natural Gas Utility Board, under the chairmanship of G. M.

Group of Petroleum and Natural Gas Conservation Board employees outside the Black Diamond office in the 1940's. Left to right: Alex Essery, Dick King, Lloyd Hicklin, Pat Webster and George Horn.

Blackstock. This Board had the delicate duty of carrying out the hearings and complex negotiations necessary to make the Weymouth plan economically agreeable to all parties. What the Natural Gas Utilities Board accomplished was fair allocation to market demand in the Turner Valley field. William Calder's 1932 ambition for Turner Valley was thus partially achieved in 1945.

While this plan was negotiated and put into effect, certain changes took place. The consolidated version of the Royalite #1 and #2 plants was renamed. By order of the Gas Utilities Board, a special act was passed by which Royalite gave birth to a subsidiary, the Madison Natural Gas Company. This new company inherited Royalite's Turner Valley plant. It was in charge of treating gas from the entire Turner Valley field and delivering the processed gas, or sales gas, to Canadian Western. The first president of the company was R. E. "Bob" Trammell, who had previously been Royalite's field superintendent at Turner Valley.

*   *   *

The idea of conservation was certainly in the minds of Canadians long before World War II, but it took the voracious appetite of war and fear of losing that war to galvanize the various parties into allowing change to occur. By war's end, the Canadian processing industry had a number of skills in its repertoire, and certain efficient means at its disposal that it did not have when war was declared. M.E.A., a more effective and flexible means of sweetening gas, was in use. A petrochemical industry, using natural gas as a feedstock, had sprung to life at public expense. While not taking a deep cut into the lighter hydrocarbons in natural gas, processors were taking a significant nibble in the form of iso-butane setting the stage for propane recovery. Perhaps most significant, Canada's largest and most complex oil and gas field to date, Turner Valley, had adopted a scheme by which the available market for natural gas was equitably shared among all producers, a necessary step down the road toward unitization.

All these developments would prove important when the industry faced its next challenge at Leduc.

Nathan Eldon Tanner (left), Alberta's Minister of Lands and Mines, opens the valve on Leduc #1. Imperial's Vern Hunter (centre) drilled the landmark well putting an end to his reputation as "Dry Hole" Hunter. Walker L. Taylor (right) was Imperial's western division manager in 1947.

LEDUC AND BEYOND: CANADIAN GAS PROCESSING BETWEEN 1947-1957

4

Our subject being natural gas and the processing of natural gas, there is little need to go deeply into the frustrating search for oil in Western Canada that characterized the oil business of the 1940's. Suffice it to say that:

— here was the Province of Alberta, literally underlain from end to end with the kinds of sediments that traditionally contain hydrocarbons;

— here too was the Dominion of Canada, oil hungry and running up a bigger bill for imported oil every year as demand grew and Turner Valley tapered toward oblivion;

— and here finally was the oil industry, led in frustration by Imperial, poking hole after hole into this vast potential and coming up dry or grassy.

It can probably be said that Alberta's 1940's wildcatters would have been better off if Turner Valley had never been found, and if geological thinking had been back with Eugene Coste and the theory of volcanic origins. Had the oil explorers of the late 1930's and 1940's been able to somehow blind themselves to the fact of Turner Valley and taken Coste's advice that oil and gas could not accumulate near the mountains, a lot of costly, complicated and fruitless drilling could have been avoided. But Turner Valley *did* exist, a foothills reservoir, and everyone continued the search in the faulted and folded geological landscape that had yielded Canada's first major oil find.

Typical of this scavenger hunt was the exploration conducted by R. A. Brown, mastermind of the Turner Valley oil discovery. After drilling a dozen good producers in the Valley, Brown moved north and settled on a location not far from Cochrane, still deep in the foothills. He went with the system that brought him his earlier success and drilled deep, over six thousand feet. This time, it brought him nothing. After four years of frustration, he handed on the torch to Shell Oil which drilled another four years before striking the Jumping Pound reservoir in 1944. Shell made its strike at 9618' in the Rundle formation of the Mississippian limestone*. It was a good find, but it was gas — wet and sour — not the elusive oil.

---

*The original name of Shell's discovery well at Jumping Pound was Shell Oil of Canada 4-24-J. It was completed on December 13, 1944.

Bob Lockwood of Canadian Gulf carried on a similar search of the foothills — but to the south. His gravity and seismic surveys in the Pincher Creek area became the subject of jokes. Was he ever going to give up all this hanky-panky, choose a location and drill? Some consolation came in 1948 when the location he did pick, Pincher Creek #1, came in with a gas flow of ten million cubic feet a day. A fabulous sour gas field, but again, no oil.

As the years piled up and the number of dusters and gassers grew, oil entrepreneurs were forced to consider the awful possibility that this lovely sedimentary landscape — huge as it was — might be barren of oil, save for Turner Valley. Evidence of how deeply the notion had taken root is the fact that, faced with an urgent Canadian oil demand and its own mounting failures, Imperial Oil seriously considered the manufacture of synthetic oil from natural gas in Alberta. Floyd Beach has even suggested that Imperial's continuation of exploration was more a search for gas to support such a scheme than a search for oil.

In any event, after 113 dry holes and over $13 million spent, Imperial finally connected in early 1947 with an oil gusher called Leduc #1, the herald of a gigantic oil field. A year later, Imperial hit again, an even richer strike at Redwater northeast of Edmonton, and the boom was on.

Associated with Leduc oil was a plentiful amount of gas. Along with the gas found elsewhere in the search for oil, it amounted to considerable gas reserves for the Province of Alberta — possibly enough to warrant export sales of natural gas. The producers who held leases on shut-in gas were obviously anxious to see it sold, even at a marginal profit, and pipeline promotors began to gather with various schemes for sending Alberta gas to faraway markets: The U.S. Pacific Northwest, British Columbia, Canada East. In the midst of it all, in 1948, the Alberta Government appointed a Royal Commission, the Dinning Commission, to study the question. As the old saying goes: "The Englishman says no; the American says yes, and the Canadian says let's have a Royal Commission.".

And that, for the time being, is where we will leave the topic of gas exports. The process by which export gas began to flow from the Province of Alberta was so grindingly slow that it did not change the fate of Canadian gas processing until the year 1957. Between Leduc #1 and 1957, much ground was covered by the processing industry in Canada, and it is to that ground that we presently turn.

WESTERN PROPANE

After 1947, the focus of industry activity quickly shifted from Turner Valley to Leduc. If an oil field can have a rough war, Turner Valley had just had one. People in both the oil and gas industries were eager to leave the fast-depleting field for the new and promising one. This is not to say that the Turner Valley gas cap was spent; it would produce for several more decades. But history had overtaken the Valley and the future lay to the north in the rapidly expanding Leduc and Redwater fields.

Under these circumstances, Turner Valley was hardly the place to expect a significant advance in Canadian processing, but that is exactly what happened in 1948 when a refrigeration-fractionation plant was built near Royalite's Turner Valley absorption and sweetening plant.

The entrepreneur behind the new plant was James Barber, a native of Boston. After attending the Massachusetts Institute of Technology and working in the Colorado oil fields, Barber arrived in Turner Valley in 1938 sporting the valuable Fisher Governor franchise. In 1940, he purchased an oilfield machine shop in Longview which he ran under the banner of the Barber Machinery Company.

James Barber came to Canada from Colorado sporting the valuable Fisher Governor franchise.

At Longview, James Barber repaired mainly oilfield equipment although his customers likely included the local gas processing plants. An important part of such a business is confidence, and to get the confidence of some of the top drillers — men like Gene Denton and Ralph Will — Barber hired Earl Griffiths from Denver. Among the drillers with American experience, Griffiths had a reputation of being the best oilfield engineer around. Griffiths accepted Barber's offer and became a very valuable part of the Barber story. He came to work for Barber in 1946, the same year the Longview operation moved into Calgary.

Sometime during this period, Barber made the acquaintance of one Adrian Cameron. Cameron had worked for the National Research Council during the war and had come up with an innovative process for making ethylene oxide from ethylene. The petrochemical industry was itself only an infant at this time, hastened into existence by the war, but those with the prophecying eye could see in it one of the waves of the future. Ethylene was then and still remains one of the fundamental building blocks of that industry.

Cameron and Barber struck up a business relationship over feedstock. Cameron was looking for a cheap and plentiful feedstock from which to make his ethylene and James Barber felt he had found that feedstock in the flare gas from Royalite's Turner Valley gas plant. The Royalite flare gas contained mainly ethane and propane.

James Barber made his deal with Royalite for its flare gas and hired James Morrison Pryde, a young Calgarian fresh out of the engineering degree program at McGill, to help him build the plant. Reasoning that the ethylene oxide application might be a little in the future yet (how far in the future would have shocked him), Barber devised the plant as a propane plant first, and an ethane plant second. That is, the plant would split the feed stream into ethane and propane, but only the propane would be marketed for the time being. This accounts for the company name Western Propane Limited. Barber constructed his Western Propane plant half a mile up the Sheep River from the Royalite/Madison plant.

Because of the H_2S content of the flare gas coming in from Royalite, the first priority for Western Propane had to be sweetening. For this purpose, Morris Pryde had a Girbotol unit installed. Virtually the same as the Girbotol unit at the Madison plant, it was in fact the last such unit ever installed under the Girdler Corporation of Louisville's Girbotol patent. A strange coincidence: the first Girbotol unit in Canada and the last one ever were operating within half a mile of one another on Turner Valley's Sheep River.

The next step in the process at Western Propane was the actual refrigeration-fractionation plant. To this day, Morris Pryde speaks of it *with* pride: "You didn't have the option of seeing how so and so did it in Kansas. They just didn't have that kind of plant anywhere else." This type of refrigeration plant was entirely new, and no other processing plant on this side of the border had ever extracted natural gas products by refrigeration. Using a deeply chilled propane reflux, Western Propane could recover propane of extreme purity: 99%. As Morris Pryde puts it, "The plant was probably overdesigned for propane." The plant had been built that way because Barber was still thinking down the road to a time when he would need extremely pure ethane overhead for making ethylene for ethylene oxide.

Meanwhile the plant made propane and lots of it, around 1000 barrels a day, which presented a slight problem in that the entire Western Canadian market for propane was a few hundred barrels a day (currently imported in cylinders from Montana). Did this faze Jim Barber? Not noticeably. If a market did not exist, they would simply have to create one. Morris Pryde started setting up distributorships, while Jim Barber attacked the problem of building cylinders for the public to put his propane in.

Western Propane found a good Alberta distributor for its product in the person of John A. Johanson. Johanson's business had been selling lubricating oils, under the company name Sturdie Oils, but he saw in propane a versatile fuel with a big future. Sturdie Propane became a successful operation. Not so successful were the distributorships Western Propane set up in Saskatchewan and British Columbia. In Morris Pryde's words, they were "financial disasters" fated to be divided up or swallowed by larger concerns. This left Western Propane to deal in those regions with the independents set up to supply local demand. One of Western's best contracts was with B.C. Electric which used propane as a standby fuel.

Despite Western's marketing efforts not enough propane could be sold in Canada to support its thousand barrel a day production. Western attempted to get rid of the surplus on the American market. Competition for space in U.S. railway tank cars was fierce after the war, but Western made some progress in the northern states with the help of a State-side marketer. The extra business could not solve Western's problems entirely, however, because the going U.S. rate of six to seven cents per U.S. gallon was slightly lower than Western's break-even rate. Still, it was better to sell at that rate than not at all and Western marketed what it could in the U.S., hoping to break even through higher priced sales in Canada.

Meanwhile in his Calgary plant, Jim Barber attacked the considerable problem of manufacturing cylinders. He plunged into what Morris Pryde calls "the painful agony of building deep-draw dies". The goal was to produce perfect half cylinders that could be united with a single, welded seam.

And, James Barber did it — except that each and every cylinder was a quarter inch shorter and narrower than specifications insisted upon by the American Interstate Commerce Commission. The I.C.C. would not allow Barber's off-spec cylinders on American trains. For a long time, the one thousand cylinders sat in Barber's Manchester shop yard, a mountain-like monument to what could have been but wasn't going to be. Finally the cylinders were cut up for other uses and James Barber went out of the cylinder business for good.

Looking back on the Western Propane experience, Morris Pryde likens it to being invited to take swimming lessons while in the middle of a lake. Everything had to be developed from scratch: the plant, the distribution system, the products for household use. The Americans were well ahead of Canada in L.P.G.* use, but often the precedents set in the U.S. were not applicable in Canada. For example, in the U.S., all farm storage systems for propane were underground. Conventional wisdom said it should be so. But, when they tried this in Canada, it just plain didn't work. In cold weather, the heavy draw would turn the tank into a mini-refrigerator. This, combined with cold ground temperatures dropped the vapour pressure and interfered with the flow. Just when you needed your propane most, it wouldn't flow into your house. Canadian propane storage tanks had to be above ground, out where the sun could warm them.

But no matter how much Western Propane learned about its product and market, and no matter how well the company innovated with its production technology, the operation continued to slide. As Morris Pryde puts it, the company was built on a bad premise: "If you don't own the market and if you don't own the raw material, there's no future as a middle man. That's a well known law."

Another Morris Pryde recollection illustrates the kind of problems a plant gets into when it does not control its raw materal. Toward the end of his time with Western Propane, Pryde received a telephone call in the middle of the night from a very excited plant operator. "Morris," the man said, "this plant is really going crazy, really working. We made 20,000 gallons *last shift!*" Wonderful, thought Pryde, except it can't be. They discussed the possibility of a water leak, but the operator was certain the product was hydrocarbon. But was it propane?

Morris hung up and phoned the Royalite plant. The operator at Royalite was not surprised by Morris' news. "Oh, ya," he said, "we forgot to tell you; we had to shut down our iso-butane unit for two or three weeks, so you got it all." Wonderful again, thought Pryde, except that Western Propane lacked a butane unit.

The shut-down of Royalite's iso-butane section lasted longer than expected and forced Morris Pryde into another scramble situation. He found a butane market in B.C., he found tank cars, he found towers (old

---

*Liquified Petroleum Gases, mainly propane and butane.

James Morrison Pryde managed Western Propane for James Barber, then became half of Pryde Flavin, a consulting company specializing in gas distribution and gathering systems.

riveted ones that he and his people worked round the clock to install); and, without too much delay, Western Propane was in the butane business.

But Western Propane was not gaining ground on its real problems. The series of oil discoveries at Leduc were quickly hastening the company's demise. In 1949, Imperial built its Devon conservation plant, complete with propane facilities. When the plant went on stream in 1950, it priced its propane at 3¢ a gallon. To quote Morris Pryde, "That put the crusher on everything".

In the end, Western Propane Limited was sold to Royalite, which itself had just been sold by Imperial to the Bronfman group. After a year of negotiation, a deal was hammered out by which everyone received their investment back, but no one profited. Gordon Barnes worked for Western Propane at the time and he recalls that when the plant went to Royalite, he went too, "just like another fixture". Pryde and Barnes worked together moving the propane plant onto the Royalite property and melding the propane facilities into the Royalite plant. Gordon Barnes compares the move to getting a chance to completely renovate a house after having lived in it for a while. They knew all the problems and they fixed them in the transition. The rebuilt and streamlined propane plant required only one operator at its new location compared to three at the old site. It took only six hours to start the plant, with specification product going to the tanks the same day.

THE LEDUC GAS CONSERVATION PLANT

The opening of Imperial's Leduc Gas Conservation plant at Devon on May 12th suggests several important things. Turner Valley flared over a trillion cubic feet, much of which could have been utilized. The flaring became almost a national disgrace although there were many valid reasons why government intervention could not be undertaken, or even action by the industry itself. Imperial Oil is the dominant operator in Leduc-Woodbend, and has so large a stake in the oilfield that they are the people to take the initiative. They have done so to the tune of $6.5 million and their action will materially reduce the flaring of gas in this field, whether the action pays or not.

Canadian Oil and Gas Industries
July, 1950

Turner Valley was very much on everyone's mind as government and industry prepared for the conservation of gas at Leduc. The Alberta Government, represented by the Petroleum and Natural Gas Conservation Board, was determined not to allow any repeat of Turner Valley. Those involved with Imperial maintain that the company cooperated willingly. As soon as gas conservation was appropriate at Leduc, Imperial went ahead with plans for the first gas conservation plant in Canada.

Main street, Devon, Alberta, 1950. Devon was created from scratch to accommodate the oil field and gas processing personnel after the Leduc strike.

In building the Leduc gas conservation plant (also known as *Leduc-Woodbend* for the fields it served and *Devon* for the nearby company town), Imperial set a standard the industry would be a long time equalling. Contractor C. F. Braun of Alhambra, California, designed the plant to operate on the refrigeration-fractionation principle, making Leduc-Woodbend the second refrigeration plant in Canada, but the first to process a raw gas stream by that means. (Western Propane's gas feed was already minus its butanes and pentanes plus.)

A key man for Imperial on the Devon design team was Jim Young. Alan Carr became the first plant foreman at Leduc, and Bill Sage was invited by field superintendent Vern Hunter to be the first maintenance foreman. Sage and Hunter had worked together for Royalite as labourers in the Dirty Thirties. During construction of Leduc-Woodbend, Carr and Sage hired several Turner Valley veterans to be its first operators. One of the recruits, Ted Deacon, (later plant foreman at Leduc) recalls sending himself on a tour of Western Propane so that he might better understand the C. F. Braun engineers who were coming to Canada to help in the start-up at Leduc.

For men like Ted Deacon, accustomed to firing a boiler when they wanted heat and cranking a valve for a change in pressure, the most impressive thing about the new plant at Leduc was its level of automation. The gas fractionator alone had an unheard-of fourteen temperature indicators charting the wide heat variation across the vessel. Every pressure and temperature in the plant could be set by the flip of a switch. But, with the benefit of hindsight, we might say that Leduc's provisions for Canadian winter were an even greater marvel. As we shall see, not all plants came to Canada equipped for winter, but surprisingly Leduc did. All its facilities were enclosed in heated buildings and, as Bill Sage points out, the heating system seldom operated beyond 25% of its capacity.

In terms of corrosion, Leduc benefited from knowledge gained in Turner Valley. No one understood perfectly yet why corrosion occurred, but H_2S and CO_2 were recognized as the culprits. Turner Valley's Madison plant scrubbed these acid gases out after oil absorption had extracted the liquid hydrocarbons. Leduc's designers saw the sense of reversing this. If they put the M.E.A. sweetening system *before* the refrigeration unit, the plant would run *sweet* and the corrosion would be confined to the sweetening unit alone.

The problem with doing it this way was that the gas at Leduc entered the plant at a very low pressure which had to be increased in three stages. To remove the acid gases at the earliest possible stage, the sweetening unit would have to operate at a mere 45 pounds per square inch (psi), and this ran counter to the common belief that M.E.A. sweetening would only work at high pressure. However, wonder of wonders, the acid gases *were* successfully absorbed by the amine wash and Leduc had for itself another important industry first. Thereafter, sour gas was always sweetened first, fractionated later.

This design variation turned out to be more of a step in the right direction than a universal panacea for corrosion. Leduc-Woodbend gas was reasonably sweet to begin with and many different problems presented themselves when the industry began dealing in later years with high percentages of H_2S and CO_2.

Residue gas from the Leduc plant sold to Northwestern Utilities Limited for the princely sum of 4¢ per thousand cubic feet. The low price was partly a recompense to the utility company for having to build a pipeline south to Leduc and partly for its having to build a modification plant to ready the gas for consumer use. Even after processing, the Leduc-Woodbend gas contained more heavy hydrocarbons than the very dry gas from Northwestern's main source, the Viking-Kinsella field. The modification plant mixed air with Leduc-Woodbend gas and reduced its heating value, or BTU rating.* Even at that, Northwestern only used Devon gas for its industrial customers for fear it would cause problems in domestic stoves and heaters.

The other products from Leduc, propane, butane and natural gasoline, had to be trucked out at first. The propane was sold directly from tanks at the plant to jobbers like Canadian Propane and Mutual Propane. (The price: 4¢/gallon). The butane went as feedstock to the Canadian Chemicals petrochemical plant at Clover Bar, while the pentanes were trucked to Imperial's Edmonton refinery for blending. In 1954, three products pipelines were built to Edmonton: a three-inch line for propane and two two-inch lines for butane and pentanes plus.

When the market for gas, propane and butane flagged, the products went to flare and Imperial found the Conservation Board quite understanding of this kind of waste. If convinced that a market did not exist and that storage was not economical, the Conservation Board recognized that little else could be done. Ted Deacon recalls that flaring was far more likely to bring reprimands from Imperial head office. The Edmonton-Calgary flight path passes close over Leduc-Woodbend and, if an Imperial boss happened to spot a flare from the air, the plant would hear about it the moment the plane touched down.

In the early '50's, Imperial devised another method for dealing with excess gas and products. Seven months after making its strike at Redwater in 1949, Imperial discovered another reservoir four miles west of Woodbend which it called Golden Spike. Golden Spike #1 had an unbelievable 544 foot pay zone, and an initial flow of 12,000 barrels per day of oil. Golden Spike #4 broke even that pay thickness record by going to 560

---

*The BTU (British Thermal Unit) is the measure of a substance's heating value when burned. One BTU is equal to the amount of heat needed to raise one pound of water one degree Fahrenheit.

feet. It was all a little bit too good to be true. As Imperial got to know its new reservoir, it found that it virtually stood on end, with a very small gas cap. As pressure in the reservoir declined and the Conservation Board looked on nervously, full of grim recollections of Turner Valley, Imperial made a decision to try gas injection. First, the company built a pilot plant with one fifty-horsepower G.M.S. compressor pumping the gas. When this proved that the reservoir would take gas, Imperial added a full-size injection plant. The Golden Spike reservoir repressured rapidly on the excess Leduc-Woodbend gas.

A natural question about Imperial's Leduc and Golden Spike ventures is, did they pay? And the answer is that they did not — not for a long time. The large initial investment, the low prices and wavering markets added up to a dependable year-in, year-out loss. But that, in the early years, was the fate of gas conservation processing in Canada.

SHELL JUMPING POUND

A month after Imperial's Leduc plant went on stream, Canadian Western Natural Gas signed an agreement with Shell Oil to purchase natural gas from Shell's sour gas field at Jumping Pound. The Jumping Pound field is twenty miles west of Calgary and the agreement called for Canadian Western to build a pipeline from the field to the city and for Shell to build a plant to sweeten and dehydrate the gas to Canadian Western's

Shell Jumping Pound; built "California-style" with a notable absence of buildings.

specifications. (Jumping Pound gas contained on average 3.5% H_2S and over 6% CO_2.) Before the end of 1951, Jumping Pound gas was also serving the Canada Cement plant at Exshaw and the national park town of Banff.

The Fluor Corporation of Los Angeles designed the Shell Jumping Pound plant. It seemed fairly straight-forward: first, scrub out the H_2S and CO_2; second, absorb the hydrocarbons with oil; and, third, dehydrate the gas with silica gel. Fluor had been using silica gel in the States and found it preferable to glycol.

Originally the H_2S at Jumping Pound was incinerated to form sulphur dioxide which was vented to atmosphere, but in May of 1951, Shell announced it would be building a sulphur plant to be completed the following summer. The Powell River Company, representing a group of West Coast pulp and paper companies, had been shopping for a Canadian source of sulphur for use in their pulp plants. This presented Shell with an opportunity to market another product from Jumping Pound, while solving the always nettlesome problem of H_2S disposal into the bargain.

From the moment Shell Jumping Pound was set out in the foothills of Alberta and put on stream, Mother Nature seemed to have it in for the place. The "open" California design lacked protective buildings like those at Imperial Leduc, which proved an invitation to disaster. On June 6, 1951, only two months after the plant went on stream, a freak blizzard hit southern Alberta. As one newspaper put it: "A small accident at Shell Jumping Pound necessitated a plant shutdown" in the middle of the storm, leaving Canadian Western minus one-third of its gas supply. The utility company maintained service thanks to Turner Valley, but just barely. A few Calgarians must have wondered what fate Canadian Western had consigned them to.

The blizzard was an omen. The winter of 1951-52 struck with vengeful ferocity, catching the California-style plant with its buildings down. The plant personnel, many of whom were from the local farms and communities and newly trained, found themselves confronted by problems that were not in the manual. The combination of sour gas, cold weather and no buildings added up to gas hydrate problems — lots of them — and a continuous ritual of thawing with steam hoses. Even the boilers at Jumping Pound froze, *while they were operating*, a fact that must have boggled the Californian mind. When a Shell field official came to the plant one day that winter and heard all the complaints about frozen boilers, he suggested that the men throw water on the inside walls of the boiler house and turn it into an igloo. No sooner said than done. The ice thickened and the temperature rose, solving one of Jumping Pound's problems at least.

One survivor of that winter is Curly Rowan, a Calgarian by birth who

Curly Rowan (left) with W. E. Saget at Jumping Pound during quieter times; studying the blueprints for an expansion.

had roughnecked on Shell's #3 well at Jumping Pound in 1943. He worked for Fluor during the construction of the Jumping Pound plant and, when it was finished, took a job there. His career with Shell spanned thirty-four years. In other words, Curly Rowan has had an enormous range of experience on which to base comparisons and, when he says that the winter of 1951-52 was a "bugger" and a "stinker" and other things even less printable, we should listen. Rowan is not in an entirely forgiving mood about that winter yet. Perhaps that has something to do with squatting in an open plant yard at thirty below zero trying to set mechanical seals in charge pumps with mitts on. Sometimes Curly would stay out at the plant for days at a stretch. With everyone as green as everyone else, it was often easier to stay than to explain to the next shift what you were trying to do.

That same year, Terry Smith, an engineer at the Imperial Devon plant, left to become the plant superintendent at Jumping Pound. Smith often phoned his old boss, Bill Sage, for advice on what to do about everything from hydrates to frost-heaved foundations. Bill's standard reply was "put up some buildings", which Smith quickly did.

Several young engineers arrived after the first winter: Bill Roman and

Bill Fisher became manager of natural gas marketing for Shell Canada; he started at Jumping Pound in 1952.

Bill Fisher from the University of Toronto, Frank Wood from Queen's and Kevin Milne from McGill. Dr. Martin Winning, a Ph.D. graduate from U of T, came slightly later, but still in 1952. They helped to work out a variety of problems and the plant had settled down considerably by the time the second winter arrived.

The summer of '52 also saw the completion of the sulphur plant at Jumping Pound. It manufactured thirty-five tons of elemental sulphur per day by the modified Claus process. This was the first sulphur plant in Canada, but it held that distinction by a slim margin. The Madison Natural Gas plant at Turner Valley began extracting sulphur by the same process later the same year. Ever since Madison had received its acid gases back from Western Propane, it had also been keeping an eye on the West Coast sulphur shortage.

At Jumping Pound, learning to dynamite the sulphur block presented a few difficulties. The dynamiters had yet to learn the niceties of the controlled, directional explosion and every blast turned into a dangerous adventure. As Bill Fisher puts it: "The first couple of times, you'd've thought the Civil War had started again." But skill came with practice in this and most aspects of the plant Bill Roman calls "Alberta's sour gas laboratory".

Shell had an interesting way of uniting its forces at Jumping Pound. It put its fleet of young Canadian engineers to whatever work was handy during the first months of their stay, thus introducing them to their fellow workers and to the end of a shovel at the same time. Bill Roman remembers being teamed with Bill Fisher and Kevin Milne at the demanding task of painting storage tanks. Fisher also dug ditch and landscaped. Even when doing engineering tasks, they "got damn dirty sometimes." It was a filtering process; those who felt they had not gone to university to wind up in the muck left for drier climes; the fellows who liked the work and the company stuck.

Initiation at Shell Jumping Pound could be swift and, if Curly Rowan was master of ceremonies, usually funny in a hair-raising sort of way. A week after Bill Roman arrived at Jumping Pound, Rowan suggested he take an inside look at one of their taller columns. It had just been cleaned and was about to be put back in service. It would be a good idea, thought Curly, for Bill to get to know the inner workings of the vessel. Roman donned his coveralls and crawled in through the lower manhole. He began wending his way through the trays and was about halfway up when he heard Rowan shout, "Okay, boys, let's button up this vessel and get her started." The manhole clanked shut, bolts slammed in and tightened, and Bill Roman made it out the top in fractions of a second. Curly Rowan was right there, of course, having a good laugh.

The camaraderie that developed, between university man and handyman, between city boy and country boy, both at the plant and over umpteen beers at the *mixed* Cochrane bar, had implications that went beyond the social. It also meant that the engineers, operators and maintenance staff cooperated. Bill Roman remembers that, in working out Jumping Pound's problems, many of the improvements stemmed from reports and suggestions by the operations and maintenance staff. For example, flaring had been the answer to all emergencies in the plant's early days. Bill Roman credits the operators with suggesting other ways of dealing with the upsets. Why not recirculate the stuff or move it somewhere else and contain it? The idea is basic to environmental practices we take for granted today.

Both Bill Roman and Bill Fisher speak with admiration of a certain

The Canadian Western Natural Gas pipeline entering the town of Banff; the source of supply was Jumping Pound.

breed of local handyman that ran Jumping Pound in the early days; men like Curly Rowan, Clarence McGonigle, Lionel Barrows and Scotty McKinnon, to name just a few. In a 1969 *Canadian Gas Journal* article, Curly Rowan was quoted as saying, "I still think some of the best people were the country boys — they didn't have the technical training, but they knew how to work, and they weren't afraid to work." For these men, pranks constituted part of an average work day. Their time was not sacred and they would often put in twelve hours to officially log eight. When things broke down, they fished in the junk bin and haywired them back together. To this day Bill Fisher speaks ruefully of the fact that industry specialization and sophistication has more or less ended the era of such men as these.

Finally, no description of Shell Jumping Pound would be complete without mention of transportation. Most of the workers at Shell Jumping Pound commuted twenty-five miles from Calgary. Curly Rowan lived near Cochrane, and his home became a regular halfway house for disgruntled drivers who had slithered off the road or sunk into it, or were waiting for a Cat to drag them through. The Cochrane Hill was so bad one spring that the company left a Cat sitting on it to pull the travellers up and down. The Cat, like most everything else to do with Jumping Pound, was strictly self-serve.

DEVELOPMENTS FROM 1953-1956

This period saw the construction of seven processing plants in Canada, all in Alberta. All were north of Calgary reflecting the drilling activity that was fanning out steadily from Leduc. All resulted from Conservation Board orders to conserve the gas.

Progas Limited of Calgary built two Grimes portable gas plants in 1954, one at Big Valley and the other at Winterburn to process Acheson gas. Gus van Wielingin, engineer for Progas, had sent Spence Pepper, a propane retailer by trade, to Ardmore, Oklahoma, for a six month crash course on how to build and operate the Grimes plant. The resulting plants at Big Valley and Acheson were small (in the five million cubic feet per day range). In 1956, the Big Valley plant became redundant due to the startup of the B.A. Nevis plant and it had to be closed. Some doubt existed if sour gas could ever be processed on such a small scale, but the Acheson plant has managed to survive to this day on residue gas sales to Northwestern Utilities.

Also in 1954, Texaco built a plant to process Bonnie Glen and Wizard Lake field gas. Texaco located the plant near the settlement of Pigeon Lake, a one time centre for the fur trade and the early Methodist missions. Like Imperial Leduc, Texaco Bonnie Glen was a conservation plant with a poor prognosis as a money maker. Its government-enforced task was to conserve the wet sour gas produced along with the oil.

Rollie Lazerte, a graduate of the University of Alberta, and then of the unofficial university of B. A. Longview, went to Houston in 1953 to participate in the design of the Bonnie Glen plant. He recalls that the winter of 1954 in which the plant came on stream was exceptionally mild, and that Americans who came up to assist this start-up in the far north arrived in parkas and mukluks. It wasn't long before they were down to their shirt-sleeves.

The designers and the contractor, Brown and Root, did a good job of incorporating the best ideas from Imperial Leduc and Jumping Pound. Bonnie Glen used the same processing sequence as these two earlier plants (scrubbing first to confine the corrosion to one place) and it followed the *enclosed* example of Devon rather than the disastrously *open* one of Jumping Pound. As a result the plant was relatively trouble free.

Most of Bonnie Glen's problems were beyond the plant's control. For example, all involved with the plant soon discovered what happens when gas production is tied to oil in a period of oil glut. At times, barely enough gas passed through the plant to keep it running. Markets for the products were also sporadic. Northwestern Utilities took the residue gas and the

local market absorbed the other hydrocarbon products — sometimes.
Tilton Adair, who has been with the plant since day-one rising finally to the
rank of superintendent, remembers that small tank trucks would occasionally be lined up first thing in the morning to load propane. At other times,
products could not be given away and had to be flared. Years later, Texaco
absented itself completely from such marketing problems by injecting its
gas and most of its other products in a miscible flood to enhance oil
recovery.

Three more plants were built in 1956, a bumper crop considering that
no gas export had yet been authorized by the Alberta Petroleum and
Natural Gas Conservation Board. Imperial Redwater, Gulf Nevis and
Western Leaseholds Hobbema were all related to oil and existed to meet
Conservation Board requirements.

Opening day at the Imperial Redwater conservation plant; 1956.

The Redwater field had been producing oil and flaring solution gas
since 1949 but, because of a low gas-oil ratio, Imperial was not obliged to
conserve the Redwater gas until 1956. Imperial patterned the Redwater
plant closely on its first and successful Leduc plant, with the exception that
Redwater gas, being more sour, called for the recovery of elemental sulphur.
The plant design took place mainly in Edmonton, carried out by an
Imperial team of Jim Haliburton, Stu Mason and Doug Howell, under the

supervision of Bill Sage. The contractor was Brown and Root and two of that company's young engineers on the project, Tommy Morimoto and Spence Landis, went on to careers that one informant calls "world class".

Though Bill Sage wryly suggests that Imperial took most of its Devon mistakes to Redwater, certain changes were made. The dehydration system differed; the vacuum assist on the glycol regeneration system had been removed, which meant Redwater could not reach as deep a chill without courting a hydrate problem. Pipe vibration at Devon had necessitated installation of over ninety pipe supports. At Redwater, this was corrected in the design. The plant supplied its own power with an Ingersoll-Rand, four-cycle generator fueled with natural gas. Stu Mason is rather proud of Redwater's graded gathering system which sloped toward the plant with no humps and hollows reducing the likelihood of hydrates and liquid plugs; it also came in handy in later years with the introduction of two-phase flow.

The consensus is that Brown and Root did a good job at Redwater, but not a perfect job. When completed, the plant's gas fractionator simply would not run. As Bill Sage and the Brown and Root representative looked on, Bill said, "I'll bet you any money someone left a pair of welding gloves in there." The contractor said that was impossible. Bill made it interesting by putting a bottle of the finest on the line and they opened up the vessel. Welding gloves it was and Bill had himself a bottle.

As for markets, Mutual Propane tanked propane from the plant for local use and some propane went by railway tank car to Ontario for tobacco drying. As much as possible, the butanes and pentanes were put back into the oil to boost the A.P.I. gravity a notch. This garnered a slightly higher price per barrel of oil. As for the sulphur, Redwater was fortunate to get a five year contract with a sulphuric acid plant in Fort Saskatchewan at $25 per ton (a price to be envied a full decade later).

The most ambitious, and troubled venture in this 1953 to 1956 period was probably the Stettler Area Gas Conservation Project. It consisted of three plants all operated by Canadian Gulf: two satellite plants in the Fenn-Big Valley and Stettler fields feeding a main plant at Nevis. The scheme was designed by a young gas engineer by the name of Don Wolcott. It was an unusual contract in that the various producers gave Gulf their gas for free (to meet gas conservation requirements) on the understanding that they would get something back if Gulf made money. As soon as Don Wolcott had clinched the deal for Gulf, he departed. He went to work for Provo Gas Producers Ltd., a subsidiary of young Dome Exploration (Western) Ltd., a company he would help to grow dramatically.

The Stettler area project involved compressing, dehydrating and chilling the field gas at the satellite plants to effect a separation into condensate and residue gas. Gulf pipelined the condensate west to Nevis for fractionation into propane, butane and natural gasoline. (A sweetening unit was added to the Nevis plant shortly after start-up.)

The system differed in many ways from the Canadian plants that had preceded it. The satellite idea was new, and so was the pipelining of sour condensate. The Nevis plant also had a quite different way of dealing with condensate CO_2 and H_2S in their fractionation plant. The deethanizer was operated in such a way that the bulk of the acid gases was driven off overhead. The propane and heavier hydrocarbons left the vessel at the bottom and were further sweetened by caustic wash.

Earl Scott, an engineer whose long career began with Gulf at Stettler, says that the Stettler Area Gas Conservation Plant was also different in that it did not conserve gas! Initially, the residue gas from the satellites was flared. Later, six-inch sour gas pipelines were built to gather the satellite residue gas into the Nevis plant for sweetening and sale to Canadian Western Natural Gas.

Project engineer for the Stettler project was R. F. "Bob" Cunningham. Cunningham had started in the industry at the same time as Don Wolcott. When Gulf handed the project to him, he had been out of school three years. In those years, it was not unusual to gain experience through such a baptism-by-fire.

The winning bid for the construction contract belonged to a newly formed company called Mannix-Gill, a hybrid of the Canadian Mannix construction company and the American firm, J.B. Gill. Chief engineer on the Stettler project for Mannix-Gill was Wally Palmer, an American who had been in the industry since the 1920's.

Wally Palmer is one of those characters about whom everyone seems to have an anecdote. Bob Cunningham remembers Palmer as a unique mixture of patience and impatience. For people who wanted to argue with him, he had no time; for those who wanted to learn, he had lots of time. An example of the impatient side of Palmer is related by Harry Wanjoe, a draftsman for Mannix-Gill on the Stettler project. One morning, Wally Palmer came into the office to find his desk locked. He asked a secretary why this was so and she told him it had been done as a new security precaution. Palmer sauntered out. Face unchanged, he returned with a hammer and reduced his deck to kindling in order to get out of it what he needed.

Bob Cunningham remembers another story that points up Palmer's decisiveness. Shortly before the three plant Stettler project was due to start up, Palmer and Cunningham went to look at the Fenn-Big Valley satellite. As Palmer walked through the plant compressor station, he stared down

Bob Cunningham (1) and Wally Palmer, about to take off for the Gordondale area where Canadian Fina was building gas gathering and compression facilities (1957).

through the iron grid at the network of pipes below the floor. "I don't like it, I don't like it," he grumbled. Finally, turning to his construction superintendent, he said, "I want all of this out." He walked over to the construction shack, drew a picture and that was that. Even at 1956 prices, it was probably a hundred thousand dollar decision.

The odd thing is that, even with this kind of experience and professional ethics at work, the completed plant was beset by a series of operating problems. First of all, reminiscent of Jumping Pound, the plant was prone to hydrates and the weather seemed determined to help point the problem out. On September 21, 1955, during the construction phase, central Alberta was hit by a vicious blizzard. The mercury plummeted and stayed huddled at the bottom of the thermometer for much of the ensuing winter. The project started up in mid-winter and problems that might have revealed themselves gradually in milder weather cropped up all at once.

In designing the aerial coolers, for example, the quite reasonable assumption had been made that water could be used as a coolant, provided it was kept in motion. Everyone was about to learn that flowing water *will* freeze if it gets cold enough! Also, gas hydrates were forming all over the system: at Fenn-Big Valley where the amine regenerator froze up, and in the pipelines between the satellites and Nevis. During construction, no drips had been installed in the pipelines. There had been uncertainty about where they should go and the idea had been to wait and put them in later. However, once the plant was operating, there was a reluctance to shut it down to make changes. Liquids built up in the low-pressure gathering system and blocked the flow. With the volume of liquids to the plant cut off, the plant would not run.

Actually, the liquid blockages only amplified another chronic problem. The plants had been designed for a far greater volume of liquids than was ever realized. The size of facilities in the Nevis plant anticipated a flow of 2000 barrels of liquids per day, and got from 600 to 800. At the lower flows, some of the automatic control valves in the plant would shut in.

All of this could be fixed, given the money; but the money for proper winterization and streamlining came slowly. To understand why, certain industry-wide attitudes and economic facts have to be understood. For one thing, these were *oil* companies, not gas companies, and the men at the top were *oil* men who, according to one informant, ran their gas plants like oil field batteries. Natural gas was looked upon as a damn nuisance; at best, a necessary evil. In Alberta, the rules of the game were such that, to be in the oil business, you sometimes had to be in the gas business too, but it was definitely obligation rather than choice.

Sound financial reasons existed for the prejudice. A good oil well would pay back a company's investment in two years; the average gas plant could take twenty years to pay — if it paid out at all.

Gordon Barnes tells a story that epitomizes this. Barnes returned to the gas business at Stettler after a brief stint in the petrochemical industry at Clover Bar. His boss at Gulf was Kelly Gibson, who Gordon describes as "a dyed-in-the-wool oil man" at the time. Early on, Gibson asked Barnes to give a talk to the Stettler community on the impact the gas plants would have on the area. Barnes consented gladly and, in the midst of his speech, he coined the bon mot: "Crude oil is fast becoming the by-product of natural gas." Barnes happened to look down to where his boss was sitting about that time and found that Kelly Gibson had turned a violent shade of red.

After his speech, Gordon Barnes stepped down from the podium wondering if he still had a job. He went to Gibson who immediately asked him who had authorized his speech. Barnes answered that no one had and that it wasn't a speech, just his opinion. In no uncertain terms, Gibson told

Barnes that he had better start remembering that he worked for an *oil* company.

Not long after this Kelly Gibson left Gulf to work for Pacific Petroleums Limited. He became deeply involved with Westcoast Transmission's scheme to supply the B.C. Lower Mainland and the American Pacific Northwest with gas. Just one year after the fiery evening in the Stettler community hall, both Gordon Barnes and Kelly Gibson were scheduled to speak at a function in Calgary. Gibson was first up and, to Gordon Barnes' total amazement, his speech led up to the resounding assertion that:

"Crude oil is fast becoming the by-product of natural gas."

When the two met after the speeches, Gibson answered Barnes' question before it was asked. "Times change, Gordon," he said. "Times change."

Kelly Gibson. When the economics of gas processing improved, he learned to like the business.

Times do indeed change and the money was found eventually to resolve most of Stettler's difficulties. According to Gordon Barnes, it cost three million to set things right, about the same amount it had cost to build the plants in the first place.

Earl Scott had the job of fixing up the Stettler area gathering system. He installed pressure taps and drips on the lines so they would not hydrate or plug as easily. Condensate was taken off the drips by the truckload and Earl suggests that, at times, this operation made more money than the Nevis gas plant. The problems with sour gas at Nevis reinforced the experience gained at Jumping Pound and contributed a valuable piece of

*Earl Scott came west with Gulf in 1954; he joined the
Goliad Oil and Gas Company in 1957.*

information to the industry: that sour gas would hydrate at significantly
higher temperatures than sweet gas.

The final change affecting the Stettler Area Conservation Project came
when British American Oil acquired controlling interest in Canadian Gulf
through an exchange of shares. It was a reverse take-over in that U.S. Gulf
owned the controlling interest in British American and, therefore, controlled the Canadian version of B.A. as well. To further confuse matters it
should be added that, in a change of name only, B.A. became Gulf Canada
Resources Inc. in 1968.

The final plant built before 1957, and just barely, was the Western
Leaseholds Limited facility at Hobbema. This simple and small plant
(three million cubic feet a day) separated the sweet solution gas from the
Samson Indian Reserve. The plant also dehydrated the gas and removed the
LPGs prior to delivery into the Northwestern Utilities system. This was
another Mannix-Gill plant, completed in December of 1956.

*   *   *

What makes all these conservation plants similar, and justifies their
separation from the many plants built after '56 is mainly their brotherhood
of poverty. Most of them would make money eventually, but it would have
been difficult to convince anyone of that fact in the early '50's. The plants
were built because the Conservation Board said they should be built — and
for no other reason. As of 1957, much of this changed. A market was

created and the industry responded with a flurry of construction. The day when you could count all the gas processing plants in Canada on two hands was over.

Another point that should be made before leaving this chapter is one in defence of all those who made mistakes in the building and operation of these early Canadian plants. These were good engineers, obeying principles and precedents that had served them well in the past. That in a way *was* the problem. Canadian climate and Canadian gas differed so much that the *tried and true* became the failed and false more often than not. It took a long time to analyze Canadian gas, to gather reliable data on its physical properties. Until those studies had been completed, construction and processing engineers had no alternative but to try things out and, when they failed, to try something else. Often, that was how the answers were found.

The Canadian prairies receive the Trans-Canada pipeline, 1957.

THREE PIPELINES: THE LONG ROAD TO MARKET

5

Growth in the Canadian processing industry has always been, and will always be, contingent on the development of access to markets in the population centres of North America. As long as that market was confined to Alberta, the industry stayed small, a poor relative to more going concerns. The primary objection to letting the gas leave Alberta was the Province's natural determination to meet its own needs first. Later, when reserves had been proven beyond Alberta's foreseeable needs, it was Canada's turn to worry about whether natural gas should be conserved for the future needs of the nation. Before more natural gas could leave Canada, reserves had to rise to a point where the whole country felt secure.

With each broadening of the market, the gas processing industry grew. It grew not only in size but in sophistication. As the market demanded more natural gas, Canadian companies had to find that gas in deeper, higher pressure sour reservoirs. From this comes the Canadian excellence in the processing of sour gas and the recovery of sulphur.

None of this would have been possible, however, without a concerted effort on the part of producing companies, pipeline entrepreneurs, gas utility companies and certain members of government who removed the obstacles and built the apparatus necessary to move natural gas to market.

GAS FOR BRITISH COLUMBIA AND THE PACIFIC NORTHWEST

The story of how Alberta natural gas began to move from its rock reservoirs to markets outside the province begins at Leduc. The quantities of gas found with the oil, and in the search for oil, infused a number of entrepreneurs with the notion that Alberta had gas beyond its needs; gas that could go for export. In the late 1940's, some of these businessmen applied to the Alberta government for permission to export gas, and the government found itself short of knowledge and methods for dealing with such a question.

This situation produced a Royal Commission known as the Dinning Commission. The Alberta government called the Dinning Commission and heard its report in 1949. It contained the key statistic that Alberta's proven reserves of gas were 4.126 trillion cubic feet. The report suggested that Alberta see to its own fifty year needs first, which amounted to a rejection of exports for some time to come. The Commission report was a setback for natural gas producers, processors and pipeliners alike but various companies managed enough pressure on the government that the legislation leading from the Commission did not slam the door on export entirely. For one thing, the 1949 Gas Resources Preservation Act gave the Conservation Board the right to set the period for which Alberta's foreseeable needs must be met. The Board decided on a period of thirty years rather than the Dinning Commission's suggested fifty years. It also gave the Conservation Board the authority to hear all future applications for export of natural gas from the province.

The Conservation Board members at this time were: chairman, Ian McKinnon; vice-chairman, D. P. "Red" Goodall; and, third member, Dr. George Govier. The Board braced for a deluge of applications and received five: three to serve Lower Mainland British Columbia and the American Pacific Northwest with gas; one to serve Montana and the last to move Alberta gas east to Manitoba and Minnesota.

The elder statesman among the applicants seeking to send Alberta gas west was Frank McMahon; he had been trying various ways of getting gas to Vancouver for twenty years. A native of B.C., Frank McMahon grew up in the ramshackle boom towns of that province's interior. He had first looked for a Pacific gas supply in the Fraser River Delta. When the Delta proved dry, he shifted his sites to Pouce Coupe in the Peace River country far to the north. It was an astute move for the Peace was one of the last large portions of Canada's western sedimentary basin to remain largely unexplored.

While McMahon founded several companies and drilled successfully at both Turner Valley and Leduc, the Peace River country and Pouce Coupe never lost their place in his thoughts. His proposal to the Alberta Conservation Board in 1950 to take gas from the Alberta side of the Pouce Coupe field was part of a larger plan to take yet undiscovered gas from B.C. and Alberta hundreds of miles by pipeline to the cities of the West Coast. McMahon created Westcoast Transmission Ltd. as a corporate mechanism for fulfilling these goals.

Westcoast's competitors for supply to the Pacific included the Northwest Natural Gas Co. * (sponsored by the experienced New York geological firm Brokaw, Dixon and McKee) and Prairie Pipe Lines Limited (originally backed by a Toronto group, but later handed over to Ray Fish, a natural gas

---

*Another company, the Alberta Natural Gas Co., was founded by this group to carry the gas within Canada. The bill to create this company in the Federal House sparked the national gas export debate, which in its various forms lasted many years.

pipeline promoter from Houston). Both of these proposals involved taking southern Alberta gas through the Crowsnest Pass into British Columbia and then down to markets in the U.S. The Vancouver area would be served in both schemes by a spur line or lateral off the main.

The only applicant in the first round battle interested in taking gas east was Western Pipelines Limited, a Winnipeg based group led by the Osler, Hammond and Nanton brokerage firm of which L. D. M. Baxter was president. The Western Pipelines plan called for Alberta gas to be piped east to Winnipeg and points in between and also for export to the American Midwest.

The final applicant was the team of McColl-Frontenac and Union Oil of California who wished to export gas to the Montana Power Corporation.

There is little need to go into the pros and cons of the various applications because all were simultaneously laid low by the Conservation Board in 1951. The Board concluded that Alberta's reserves were 4.439 trillion cubic feet, only marginally higher than those found by the Dinning Commission. This was not enough for the thirty year needs of Albertans and export remained out of the question. But again the Alberta government left the door to export open a crack. Although the Board could not recommend export at this time, it encouraged companies to explore and prove up new reserves that might be exportable in future.

This decision was unequivocal and seemed likely to set export aside for at least a few years, but the granting of the first permit for export of gas from Alberta came quickly on June 11, 1951. The permit went to McColl-Frontenac and Union Oil for the export of ten billion cubic feet per year for five years to the Montana Power Corporation from the Pakowki Lake area of southeastern Alberta. At first glance, the permit seems to contradict the legislation that preceded it, but actually it represented no change in policy. The granting of this export came as a result of special lobbying from the U.S. military and special pressure from the Canadian Federal Government on the Alberta Provincial Government. The Anaconda Copper Mining Company in Montana needed gas in order to run its Butte smelter and both the U.S. and Canadian governments regarded the supply of copper from this smelter as necessary to North American defence during the Korean War. The Alberta government obliged these interests with a special Gas Export Act to allow the gas export to Montana, but the Conservation Board made certain everyone knew that the Pakowki Lake gas was not regarded as surplus to Alberta's needs and that other companies seeking gas export could expect to continue their wait. The first gas export from Alberta owed more, therefore, to the Korean War than it did to any particular desire by Alberta to part with its gas.

Canadian Gulf, with its huge shut-in reservoir at Pincher Creek, felt particularly unhappy about the Board's decision. Gulf along with others in the industry saw Alberta's insistence on proven reserves as overly cautious. Ironically, Dr. G. S. Hume, whose reserve estimates had been used by the Dinning Commission to quash export in 1949, was one of those who felt proven reserves were not relevant to the export question. In a 1949 article in *Canadian Oil and Gas Industries*, Hume wrote:

> Widespread evidence of gas together with the favourable geological condition of its occurrences makes it safe to infer that the potential gas reserves of Alberta are enormous, exceeding by many times the proven and indicated reserves of 4.2 TCF* as of November, 1948.

As proof by comparison he brought up the American situation:

> The history of gas fields in the gas producing areas of the U.S. has clearly shown that an assured market develops large reserves.

But, for the time being, it remained a dismal *Catch-22* situation. Without a market, most companies could see no sense in drilling for gas. Without reserves proven by successful drilling, the government was not about to allow the market to come into existence. To break the stalemate, true gamblers were needed and, in timely fashion, Clint Murchison paid Canada a visit.

Clint Murchison was a very successful Texas businessman (not to be confused with his son of the same name who until recently owned the Dallas Cowboys). Murchison had watched the Leduc strike with great interest, matching in his mind the great gas potential of Alberta with the serious energy drought in the cities of Canada's East. After a trip to Ottawa in 1949, he decided to turn that daydream into a pipeline.

Murchison was president of the Delhi Oil Corporation in the U.S. and, to pursue his Canadian plan he founded a subsidiary called Canadian Delhi Oil Ltd. When Canadian Delhi entered the exploration scene in 1950, heads turned immediately, for out of the many companies exploring the Canadian frontier, only Canadian Delhi was looking for *gas*. Murchison's plan was to find enough natural gas to boost Alberta's reserves to an exportable level. Then, to transport that surplus to the Eastern market, Clint Murchison created another company, Trans-Canada Pipe Lines Limited (TCPL).

In September of 1951, the Alberta Petroleum and Natural Gas Conservation Board reopened its gas export hearings and brought on another deluge of work for its small gas department, anchored in Calgary

---

*trillion cube feet

by veteran field staff member Dick King, and his associates Vern Horte and Ed Foo. Board Member Dr. George Govier became so busy during the hearings that he often had to call upon one of the Board's bright young engineers, Doug Craig, to stand in for him as a lecturer in the engineering faculty of the University of Alberta. The situation became more difficult still in 1952 when Verne Horte left the Board to work for reservoir specialists DeGolyer and McNaughton. This resulted in Jack Stabback's being brought in from the field to serve as gas engineer in Calgary. In a sense the Board intensified its own staffing problems by its high employment standards. It was always the philosophy of the Board to hire top technical people who could talk to the industry at its own level. This meant competing with industry for the brightest young technicians and engineers.

The applicants before the Conservation Board in 1951 again numbered five. McColl-Frontenac and Union Oil were gone (having received their special permit for export) and Trans-Canada Pipe Lines was in. After looking Canada over carefully, Clint Murchison geared his proposal to a probable upswing in Canadian nationalism. He reckoned on a certain amount of anti-American bias and hoped to counter it with an all-Canadian route. Despite the economic disadvantages, he proposed to crack a path across the Canadian Shield.

Another Murchison device for winning Canada's favour proved less astute. Recalling the Canadian popularity enjoyed at one time by Edward,

Edward Prince of Wales sharing a corral rail with Archie McClean (left) and George Lane (centre), two of Calgary's Big Four, in 1923.

Prince of Wales, especially after World War I when his EP Ranch in southern Alberta had been a social centre for the elite, Murchison asked Edward, now Duke of Windsor, to be TCPL's chairman of the board. Edward accepted and received 61,000 shares of Canadian Delhi for the exceptionally good price of 10¢ apiece. When Murchison's Canadian lawyers heard of this, there was much anguished muttering about abdication, marriage to a divorcee and other well-known reasons (well known in the Commonwealth at any rate) why Edward was the darling of the Canadian public no longer. The announcement of the Duke's chairmanship was never made. The Prince of Wales held onto his shares for a judicious period of time, reportedly selling out in the vicinity of $10 per share.

Edward Duke of Windsor with the Duchess and Royalite's R. E. Trammell during a 1940's visit to Turner Valley.

But once again all the maneuvering was robbed of its consequence when the Conservation Board published its conclusions in March of 1952. Again the Board ruled out all projects (including TCPL's) based on gas from southern Alberta. The Board did not rule against all the applications, however. Alberta's reserves now stood at 6.8 TCF, with excellent and obvious prospects of growth beyond that to at least 8 to 10 TCF. The amount needed to serve Alberta's thirty year needs was calculated at 4.2 TCF for which 6.5 TCF of proven reserves would be needed to meet the deliverability requirements. That left a relatively slim margin of 300 billion cubic feet of surplus. At this point, Westcoast Transmission was rewarded for the remoteness of its reserves. The Conservation Board deemed Westcoast's Alberta gas reserves near Peace River beyond the economic reach of Alberta's population centres and gave the company permission to export 42 billion cubic feet of that natural gas per year for the next five years.

Westcoast was on a roll. Five months earlier its exploration in northeast British Columbia had finally paid off with a 71 million cubic feet a day gas well near Fort St. John. The 650 mile transmission system which had seemed so incredible at first was now showing definite signs of feasibility. Not everyone agreed, of course. One oil executive called the permit granted to Westcoast by Alberta "a license to commit suicide".

Westcoast still had two regulatory hurdles to jump: the Canadian Federal Government and the U.S. Federal Power Commission. The Canadian government was not much of an obstacle because the powerful Minister of Trade and Commerce, C. D. Howe, had already expressed his determination to see Canadian gas in the Pacific Northwest. Howe considered the lack of reliable fuel supply in that region one of the major weaknesses in North American defence.

At the Federal Power Commission (FPC) hearings, however, Westcoast found itself opposed once again by Ray Fish. This time, the Houston entrepreneur sported an *All-American* plan to bring gas to the Pacific Northwest from Texas. Everything that had worked for Westcoast in Canada worked for Ray Fish in the United States. His project would supply America *from* America; all capital expenditures would be made *in* America. The Westcoast application was denied.

One has to marvel at Frank McMahon's tenacity. When many would have given up, he did not. All he gave up at this point was his plan for distributing gas in the U.S. through his own American subsidiary. By late 1954, after a tremendous amount of hard bargaining, he reached an accommodation with the Ray Fish interests, with El Paso Natural Gas and with Pacific Gas and Electric of San Francisco such that Westcoast would bring its natural gas as far as the international boundary. American companies would take it from there.

The FPC gave its approval to the revised plan and the long regulatory war ended. After that long struggle, the building of 650 miles of pipeline through some of the world's most rugged terrain and the construction of a gas processing plant farther north than ever attempted before probably seemed like *relatively* minor obstacles.

Frank McMahon. *When most would have given up, he held on.*

GAS FOR EASTERN CANADA

The decision to grant an export permit to Westcoast thinned the ranks of applicants to the Conservation Board in Alberta. For a time, only Western Pipelines and Trans-Canada Pipe Lines persisted, both vying for the right to take southern Alberta gas east.

The stumbling block remained the quantity of proven reserves and Canadian Delhi kept drilling wells to up that number. Smiley Raborn, a Louisiana man in charge of exploration for Canadian Delhi, had in three years managed participation in 98 wells, including 36 gas producers and five oil wells. (What a switch to be finding oil while in the pursuit of gas!) The program's most significant achievement was the discovery of the Cessford field, a large accumulation of sweet, dry gas about 100 miles east of Calgary.

The other major increase in gas reserves came from oil exploration. The oil explorers of the early 1950's were beginning to understand that the oil finds of the late '40's were from reefs of Devonian age. As they followed the trend of these reef systems, more oil was found — and more gas*. The Conservation Board and the gas export applicants kept careful track of all gas found because each find increased the magic proven reserves number and brought expanded gas export a bit closer.

A bugbear in the calculation of reserves for all concerned was the Pincher Creek field. This sizeable wet sour gas field had a reservoir rock of low porosity and low permeability. The joker in the pack was a fracture system that crossed the reservoir. Some of the top reservoir engineers in the world differed in opinion when it came to a calculation of reserves for the Pincher Creek field. Some believed that gas from the tight reservoir rock would bleed into the fracture zone as it was emptied of gas, thus improving deliverability. Others held that the fracture zone would fill with water when it was emptied of gas, killing the field. Reservoir expert Ralph E. Davis represented Alberta's gas utilities during the gas export hearings of the 1950's and he was one of those who doubted the deliverability of the Pincher Creek reservoir. The majority of people in the industry sided with the optimistic assessments, however, and deliverable reserve estimates for Pincher Creek were set as high as three trillion cubic feet and seldom lower than 1.7 trillion.

---

*The oil finds followed two reef systems. The first, known as "The Golden Trend" included (from north to south): Glen Park, Wizard Lake, Bonnie Glen, Westerose, Westerose South, Homeglen and Rimbey. The second trend (also from north to south) included: Duhamel, New Norway, Bashaw, Clive, Erskine, Stettler, Big Valley and Drumheller.

In any case, finding gas remained a much less formidable problem than the politics of moving it. Smiley Raborn, who later became president of Canadian Delhi and a member of the TCPL board of directors, summed up TCPL's propects for 1953 this way: "The political problems looked insurmountable and we had no assurance of eventually succeeding; but we were too involved now to withdraw."

Early in 1953, C. D. Howe wrote the Alberta Premier, Ernest Manning, to let him know that Ottawa would not allow any additional gas

Ernest Manning in 1943, the year he became Alberta's Premier.

export to the U.S. until the needs of Ontario and Quebec had been met. In March, 1953, Howe made a similar *Canada-first* statement to the House. All this looked very good for the *All-Canadian* approach championed by Clint Murchison and TCPL, and very bad for Western Pipelines whose proposal did not extend to Ontario and Quebec. However, late in 1953, Alberta agreed to supply gas for *both* schemes, and C. D. Howe delivered an ultimatum instructing TCPL and Western Pipelines to merge their projects. The 50-50 amalgamation of companies that resulted (or "shotgun marriage", as Smiley Raborn calls it) was distasteful in the extreme to the backers of TCPL. But it was clearly that or nothing.

The new company retained the Trans-Canada Pipe Lines name. Its immediate needs included the appointment of a president who could deal effectively with the levels of government involved, and the hiring of an engineer who could actually build a pipeline. The top candidate for president (some say on the advice of Ernest Manning) was Nathan Eldon Tanner, the former Alberta Minister of Lands and Mines. Tanner was enjoying his business ventures and the prospect of wading into a long regulatory battle with government did not entice him particularly. He drove a hard bargain, the fruits of which (stock options and a retirement allowance) would be much criticized in years to come.

In a somewhat amazing coup the new president lured Charlie Coates, one of the top pipeline men in the world, away from the world's largest pipeline company, Tennessee Gas Transmission in the U.S.A. Coates became Tanner's executive vice-president. Western Pipelines was represented on the new TCPL board by four people including Ray Milner, president of both Canadian Western Natural Gas and Northwestern Utilities.

Even this powerful team came close to defeat in the political machinations to come. The U.S. Federal Power Commission looked upon the TCPL application to move Canadian gas into the American Midwest with the same jaundiced eye it was casting on Westcoast's plans for the U.S. Pacific Northwest. Among other things, TCPL had not signed up sufficient reserves in Alberta. The situation took a long step in the wrong direction when TCPL was forced to accept government assistance in order not to lose a contract for U.S. pipe. In exchange for its help, the Bank of Canada insisted on control of the company. Gulf, which had a policy against doing business with government-controlled entities, promptly refused to sell TCPL any gas. As Gulf now controlled B.A. and thus owned the Pincher Creek field on which TCPL was counting for supply, TCPL's chances before the FPC looked very gloomy.

Then two events occurred which, when put together, were like a hammer and a blasting cap. First, Mitchell Sharp, C. D. Howe's deputy minister, came up with a plan by which the unfinanceable Canadian Shield portion of the pipeline could be built. The government would simply create a crown corporation which would build that segment and then lease it back to TCPL. It seemed a good idea until TCPL, in desperate need of money for pipe once again, sold 51% of itself to three American companies: Hudson's Bay Oil and Gas (HBOG), Gulf and Tennessee Gas Transmission.

The press and the opposition had a field day. For the nationalists, it had been bad enough that an American had originated the all-Canadian pipeline idea; it was worse that an American company, Gulf, had been telling Canada of late what proportion of its pipeline the nation might own; but it was the very final straw that the national pipeline was now no longer Canadian, and that the government was introducing a bill to the House asking for money to build it on behalf of the American companies who owned it.

The controversy focussed during the spring sitting of the House of Parliament, 1956. C. D. Howe had to get the bill to create the Northern Ontario Pipeline Crown Corporation through the House by the end of session or at least another year of pipeline construction would be lost. Faced with the determination of the opposition parties to obstruct the bill's passage, Howe did an incredible thing: he invoked closure of debate before debate had begun. As the opposition would point out many times (especially Stanley Knowles of the CCF), such a stifling of debate ran absolutely counter to the traditions of Canadian parliamentary democracy. To let the action pass would create a situation where any party enjoying a majority could merrily pass any legislation it wished without discussion. Dictatorship of the majority, by George, and Canadians weren't going to stand for it!

The resulting conflict goes by the name *The Great Pipeline Debate of 1956*, but the pipeline was in a sense forgotten in the grand procedural wrangle that occupied the House. The opposition employed every tactic, exploited every technicality; but, on the very last day, the bill *did* pass, and construction of the pipeline was finally able to begin.

CONSTRUCTION OF THE WESTCOAST AND TCPL PIPELINES

It is interesting to contemplate that 150 or so years before Frank McMahon built his pipeline from Peace River to Vancouver, explorer David Thompson began to use a similar route in his fur trade with the Indians. Thompson overcame the obstacles of topography and climate to supply the

Construction of the Trans-Canada pipeline begins; thirty-four inch pipe being unloaded at Burstall, Saskatchewan, in 1956.

West Coast Indian people with the guns, tools and household goods that vanquished the Stone Age and changed their way of life forever. By late 1957, Frank McMahon had overcome the same physical obstacles, plus a mountain of paper, to perform a similar function for the West Coast inhabitants of the 20th century. Though hardly in the Stone Age, the Pacific Coast on both sides of the 49th parallel was being held back in its development by a lack of economical fuel. The supplies of natural gas McMahon brought west represented an opportunity for industrial growth that has translated into prosperity ever since.

The fur trade analogy does not work nearly as well for the TCPL transportation route, but another kind of analogy does. As William Kilbourn has pointed out in his fine book PIPELINE, the incredible TCPL undertaking is comparable to the construction of the Trans-Canada railway at the end of the 19th century. For more detail on the financing and construction of both pipelines, we refer you to Kilbourn's PIPELINE and another good book on Westcoast Transmission's development: WILDCAT-TERS by Earle Gray.

For the purposes of this book, suffice it to say that the Westcoast Transmission line was completed on August 28, 1957, at a cost of $180 million (230,000 tons of steel), while the final weld on the longer TCPL main line was made at Kapuskasing in northern Ontario in October of 1958. The big construction year for TCPL was 1957 when they completed the line from Alberta to Winnipeg, from Winnipeg to the Lakehead, and from Toronto to Montreal and Ottawa.

ALBERTA GAS TRUNK LINE

For TCPL to carry Alberta gas from the Saskatchewan-Alberta border to Eastern Canada, someone had to collect that gas within Alberta and deliver it to the point of exit. For that purpose, the Alberta government created a new corporate entity, Alberta Gas Trunk Line (AGTL). This new company was conceived in the heat of the first export hearings before the Conservation Board in 1950. During the joint hearings that year, Alberta Interfield Gas Lines Limited presented itself, offering to act as the sole, integrated, gas-gathering body for the province. Behind Interfield stood

Behind Interfield stood Ray Milner of Edmonton, a sort of Alberta entrepreneurial colossus. Milner was president of both Alberta gas utilities, a principal backer of the Western Pipe Lines scheme and thus an eventual TCPL director.

Ray Milner of Edmonton, a sort of Alberta entrepreneurial colossus. Milner was both president of Alberta's gas utilities and one of the principal backers of the Western Pipelines scheme. Later he became a TCPL director and a promoter of the Alberta and Southern Gas Company.

The Conservation Board liked the Interfield concept; what it did not care for was the idea of such an influential company being solely in the hands of the utilities. The Board recommended to the Alberta Government the creation of the same *type* of company described by Interfield, but one controlled by all interested parties: the utilities, producers, pipelines and government. The Government took the Board's advice and, on April 8, 1954, by a special act of the Alberta Legislature, Alberta Gas Trunk Line was born.

The first executive of AGTL contained quite an assemblage of experience. The first president was Vernon Taylor. Back in the 1930's, Taylor had been a resident geologist in Turner Valley for the Alberta government. Later, he joined Royalite, rising through the Royalite/Imperial ranks to the status of senior vice-president. William Knode, the Texan who had been the first chairman of the Conservation Board in 1938, consented to be AGTL's first general manager. James C. Mahaffy, Q.C., legal counsel for Interfield was named secretary-treasurer.

The timing of AGTL's incorporation had been geared to the probable date of construction of the Trans-Canada pipeline, but as we have seen there is no such thing as probability when it comes to pipelines. In late 1956, after two inactive years, AGTL began laying pipe and issued its first common shares. Share sale was initially limited to Albertans and a stock bonanza ensued the like of which had not been seen since the glory days of Dingman #1.

Fulton-Banister Ltd.*, "Canada's first wholly Canadian-owned major pipeline constructors", received the contract to build the first leg of the AGTL line from the South Bindloss field across the Red Deer and South Saskatchewan Rivers to the TCPL border gate near Burstall, Saskatchewan. For the most part, the line crossed flat land, but the river crossings presented some technological challenges. To cross the South Saskatchewn, two 120 foot high towers had to be built and the pipeline suspended between them.

---

*Before AGTL began construction of its lines, Banister Construction had done big-inch contract pipeline work for Interprovincial Pipe Line and Saskatchewan Power Corporation. Fulton, an Oklahoma pipeline contractor, joined forces with Banister to provide expansion capital in anticipation of the Trans-Canada pipeline.

James C. Mahaffy; secretary-treasurer, then general manager, then president of AGTL.

The first leg was completed by July 10, 1957, and a ceremony took place two weeks later near Cavendish, Alberta, to celebrate the turning of the valve that sent export gas into the system for the first time. Premier Manning supplied the muscle and a crowd of 300 stood on the wind-swept prairie to watch him. Among the celebrities on hand were Vernon Taylor, William Knode and James Mahaffy of AGTL. (Knode had just handed the cudgel of general managership on to Mahaffy.) Alex G. Bailey of the Bailey Selburn Oil and Gas Company represented the Bindloss producers who owned the gas that was being delivered. Frank McMahon also attended.

As McMahon looked on, he must have been a little distracted. It would have been understandable if his mind, rather than being on the speeches, was off in the Rocky Mountain Trench where his crews were putting pipe in the last gap in the Westcoast system. One wonders if he found it odd or ironic at all that, after all the years of struggle and separate destiny, gas was entering the TCPL line for the first time within about a month of Westcoast's completion.

As for AGTL, it did not stop building with the connections at Bindloss, Alberta, and Burstall, Saskatchewan. Even as the ceremony at Cavendish took place, Fulton-Banister's crew was pushing the eighteen-inch line north beyond Bindloss en route to the Provost field. But Provost gas was not quite as dry as that at Bindloss and would require some processing before it could go on stream.

HOW EVERYONE WAS SCOLDED AFTER THE JOB WAS DONE

By 1958, two giant natural gas pipeline systems lay at right angles to one another across Canada, with laterals spurring off in all directions to feed the cities and towns along the main. What that would mean to the country was a hot topic of debate steadily consuming editorial ink. Here is part of what Alan Phillips had to say on the subject in a 1957 *Maclean's* article:

> First, (natural gas is) fuel, the purest known, refined in the bowels of the
> earth by nature from organic ooze. It's invisible, silent, clean, convenient
> — "the wonder fuel" it's called in the U.S. Second, it's raw material, the
> source of a thousand chemicals.

Luckily for the gas processing business, nature did not quite complete the refining process in the bowels of the earth, but the gist is clear: Eastern Canada and West Coast industry would surely bloom now that they had a ready and economical supply of this fabulous stuff.

Strangely, the enthusiasm for the wonder fuel did not extend to the people responsible for getting it from source rock to city. For starters, the St. Laurent Liberal Government which had supported TCPL and championed its pipeline through the House was tossed out of power in the summer of 1957, replaced by Diefenbaker's Conservatives. Often cited as the key reason for the Liberal demise of '57 is the conduct of the party during the Great Pipeline Debate of 1956. C. D. Howe, who of all government members had worked hardest to see the Trans-Canada line built, lost his seat to a Conservative.

Once elected, the new government put the pipeline issue on a back burner by making it the subject of a Royal Commission chaired by Henry Borden, nephew of former Conservative Prime Minister Borden. During the hearings of the Borden Energy Commission, the Westcoast and TCPL entrepreneurs received a severe hiding. In early 1958, Henry Borden startled his own Commission by accusing Westcoast of subsidizing its export prices to the U.S. with higher prices to Canadian purchasers. (The fact that Canadian gas already cost more than American gas by the time it reached Californa he neatly overlooked.) Then Borden took a swipe at Westcoast for having sold shares in the company to insiders at 5¢ when the first public offering of the stock was for $5.00. In Westcoast's defence, legal counsel D. P. McDonald reminded the Commission that when the "insiders" bought these nickel shares you couldn't have sold a Westcoast share publically at any price. The whole Westcoast system had been nothing more than a slightly incredible notion at the time. He also pointed out that Frank McMahon had also bought a good deal of Westcoast stock at $5.00, bringing the average cost of his holdings to $3.78. Still the Commission and the public found it difficult to overlook the fact that Westcoast Transmission stock had risen far beyond the initial $5.00 and had made glamorous fortunes for its first investors.

When TCPL came under the Borden Commission's stern gaze, it too received criticism. The Commission pointed to stock options and other enticements given to Eldon Tanner and Charlie Coates to bring them to TCPL. The TCPL spokesman argued back that such carrots are not uncommon in business and that, without them, TCPL would never have received the services of such able and experienced men. Again, it is hard not to smile at the critics. Had the Trans-Canada scheme failed, which seemed likely on many occasions, Coates and Tanner would have lost money, preferred rate of purchase notwithstanding. Or, had Canadians not flocked to buy TCPL shares, driving up the price, the much criticized fortunes would not have been made. But the fortunes were made and a pall was cast over anyone on the inside who made money. To this day, when you ask people in the oil and gas industry to comment on Eldon Tanner, they usually begin by speaking of his fairness, his honesty, his square dealing. After twenty-five years they are still trying to set the public record straight.

Clint Murchison, the realist, had expected to be the subject of a certain amount of anti-American, anti-entrepreneurial sentiment when he undertook to build the Trans-Canada pipeline. It is doubtful that cartoon depictions of him as a gun-toting cowboy capitalist from Texas, standing astraddle the map of Canada, bothered him very deeply. But a candid glimpse provided by Smiley Raborn does show a side of Murchison most people might not have expected. After TCPL's financing was in place and the company shares had risen dramatically, Smiley Raborn approached his boss and suggested that they sell a block of Canadian Delhi's TCPL shares and thereby establish a powerful exploration budget. Raborn suspects that, at that moment, he stood perilously close to losing his job. Clint Murchison gave him a cool look and replied that he would absolutely *not* sell out for a quick profit. He had made a promise to C. D. Howe.

One of the more astute summaries of all this came in a 1958 editorial in the new Calgary publication *Oilweek*. *Oilweek* likened the Borden Commission and the general bashing of profiteers that followed the building of the pipelines to the fable of the Little Red Hen. When the Little Red Hen wanted to plant some grain and asked who would help her, the rat and the cat and the little dog all replied, "Not I." Later, after the Little Red Hen had planted the grain herself and harvested it herself, she asked who would help her *eat* the grain. "I will," said the rat; "I will," said the cat; and "I will," said the little dog. Being no one's fool, the Little Red Hen told her chums that she would be eating the grain all by herself. Luckily for the Little Red Hen, her dealings were not widely covered by the press, nor were they the subject of any Royal Commissions.

Nathan Eldon Tanner in his days as Alberta Minister of Lands and Mines turning on the Imperial Devon conservation plant (1950).

B.A. Pincher Creek, on stream on December 31, 1956; selling gas to TCPL in 1958.

1957-1959:
THE FIRST WAVE OF
PROCESSING
EXPANSION IN WESTERN
CANADA

6

At the end of 1956, eleven gas processing plants were operating in Canada with a total nominal capacity of 376 million cubic feet of raw gas a day. All except for the gas treating facility at Port Alma, Ontario, were in Alberta. A look at the same total three years later gives a good indication of the effect the completion of the TCPL and Westcoast pipelines had on the gas processing industry. By year-end, 1959, the number of plants in Canada had tripled to thirty-three, and total raw gas capacity had quadrupled to over a billion and a half cubic feet a day. Elemental sulphur production was just beginning its surge, having expanded over the same period from 130 to 1686 long tons a day. Though some of this expansion has to be credited to the ongoing conservation of oilfield solution gas and the opening up of a small industrial market for gas, the vast majority of construction related directly to the demand created by the pipelines. Another feature of the first expansion is that, by 1959, both British Columbia and Saskatchewan had processing facilities of their own.

For personnel in the industry this growth translated into new opportunity. Experience at any of the conservation plants became a ticket to mobility after 1957. A good operator or engineer from, say, Shell Jumping Pound or B.A. Nevis could be fairly certain of a welcome at one of the new plants if he had a mind to move. The shortage of experienced hands lasted throughout the period and companies had to concentrate on fast and effective training of green men with aptitude, ingenuity and courage.

THE McMAHON PLANT AT TAYLOR

The big news in 1957 processing (though it did not go on and stay on stream until 1958) was the enormous processing and refining complex being built at Taylor Flats near Ft. St. John, British Columbia. When finished, the gas processing plant would serve the Westcoast Transmission pipeline. The first gas into the Westcoast line came from the Pouce Coupe field, sweet dry gas that made pipeline specification without having to be processed. But to meet the supply obligations of the winter of 1957-58, Westcoast would need gas from its sour gas fields, gas that would have to be sweetened, dehydrated and processed for hydrocarbon liquid removal at Taylor.

Complex is a good word for the Taylor facilities, because they *were* complex both technologically and financially. Taylor was a gas processing plant, a sulphur plant and an oil refinery. The gas plant had a capacity of 350 million cubic feet of raw natural gas per day, which made it almost as large as all eleven plants operating in Canada prior to 1957 *put together*. Westcoast Transmission owned the gas plant and Pacific Petroleums Ltd. operated it. The Jefferson Lake Sulphur Company owned and operated the sulphur plant. The refinery was jointly owned by Pacific and the Phillips Petroleum Company. Pacific operated the refinery, but several Phillips employees participated in key positions during start-up. In 1960, this complicated ownership arrangement underwent additional changes. Phillips and Pacific merged in a way that left Pacific as sole owner of the Taylor oil refinery, but Phillips had meanwhile attained 39% ownership of Pacific. As Pacific held a considerable amount of Westcoast Transmission's stock, Phillips thereby attained a large interest in the gas processing, compression and transmission side of the Taylor complex as well.

Westcoast's overriding concern in the design of the gas plant had been the absolute need for uninterrupted operation. Never before had a plant been built so far north, and never before had an entire gas transmission system relied upon a single plant. The designers could borrow some aspects of earlier plants like Shell Jumping Pound, but the fact remained that Jumping Pound supplied only part of Calgary's natural gas needs and could shut down without disaster. Taylor could not.

For better or worse, the obsession led to two decisions: that the plant should be completely housed, and that there should be four totally separate trains. A California design would be used and, thanks to well-heated buildings, it would operate in a California-like environment. If one train shut down, the transmission system could still be supplied by the other three completely isolated trains. This design cost a great deal to build and operate. Housing the sour gas equipment was also thought to increase the inherent dangers of hydrogen sulphide. Still, it seemed like the best approach.

To celebrate construction of the Taylor plant and completion of the pipeline, a grand opening was scheduled for October, 1957. Invitations went out to hundreds of dignitaries, investors and business friends of Frank McMahon for an opening celebration, a tour of the Taylor plant and a meal in the construction camp. Much of the responsibility for organizing this

Al McIntosh, Pacific's general manager of production at Taylor. His duties included building golf courses, conducting Royal Tours, and seeing to it that opening day visitors did not muddy their shoes.

event fell on the shoulders of Al McIntosh, an Albertan with nine years in the Pacific Petroleums organization. McIntosh was the first general manager of production at Taylor.

As the day approached, everything seemed well in hand. A fleet of buses had been rented in Edmonton that was to come up in convoy to ferry the guests from the Fort St. John airport to the plant site. The cooks at the construction camp had pots, pans and spatulas at the ready. Then it began to snow.

Day after day, the snow fell until thirty inches of the stuff lay piled on the ground; "like Al Capp's Lower Slobovia" is Al McIntosh's recollection. Not knowing if a single bus would make it through the blizzard, McIntosh began frantically lining up cars. Like the Little Boats of Britain to the rescue at Dunkirk, every car and truck in Ft. St. John had soon been pledged to act as a taxi should the buses fail to show. The buses did make it in the end and, when the celebrities fell from the skies, they were moved in comfort to the camp. Frank McMahon had purchased all the available overshoes in Calgary to ensure that no guest would dirty a shoe on the plant site. The cooks "really put on a spread" and some of the members of the press so enjoyed the various bars set out for them that it was difficult to make them leave.

By taking a look at a few of the people who worked at the Taylor plant in its first year, we get a good impression of how processing experience was acquired in or imported to Canada, and how it spread through the industry once it existed here. The first gas plant superintendent in Taylor, Terry Smith, was a graduate of Queen's University who had worked at the Imperial Devon plant and served as the first superintendent at Jumping Pound. Fluor, the contractor at Jumping Pound often said it had more money invested in Jumping Pound than Shell did; it had spent that money as an investment in the understanding of sour gas. But Fluor and Shell were not the only ones to profit by that investment. When Terry Smith and another Jumping Pound engineer, Kevin Milne, brought their know-how to Taylor, Westcoast and Pacific Petroleums came out ahead as well.

In the elemental sulphur area, American expertise was imported in the person of Jim Leeper. Leeper was Jefferson Lake's superintendent at the Taylor sulphur plant after having filled the same post at a sulphur plant in Wyoming.

Andy Younger, the Canadian operations superintendent at Taylor, brought an unusually high level of academic preparation into the area of gas processing. He held a Ph.D. in engineering from Purdue. Clayton Edgelow, a shift foreman at Taylor, represented a trend toward finding gas plant operations people in the refinery and petrochemicals industries. Prior to coming to Taylor, Edgelow had worked in refining at Lloydminster and in the petrochemical industry with C.I.L. in Edmonton.

These are just some of the people who participated in the on-again, off-again start-up of the gas processing plant at Taylor in late 1957. Given

After a few days like the day they pigged the line at Tayor, Terry Smith went farming at Charlie Lake.

the number of companies involved, it isn't surprising that coordination became one of the plant's key problems. Another minor vexation was that the Peace River Bridge collapsed.

It all started when the plant's water lines, which passed under the bridge, began to break for some unknown reason. Finally, Andy Younger shut the plant down for lack of fire water. At 7 a.m., the shift foreman roused Younger bearing this almost poetic message:

> "The pumphouse is falling in the river, the bridge is falling in the river, and your house is going to fall into the river!"

Only the middle observation proved true. One of the giant foundations supporting the bridge had begun to move, breaking the water lines in the process. The suspension cables above snapped and the bridge crashed into the Peace River.

The collapse of the Peace River bridge at Taylor; one of the minor setbacks during the first surge of growth in Canadian processing.

Jim Carveth, a start-up engineer at Taylor for the Stearns-Roger engineering firm, estimates that the bridge disaster cost the project six weeks. Eight hundred men were working to complete the plant and all their food and equipment had to cross the river in small boats. Finally, when the railway bridge across the Peace was completed, the Board of Transport Commissioners gave permission for its use as a bridge for cars and trucks*. Beside the railway track, on planking barely the width of a vehicle

---

*The Fort St. John plant and refinery needed access to markets and this, added to other regional needs, resulted in the building of a railway line to Fort St. John, with a spur line to the gas plant and refinery on Taylor Flats, nearby.

— and no guard rails — the cars and trucks crept across. Andy Younger's comment: "I wouldn't go near it." The plant finally went on and stayed on stream during the final days of 1957 and the first days of 1958.

But the best possible summation of the kind and number of problems met with at Taylor has been left by George Bishop, Phillips Petroleum's manager at Taylor. Phillips had been nagging Bishop for some report of development and, finally, he replied with this telegram:

TO: W. L. PHILLIPS — PHILLIPS PETROLEUM CO BARTLESVILLE OKLA
FROM: GEO F. L. BISHOP
HAVE NOT SENT YOU A REPORT BECAUSE WE HAD NOTHING TO REPORT BUT TROUBLES. HOWEVER, IF YOU NEED A REPORT HERE IT IS:
HAVE HAD DIFFICULTIES WITH AMINE PUMPS, TURBINES DRIVING AMINE PUMPS, GOVERNORS CONTROLLING TURBINES DRIVING AMINE PUMPS, PRESSURE REGULATORS, CONTROL VALVES, MOTORS DRIVING CONTROL VALVES, ELECTRONIC DEHYDRATION FURNACE CONTROLS, LEAKS IN SCREWED CONNECTIONS, LEAKS IN LARGE CONNECTIONS, LEAKS IN VALVE BONNETS, FAILURES OF VOLTAGE REGULATORS, BURNED UP 2500 KW GENERATOR, WORKMAN BREAKING LEG WHEN HE JUMPED OUT OF SECOND STORY WINDOW WHEN GENERATOR BURNED UP, COLLAPSE OF THE PEACE RIVER BRIDGE, NEWS REPORTS AND MAGAZINE REPORTS ON WHO-DONE-IT, COLLAPSE OF WATER LINES, DAMAGE TO PUMP HOUSE AS A RESULT OF MOVEMENT OF WATER LINES, FAILURE OF FIRE PUMP, MUD ANKLE DEEP, MUD KNEE DEEP, MOTEL RESERVATIONS FOR MANUFACTURER'S REPRESENTATIVES, MOTEL RESERVATIONS FOR AUDITORS, TEMPORARY OFFICE SPACE FOR AUDITORS, TEMPORARY QUARTERS FOR ARMY, TEMPORARY OFFICE SPACE FOR OURSELVES, INEFFICIENCY OF PROCESS WITH GAS GOING TO ONE CONTACTOR AND AMINE TO ANOTHER, SLOWNESS GETTING FERRY STARTED, ICE IN RIVER FREEZING UP FERRY, GETTING PIPE ACROSS THE RIVER, GETTING PEOPLE ACROSS THE RIVER, GETTING MESSAGES ACROSS THE RIVER, BRIDGE EXPERTS IN OUR HAIR, ARMY IN OUR HAIR, INSURANCE PEOPLE IN OUR HAIR, TELEPHONE OUT OF ORDER, TELETYPE OUT OF ORDER, TWO-WAY RADIO OUT OF ORDER, REPLACEMENT FOR TWO-WAY RADIO OUT OF ORDER, REPLACEMENT FOR REPLACEMENT FOR TWO-WAY RADIO OUT OF ORDER, CAR OUT OF ORDER, RENTAL CAR REPLACEMENT OUT OF ORDER, REPLACEMENT FOR RENTAL CAR REPLACEMENT OUT OF ORDER, TRUCKS OUT OF ORDER, REGULATORS FOR RUBICON LOST, SPRINGS FOR REGULATOR FOR RUBICON WRONG SIZE, WET TEST METER

TO CALIBRATE RUBICON LOST IN ROUTE, LABOUR UNION
BEEFING ABOUT NON-UNION PEOPLE DOING EMERGENCY
WORK ON WATER LINES, LABOUR UNION BEEFING ABOUT
NON-UNION PEOPLE DOING EMERGENCY WORK ON CRUDE
AND PRODUCT EMERGENCY PIPE LINE RIVER CROSSING,
MINOR DIFFICULTIES OF FOUR COMPANIES TRYING TO OP-.
ERATE ONE PLANT AND TROUBLE ABOUT WHO PAYS THE
ELECTRIC AND WATER BILLS FOR THE AUTOMATIC LAUNDRY
IN OFFICE GIRLS APARTMENT BASEMENT.
HOPE TO TURN GAS INTO WESTCOAST SOMETIME THIS AF-
TERNOON.

However many problems were encountered and conquered at Taylor
in 1957 and 1958, the plant has to be viewed as a success. An uninterrupted
flow of northern B.C. gas moved south and burned as fuel in the homes and
industries of Vancouver, B.C., Seattle, Washington, and Portland,
Oregon. Despite some early scares when the fields at Fort St. John and
Pouce Coupe proved smaller than originally estimated, Westcoast found
enough natural gas reserves to cover its commitments for several years to
come. Frank McMahon's dream of 1930 had come fully true by 1958.

*Princess Margaret and Frank McMahon enjoy a lingering look
across the Peace River. McMahon enticed the Princess to Taylor in
the early years of the plant's operation.*

FORT ST. JOHN

When the oil and gas boom hit the tiny community of Fort St. John in the early '50's, the townspeople were not exactly in awe. With no exaggeration they could say that they had seen as good or better before. A decade earlier, during wartime, the hundred person town had become the overnight home of 10,000 American soldiers. Fort Alcan was built a half mile west of the village as the jumping off place for construction of the Alaska Highway. For a time the brand new Canadian Bank of Commerce at Fort St. John handled a payroll of $2½ million per month, doled out from cardboard boxes at the tellers' feet.

The local residents had watched that boom peak and peter out, and were not about to kiss the ground upon which the next wave of saviours walked. The local newspaper, The *Alaska High-*

Ma Murray of Fort St. John. Her acid editorials were read all over North America.

way News, run by the legendary Ma Murray, recalled the old boom in its first articles about the new one. Ma Murray wrote: "This is the second time this little town has been knocked into God's breast pocket."

Ma Murray covered the progress of the plant and pipeline so carefully and colourfully that the *Alaska Highway News* became required reading in faraway Bartlesville, Oklahoma, headquarters of Phillips Petroleum. But the years of halting progress and frequent stalemate finally got on her nerves. The ready vitriole for which she was famous flowed without stint in the direction of Frank McMahon, the Taylor plant, the B.C. Government and the Westcoast pipeline. One of Al McIntosh's tasks as production manager for Pacific was to befriend this prickly opponent and convince her that Westcoast and Pacific were not all that bad. Having heard how she had once expressed her annoyance with the local townspeople by threatening to publish the local hotel registers, he approached with care. This courting of Ma Murray took time and there were occasional relapses into acid prose. But, in time, McIntosh and Ma Murray became friends. "She was a crusty old gal, I'll tell ya," says McIntosh, but his voice contains a definite note of admiration. Ma Murray died in 1982 at the age of 95.

When the Taylor plant began construction, Westcoast Transmission built 192 houses. The company did not want to be in the housing business but as Al McIntosh says, you had to be if you wanted to be in the gas business. Plant construction doubled the population of the town, and for a time resentment existed about the standard of living gap between those who came and those who had been there before. Al McIntosh spent a good deal of time worrying about local morale and the integration of his newcomers. Finally, he decided on a golf course as an excellent way of improving both. Every time McIntosh came to Calgary, he hounded George McMahon, Frank's brother and a Westcoast vice-president, for a building he could use as a club house. Finally McMahon said, "Okay, you'll get your hut. Now I don't want you to ever come in here talking golf course again." The golf course at Charlie Lake was completed with much volunteer help and, over the next few years, the residents who had preceded the gas industry at Fort St. John became some of the club's most avid supporters.

SWEET GAS FOR TCPL

The first plant to process natural gas for the Trans-Canada pipeline was the Provo Gas Producers Ltd. refrigeration plant in the Provost field near Consort, Alberta. Designed for 55 million cubic feet of natural gas per day, the Consort plant was tied into AGTL's system by an eighty-five mile extension of the line recently built to collect gas at Bindloss.

Imperial put the original plan together for a processing facility at Provost, but Imperial had little interest in the gas processing business, despite its successful ventures at Devon and Redwater. Imperial preferred to deal in oil and, when the chance came to sell out at Provost, the company took it. The purchaser was Provo Gas Producers, a group led by Max Bell (publisher of the Calgary-based newspaper *The Albertan*) and George Gardiner of Toronto. On behalf of Provo, Max Bell approached Jack Gallagher, head of Dome Exploration (Western) Ltd., a young company involved in the Provost field, and asked him if he would merge Dome's gas reserves at Provost into those of Provo Gas Producers, then build and run a gas processing plant there. Gallagher said he would do so only if Dome controlled the enterprise. Eventually arrangements were made to give Dome that control.

Dome Exploration (Western) Ltd., a subsidiary of Dome Mines Ltd., was young and small in 1957 but hoped to finance great oil explorations with bread-and-butter gas operations like this one. To look after this potentially lucrative part of Dome's business, Jack Gallagher brought in Don Wolcott from Canadian Gulf. Wolcott was fresh from setting up the Stettler Gas Conservation Project for Gulf with the help of Bob Cunningham. Imperial originally planned a 100 million cubic foot per day plant for Consort, but Don Wolcott proceeded with a plant about half that size, in closer accordance with Provo's sales agreement with TCPL. Wolcott and a young Dome engineer by the name of Harry Palmer also decided to go with a different plant location. Imperial had chosen a place near the geographical centre of the field and Wolcott and Palmer went with a spot at the reservoir's centre of gravity. The plant used ammonia refrigeration to fractionate the sweet, dry Provost gas and to extract the small amount of liquid hydrocarbons necessary to meet TCPL's hydrocarbon dew point specification*.

The Provost field and the Consort plant represented early building

---

*A pipeline dew point specification defines the quantity of liquid hydrocarbons in the gas by setting a temperature and pressure at which the first drop of liquid will form from the vapour phase. The TCPL dew point specification was 15°F at 800 psi.

blocks in what would one day be a considerable processing and gas liquids empire owned by Dome Petroleum. Don Wolcott retained much influence over that aspect of Dome's operations for almost two decades. In 1957, one would have needed an extremely good crystal ball to see a budding mega-corporation in this thirty person company, but in some ways the kernel of growth was there. Already in 1957, Dome's short roster contained many of the names responsible for its ultimate growth: Jack Gallagher, Don Wolcott, Charlie Dunkley and a young Manitoba lawyer by the name of Bill Richards.

In the winter of 1957-58, the Consort plant supplied 77% of TCPL's needs, with Bindloss making up the rest. If Consort had gone down for any length of time, it would have meant chilly days for Winnipeg and Regina. The responsibility for preventing any disruption of service fell on Joe Burge, the man Don Wolcott brought in from Gulf Nevis to be superintendent at Consort. Burge found it frustrating at times to keep up with the heavy and uneven load requirements of TCPL, but his plant stayed on stream for the entire winter.

By the heating season of 1958-59, Consort was no longer alone in supplying TCPL. Canadian Delhi's long wait for a pay-off on Alberta exploration ended that winter when AGTL linked the Cessford field into the TCPL line. Despite its long history in the Cessford field, Canadian Delhi was not the gas plant operator. The other major Cessford producer, Hudson's Bay Oil and Gas (HBOG), built and ran the 125 million cubic foot per day plant.

HBOG had a reputation for being a *lean* company. Howard Becker, who oversaw the design of the Cessford plant, was good evidence of that. When he started with HBOG in 1955, Becker was *the* gas engineer. At Cessford, his task was fairly simple; the sweet dry gas made the pipeline specification easily after refrigeration took out a small quantity of liquids. Becker credits his "excellent process man" Aki Masuda with much of the preparation that led to Cessford's uneventful start-up. Bill Humphreys, who was with Hudson's Bay at the time (between a stint with Mannix-Gill and a career with Canadian Pacific*) had responsibility for Cessford's wellhead dehydrators and gathering system. Humphreys still looks back fondly on Cessford which he calls "one of the best fields Canada ever had." Sweet, dry, deliverable, medium-pressure gas: what more could a gas man want?

The other plant brought to life on the plains of eastern Alberta in

*Canadian Pacific Oil and Gas later became PanCanadian Petroleum Limited.

1958 belonged to the Canadian Export Gas Co. (Canex). This Wardlow plant processed gas from the Cessford field, another sweet dry gas accumulation. The gas was so dry, in fact, that Canex decided it did not warrant the expense of a refrigeration plant. Harvey Doyle, the company's gas engineer since 1955, took a shopping trip to Texas to investigate the new dry dessicant adsorption plants that were making an appearance there. After seeing how cheaply the solid dessicant system could process dry gas, Doyle purchased a two-tower, solid dessicant plant from National Tank. The prefabricated plant was transported to the site on five trucks and assembled in one day with a single crane. It could process 22 million cubic feet of gas a day at up to 1000 pounds per square inch (psi).

In his days with Canada Export Gas, Harvey Doyle brought the first dry dessicant absorption plant to Canada.

Gas flowed through one tower until that tower's bed of dessicant was saturated with natural gasoline. Then the system would switch to the other bed while the first was regenerated with hot gas. The dessicant beds also caught any water that got by the wellhead dehydrators. This type of plant required virtually no attendance, and ran off pneumatic instruments, thus eliminating the need for electricity.

These dry dessicant plants were, in other words, ideal for sweet dry gas fields in remote locations like eastern Alberta. After Canex installed its Wardlow plant, everyone in that part of the country followed suit. Of the eleven plants that came on stream in Alberta in 1959, seven were dry dessicant plants of various sizes. When sales gas demand necessitated an expansion of Dome's Consort plant to 90 MMCF*, a solid dessicant plant was added to the existing refrigeration facility.

*Millions of cubic feet.

SWEETENED GAS FOR TCPL

Moving from east to west across Alberta, the natural gas is generally found at greater depths. The deeper in the earth gas is found the more likely it is to be *sour* (containing hydrogen sulphide) and *wet* (containing liquid hydrocarbons). B.A.'s gas field at Pincher Creek is a good example. The reservoir is deep, faulted and fractured; the raw natural gas is sour, wet and under very high pressure.

As mentioned in the previous chapter, Pincher Creek gas had been part of most everyone's plans for export since the early '50's. Finally, in 1958, after a year of cycling, AGTL arrived and Pincher Creek sales gas went on stream to TCPL.

B.A. had encountered a number of severe and unusual corrosion problems in its equipment while developing the Pincher Creek field. The company knew, therefore, that no simple, inexpensive plant would be capable of processing Pincher Creek gas. Over a million dollars in research preceded design and construction of the Stage I plant by Stearns-Roger. As will be seen in Chapter Eight, knowledge didn't progress far enough, fast enough to prevent the almost incredible problems that besieged the first operating staff. With its combination of high acid gas concentration (11% H_2S and 6% CO_2) and its high pressure (the plant operated at 1500 psi), B.A. Pincher Creek was destined to become the next unofficial university of the Canadian processing industry.

The first class in that university was certainly a freshman one. Out of all the salaried and operating staff, only the superintendent Martin Bretz had extensive experience in sour gas processing. One other engineer, UBC graduate Ron Pauls, had participated in the construction of the Stage I Pincher Creek plant and had received two years of gas plant training in the U.S. Even the area manager for B.A. at Pincher Creek, Cliff Stewart, knew nothing of gas plants. His experience at home in Oklahoma and in the Pincher Creek field where he had worked on Gulf's 1948 discovery well was strictly in drilling. B.A. Nevis had difficulties of its own and could not spare experienced men for Pincher Creek's start-up. Efforts to lure seasoned sour gas men away from the Shell Jumping Pound plant also failed.

One of the most experienced employees at Pincher Creek was shift foreman Murray Wright. Wright had worked in the petrochemical industry for eight years at Cominco's ammonia plant in Calgary and at the Canadian Chemicals plant near Edmonton. At the latter operation he had made the acquaintance of natural gas, compressors and a Girdler-type sweetening unit. He brought to Pincher Creek valuable experience of the dangers of hydrogen sulphide.

The rest of the first crew at Pincher Creek was largely made up of green trainees off the seismic crews, the drilling rigs and the local farms. The handiness of these men and their ability to learn made them good candidates; nevertheless, they were starting from scratch.

On the engineering side, an early Pincher Creek recruit was Elmer Berlie who took over as plant engineer from Ron Pauls. After several years with the Conservation Board, Berlie had decided he wanted to experience processing from the industry side. After being recruited for B.A. by Floyd Aaring of Gulf*, Berlie was handed over to Gulf's famous chief gas engineer Charlie Buskel for orientation. This introduction consisted of a half hour chat, during which Buskel corrected a report. When finished, he said to Berlie: "Well, Elmer, the work is in Pincher Creek; you'd better be on your way." Elmer Berlie brought a strong knowledge of the industry to B.A. Pincher Creek, but he had never worked in a gas plant before.

Luckily for all concerned, the one man at Pincher Creek who did know about sour gas plants knew more than practically anyone. That man was Martin Bretz, the first plant superintendent at Pincher Creek. After graduation from Oklahoma A & M, Bretz had worked for Stanolind Oil and Gas during the war and as Stanolind's gas plant superintendent from 1948-56. When asked why he left the U.S. for Canada, Bretz gave as his principal reason the "bugs and sand" in West Texas. Stanolind had transferred him to Texas and he didn't like the place. When the Pincher Creek offer came, he nabbed it and moved to Canada, sight unseen.

The Stage I Pincher Creek plant over which Martin Bretz had charge in the winter of 1956-57 had a raw gas capacity of 60 million cubic feet per day. Its one sulphur train could recover 225 long tons a day. The plant was also equipped to stabilize condensate. Because AGTL had yet to reach Pincher Creek, the residue gas was reinjected to the reservoir at 5400 psi and 520°F. The second stage of the plant went on stream with the first sale of gas to TCPL in the fall of 1958. Two more sulphur trains had been added bringing the total capacity of the sulphur plant to 675 long tons per day. LPG extraction facilities went into operation that fall and gas capacity increased to 180 MMCF/day. The plant was to get even larger after that. Stage III was to push capacity to 240 million a day and a fourth stage was being contemplated.

There was just one problem with all this growth. While plant capacity went up, the reserve estimates for the field went down. The earliest reserve estimate for Pincher Creek had been a whopping three trillion cubic

---

*Gulf was at that time acquiring control of B.A. through an exchange of shares, though the B.A. name continued to be used for the company's processing units in Canada.

feet. By the time Elmer Berlie arrived, the estimate had slipped to 1.7 trillion. As Berlie puts it: "Every time a well was drilled, the reserves estimate dropped."

The argument among reservoir experts was fast being decided in favour of those who had predicted that the fracture zone in the Pincher Creek reservoir would fill with water when it emptied of gas. Martin Bretz could see it plainly in the production graphs of the Pincher Creek wells; the line for water production rose steeply and steadily. His Wyoming way of describing the problem: "There's two or three zones and the fractures in them are vertical. If you get pulling too hard, the water'll come up and kill you right out."

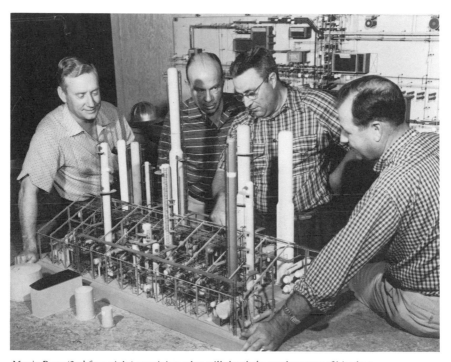

Martin Bretz (2nd from right) scrutinizes what will shortly be another stage of his plant.

Whatever the reason, the result was undeniable. The great Pincher Creek reservoir, touted as the backstop for every second pipeline scheme to the south or east, had turned out to be a bit of a clunker. Far from three trillion or even 1.7 trillion, the real recoverable reserves at Pincher Creek were well below one trillion. Thus, it could truly be said that gas export from Alberta and the Trans-Canada pipeline were both approved on the basis of gas that did not exist.

MARTIN BRETZ

Wyoming native, Martin Bretz, represents a generation of American engineers and operators who came to Canada in the '50's to fill an experience gap created by the sudden growth of the processing industry. Though thousands of Americans made that trip north, Martin Bretz was one of only a handful who brought with them a knowledge of sour gas. In windy Wyoming, he had been in charge of a couple of small, low-pressure sulphur plants, and he owed his opportunity in Canada to that experience.

Put in charge of the unpredictable plant at Pincher Creek, Bretz soon learned that sour gas processing was a different game in Canada, complicated by pressures and trace compounds he had never encountered down south. Luckily, he is an unflappable person and was able to hang in there until things ran smooth.

Gruff and blunt, Martin Bretz always expected a great deal from his salaried employees. For his operators, he had a little more patience and most who worked for him speak of a generosity he

Martin Bretz.

concealed in a mostly unsmiling exterior. Dome president John Beddome, one of the many engineers to have worked for Bretz at Pincher Creek, comments that Martin Bretz literally lived at his plant. When he took a break, it was usually to slip down over the hill to the dam that supplied the plant with water. At that dam, Bretz had a favourite fishing hole. Staying away from that fishing hole was one of the prerequisites to getting along with Martin Bretz.

Between Bretz and Cliff Stewart, his area manager at Pincher Creek, a strange relationship existed. Stewart, a classy Oklahoman, never quite got over Martin Bretz' eccentric habits of dress. Stewart believed that a superintendent's place was in the office and that he should set an example by dressing in suit and tie. That Bretz could usually be found deep within his plant in a hair shirt and grubby workboots trailing their laces was one of many bones of contention between them. But Stewart needed Bretz' plant experience badly and a truce generally maintained, broken only on those occasions, as one informant put it, when the two "confused the hell out of one another."

Martin Bretz left Pincher Creek for Rainbow Lake in 1967, the day B.A. gave him his ten-year pin. "They gave me my pin and I told them I quit." He ran the Rainbow plant for Banff Oil until 1975 and then worked on various projects for Aquitaine up until his retirement.

Among today's industry veterans, Martin Bretz is remembered as a character, but also as a teacher, the man who probably trained more people for the industry than anyone else. A list of those who worked for him reads like a roster of current industry leaders: John Beddome, Howard Guin, John Martin, Elmer Berlie, Lew Cameron, John Law, Ron Pauls, Joe Lovecky, Graeme Tuttle, Bill Masson and Leo O'Rourke, to name just a few. When asked to pinpoint Martin Bretz' contribution, many mention his insistence on safety procedures and the fact that he demanded that all pollution complaints be responded to without delay. He worked his men very hard, but he always worked himself harder.

Martin Bretz is now retired to the fishing holes of Vancouver Island. He says: "There's a lot I've forgotten about sour gas. And I'll tell you something, I intend to leave it forgotten too."

THE OTHER GAS PLANTS OF 1957-1959

The expansion of Western Canada's processing industry in the years 1957-1959 went beyond that stimulated by the completion of the Westcoast and TCPL pipelines. Gas conservation continued to be a concern of the Alberta government and was fast becoming a concern of the Saskatchewan government as well. These local forces of conservation stimulated the construction of plants which tied into markets other than the two major pipelines. Two of the Alberta plants, Ajax and Mid-Western Industrial Gas, both situated near Edmonton, existed to provide feedstock to the budding petrochemical industry. Another three of Alberta's new plants sold to the utilities, Canadian Western and Northwestern Utilities. Saskatchewan's four new plants sold residue gas to the Saskatchewan Power Corporation, serving a new market in the cities and towns of that province.

The most ambitious of these *other* plants were the Dome and Goliad solution gas processing operations at Steelman, Saskatchewan, and Pembina, Alberta; and the Texas Gulf sulphur plant at Okotoks.

Texas Gulf Okotoks represented a new horizon in sour gas processing for Canada. The plant processed raw gas containing 10% CO_2 and 35% H_2S, thus producing enormous quantities of elemental sulphur relative to the amount of gas. The Texas Gulf Sulphur Co. also enjoyed a high level of experience in sour gas processing. The company had been running an amine treating and sulphur plant in Worland, Wyoming, since 1949. *(The plant will be discussed in more detail in Chapters Eight and Nine.)*

Dome Steelman and Goliad Pembina were somewhat similar operations. They were both solution gas conservation projects, and they were both "third-party" schemes; that is, neither company had a major stake in the oil fields from which the gas was gathered. It was a definite sign of things to come that these companies approached oil producers who were under government pressure to conserve their gas and made *business deals* to process the gas for them. The big difference between the two was that, in Goliad's case, the deal left ownership of the residue gas in the hands of the producers, Goliad's share being ownership of the liquids removed from the gas. This was the first time anyone had tried to make a profit in Canada out of gas liquids alone. The deal Don Wolcott made on behalf of Dome with the producers in southeastern Saskatchewan gave Dome ownership of both the residue gas and the by-product liquids and sulphur.

The other interesting fact about these deals is the number of parties involved. Seventy-six producers participated in the conservation agreement at Pembina. Goliad Oil and Gas gathered gas from 350 oilfield batteries into eight, extensively automated area compressor stations where the raw gas was stripped of its natural gas liquids (or NGLs)*. The gas at this point met Northwestern Utilities' specification and was ready for sale to that utility. The wild natural gas liquids mix went to Goliad's central fractionating plant at Buck Creek. The compression and NGL stripping facilities all belonged to Goliad and were leased to the producers. Goliad operated the facilities on behalf of the producers for a fee.

The whole concept was a monument to co-operation and common sense. Goliad Oil and Gas was an H. W. Bass company, created solely for the Pembina gas liquids venture. Bass was an experienced operator in the U.S. and was familiar with the post-World War II joint-ventures instigated by the U.S. government in the name of conservation. Goliad's proposal for Pembina was laid out along similar lines. H. W. Bass had hired the consulting firm of Purvin and Gertz to work out the Pembina joint-venture for Goliad, and Purvin and Gertz employee Otto K. Wetzell is credited with doing the leg work that got the ink on the contracts. Among the many others who provided leadership in the Pembina conservation agreement for their various companies were: Charlie Yarbrough of Mobil, Don McEachern of Imperial, Bryan Edwards of Pan Am, C. T. Wells of Goliad and Charlie Drake of the Honolulu Oil Corporation. One major producer at Pembina chose not to join in the Goliad scheme. Texaco went it alone with its own processing plant at Cynthia.

The Steelman venture was significantly smaller. Dome gathered solution gas from many oil producers in southeastern Saskatchewan and brought it into a central processing plant where LPGs, natural gasoline, sulphur and specification residue gas were produced for market. To lower the BTU rating of Steelman's residue gas, Dome mixed the gas with air much as Northwestern Utilities had done with the sales gas from Leduc-Woodbend.

The Steelman and Goliad ventures were enlightened, but slightly before their time. The market for hydrocarbon liquids, especially the LPGs, had not matured to the point where either Dome Steelman or Goliad Pembina could easily profit, despite favourable agreements with the producers. Creative salesmanship was needed and, fortunately for both companies, they had the kind of personnel needed to create markets where none existed, and to find markets where they were well hidden. Don Wolcott of Dome and Dan T. McDonald of Goliad were two of the men who had that kind of insight. Through them, the LPG industry developed the storage and outlets it needed to be viable in Canada.

---

*Natural gas liquids (NGLs) are defined as any mixture of ethane, propane, butane and pentanes plus.

Dome Steelman, 1959; processed solution gas from the oilfields of southeastern Saskatchewan.

*   *   *

By the end of 1959, many major trends in the Canadian gas processing industry had achieved a certain momentum. Sour gas technology was making important strides forward at Pincher Creek and Okotoks. Solid dessicant plants had improved the economics of sweet dry gas processing and had allowed small holdings to be produced. This in turn brought a number of small companies — many of them Canadian-owned — into the business. The LPG industry was also showing signs of life through the aggressive and innovative strategies of companies like Goliad and Dome.

The industry was also beginning to appreciate the economic value of cooperation; it was finding that the way of swiftest progress lay in that direction. It is almost certainly no coincidence that the individuals who provided the leadership in the conservation agreement for Pembina gas and liquids also provided the leadership in the founding of the Canadian Natural Gas Processors Association. A year after the Pembina project started up, the CNGPA and its affiliated association, the Canadian Natural Gas Processors Supply Men's Association, were founded. For a long time, individual engineers and operators had been crossing company boundaries to compare notes and share knowledge. The founding of these associations in a sense formalized that practice and confirmed the fact that Canadian processing problems could best be solved by those working in Canada through a pooling of experience and knowledge.

However, for these various trends to hold their momentum, there had to be continuing growth in the industry brought about by dramatic growth in the market. Market expansion on the scale needed could only be achieved if the untapped reserves of Canadian gas were allowed to flow south into the United States.

GAS EXPORT TO THE UNITED STATES: THE SECOND WAVE OF EXPANSION IN CANADIAN PROCESSING

7

The second wave of expansion in the Canadian processing industry began so much like the first that those participating must have had an unsettling feeling of déjà vu. It began with export applications, with lengthy hearings and, finally, with a pipeline. For TCPL, it was more than just a similarity between first and second effort, it was a continuation of the first effort. For that company, the struggle to get permission to export gas to the American Midwest via the border gate at Emerson, Manitoba, continued.

TCPL had a new problem in that regard: success. After grave predictions in the Eastern press that TCPL might yet fail if it did not do a gung ho marketing job in Ontario and Quebec, consumer sales in that quarter skyrocketed beyond all predictions. The same Pipeline Debate that washed the St. Laurent government out of office gave natural gas and the Trans-Canada pipeline more promotion than money could buy. The irony for TCPL was that the company's success in selling its product domestically again raised the question of whether Canada had any real surplus of gas to export.

On top of that, TCPL had a new and aggressive competitor for Alberta gas in the Alberta and Southern Gas Company (A & S), a wholly owned subsidiary of Pacific Gas and Electric (PG & E), the largest California utility. PG & E's plan was to have A & S negotiate long-term contracts with the gas producers who were currently beyond TCPL's reach. The major new Alberta gas fields that fit this description followed a trend through the Rocky Mountain foothills; deep faulted reservoirs full of mostly wet and sour gas. AGTL would pick up this gas with a new foothills pipeline and deliver it through the Crowsnest Pass to the B.C.-Alberta border where it would enter a pipeline owned by PG & E. The pipeline would cross the southeastern corner of British Columbia to the Kingsgate border point. There the gas would be sold to another PG & E subsidiary for conveyance through Idaho, Washington and Oregon to the State of California.

The third company in this new gas derby was Frank McMahon's

Westcoast Transmission. The Westcoast plan had a lot in common with that of PG & E. It was based on two reservoirs: the Savanna Creek field in the Rocky Mountains southwest of Turner Valley, and the East Calgary field, northeast of that city. The target markets for the residue gas were in the U.S. and, like the PG & E project, Westcoast's called for a pipeline through southeastern B.C.

The various applications proceeded along their well-worn paths until Prime Minister Diefenbaker decided to investigate the doings of his predecessors using that dreaded instrument of torture, the Royal Commission. The Borden Commission on Energy started and progress on all export applications stopped.

Besides scolding risk-takers in the pipelines for making a large profit, the Borden Commission came up with two things of importance to the gas industry: it approved in principle the export of natural gas from the country and it recommended the creation of a national energy board to be the federal authority over such matters in future.

During the Borden Commission and the parliamentary proceedings which stemmed from it, the export companies continued applying to the Alberta Oil and Gas Conservation Board. Getting permission to take gas from Alberta remained the first step in every export scheme. The Board refused A & S on its first application on grounds that it did not have sufficient gas supplies under contract. Broad hints were also dropped that A & S and Westcoast should consider amalgamating the parallel aspects of their projects.

In mid-October, 1958, Frank McMahon and A & S president J. K. Horton issued a statement announcing their plans to join forces for the building of the southeastern British Columbia pipeline to Idaho. This would be done through a company called the Alberta Natural Gas Co. (ANG) controlled by A & S and Westcoast. In March, 1959, the strategy paid off; both the A & S and Westcoast requests for export were approved (albeit at lesser volumes than applied for) by Alberta's Conservation Board.

As for TCPL, it was once again clear from the Borden Commission and TCPL's hearings before the U.S. Federal Power Commission that the key to success in its quest for export was reserves, signed and ready for delivery. Vern Horte, who became TCPL's chief gas supply engineer in 1957, continued his ardent search for contracts and, eventually, in December of 1959, the Conservation Board approved TCPL's export request as well.

Still, no gas could move from Canada until the newly legislated National Energy Board (NEB) completed its formal investigations. Three months after the NEB's formation came the choice of its first chairman. Ian

McKinnon consented to take the job, leaving the Alberta Oil and Gas Conservation Board* chairmanship after eleven years. (Red Goodall succeeded McKinnon as Alberta Conservation Board chairman.) Premier Manning of Alberta applauded the choice of McKinnon, as did most everyone in the oil and gas industry, but Manning added that Alberta "did not want to lose him." McKinnon had been given "a two year leave of absence only." Pleasantries aside, Manning went on, at the same news conference, to lambaste the feds for their "attitude of procrastination".

In February of 1960, after five weeks of hearings before the NEB, *Oilweek* felt able to confidently predict the authorization of export. Only one "die-hard opponent" remained and who was it but the City of Calgary, the burg most apt to profit from the growth engendered by export? The gas processing industry, which largely resided in Calgary, was not amused. As the thing wore on, it became obvious that only one person wanted to block the export, the veteran engineer the City of Calgary had hired to represent it. He felt strongly that the NEB should not export gas unless that body also controlled the price (a concern that seems prophetic in hindsight). Meanwhile in Calgary, Mayor Harry Hays went on record as saying that he did not want the city's arguments to hold up export. When Calgary's consulting engineer made a miscalculation of Canada's future reserve needs, general impatience took command. Ian McKinnon told the engineer that his estimates were of no use to the Board; the engineer retired to recalculate them and, in the process, the final objection dissolved.

PROCESSING TO SUPPLY THE EXPORT DEMAND

Most of the contracts between A & S and the producing companies called for the supply of specification gas by New Year's Day, 1962. A tremendous amount of construction had to be done in a tremendous hurry. As can be seen from the following remarks in the April 25, 1960, issue of *Oil in Canada*, it took a little while for the industry to overcome its inertia:

> The processing industry has apparently not yet recovered from the shock and surprise of the fact that the Dominion Government has finally made a decision and plans for future field development and gas plant construction seem to be at a standstill.

Within the year, the situation resolved itself in a flurry of construction. There were signs, however, that purchasers south of the border were not entirely confident that the plants would be finished on time or that they would be able to successfully process such sour gas. Bob Blair,

*The Petroleum and Natural Gas Conservation Board became the Oil and Gas Conservation Board in 1957.

then vice-president and manager of A & S, felt the need to monitor progress on the plants in a way that would reassure his customers. He hired Jim Richardson, a consulting engineer with an established U.S. reputation, to fly up and down the AGTL's new foothills lateral, stopping at all the new plants to see that construction was sound and on schedule.

Jim Richardson (right) and his pilot; flying along the foothills trend for Alberta and Southern.

These qualms were not unreasonable. The gas analyses on the new reservoirs showed them to be very sour. Some were rich in liquid hydrocarbons; some were lean. Gas of this sort had never yet been processed without extensive start-up problems, corrosion problems and embrittlement problems. In the existing plants like B.A. Pincher Creek, the problems were dealt with as they showed themselves, but no one could really say with confidence that he understood them well enough to design a plant in which they did not exist. Nonetheless, the plants were built and most went on stream through the AGTL Foothills Division in time to meet the A & S and Westcoast deadlines.

Many plants were also constructed to meet the TCPL demand engendered by U.S. export. Although the majority of these were dry dessicant plants processing sweet dry gas, TCPL was reaching farther westward all the time and was encountering sour gas of its own. The fact that two of the new sour gas plants, Carstairs and Rimbey, sold to both TCPL and A & S illustrates that the two systems had overlapped in the middle of Alberta and were beginning to compete.

The period 1960-62 saw a total of thirty-eight new processing plants built in Canada. In 1961 alone, capacity jumped 815 million cubic feet a day, an investment of over $90 million. The following pages profile the most significant of these plants: the cornerstones of pipeline supply, and the sources of innovation which improved the safety, economics and efficiency of sour gas processing. Within the profiles are introductions to some of the people who enabled the industry to meet the challenges of a growing market and a scientific frontier.

1960: HOME OIL IN THE PROCESSING BUSINESS AT CARSTAIRS

The first major plant designed for the new U.S. export market was Home Oil's processing facility at Carstairs. This plant represented Home Oil's debut as a plant operator though the company had been involved with gas plants before in other ways. Home, Gulf and California Standard were the major producers in the Nevis field and, back in 1953, a handshake agreement had taken place such that, if export was ever realized, they would go in together on the building of a plant. But, long before export, the Conservation Board urged Gulf to conserve its Stettler, Fenn and Big Valley solution gas which the company subsequently did with the Stettler Area Gas Conservation Project. When TCPL finally received its permission to export gas, Gulf (now B.A.) decided to expand its existing plant to process Nevis gas. B.A. did not look for partners, reasoning that the old undertaking with the Nevis producers had been nullified by more current events. The other Nevis producers felt differently; they also felt that B.A.'s proposed fee for processing their Nevis solution gas was too high. As a result of all this, Home Oil approached California Standard and proposed that they join forces and build a producer-owned plant for Nevis.

When the new Nevis plant was built in 1959, California Standard had taken the role of operator. Home Oil chose not to operate the plant in order to focus all of its attention on another project. In 1958, Home had discovered a rich gas field at Carstairs and it wanted to build another joint-venture processing plant to serve it. Home had numerous partners in this Carstairs joint venture: Canadian Superior, HBOG, Tennessee, Alminex, Shell and Texaco among them.

The man in charge of the Carstairs project for Home Oil, also responsible for the joint-venture agreement that launched it, was Ian Drum. Drum came to the oil business via the chemicals industry. After training in the Royal Military College at Kingston and earning a chemical engineering degree from Queen's, he worked for several years at Dye and Chemical of Canada. But long before this, Ian Drum had been a University

School boy in Victoria, B.C., where one of the younger boys had been Bobby Brown (R. A. Brown Jr.). Drum remembers the younger lad as "a very useful wing three-quarter" at rugby. Their paths crossed a few times during the next two decades. In 1937, while Drum was with the military stationed at Sarcee in Calgary, he and Brown took a flying trip round Turner Valley in Bob Brown's car (a view of the oil boom R. A. Brown Senior had

R. A. Brown Sr. and R. A. Brown Jr.; after taking over his father's enterprises, Bobby Brown merged Federated Petroleums into Home Oil Ltd.

recently sparked). In 1943 they visited in Brown's suite at the Chateau Laurier. Brown had been appointed to work in petroleum supply for the navy. Then, in 1950, Ian Drum came to Calgary looking for work and found it in Bob Brown's growing oil enterprises. After his father's death, R. A. Brown Jr. had taken over the family businesses and, recently, had merged one of his father's companies, Federated Petroleums, into Major Jim Lowery's Home Oil Ltd., taking the latter over.

By 1960, Ian Drum had risen in Home Oil to vice-president in charge of special projects. The Carstairs plant, being something new for the company, fell into his bailiwick. Drum decided he needed a gas expert to help him and was able to get Kevin Milne whose extensive experience at both Jumping Pound and Fort St. John recommended him highly. Milne oversaw the design and construction of Carstairs (by Fluor) and, after start-up, left the plant in the hands of its first superintendent, Howard Geddes. Geddes had previously been a gas engineer for Shell at Jumping Pound.

The largest plant built in 1960 (at 75 million cubic feet of raw gas capacity), Home Carstairs has been described as a carbon copy of B.A.'s Nevis plant. Some things did differ, most importantly the analysis of the gas. Operating engineer Fred Brooks of Hillspring, Alberta, recalls that the CO_2/H_2S ratio in the acid gas was so high it would not burn to make sulphur. The plant also had an interesting marketing relationship with the Canadian Oil Companies refinery at Bowden. Borrowing an American idea which had already been used in Canada at Pacific's Taylor refinery, the Bowden refinery was designed to produce high octane gasoline using condensate as a feedstock. The process had the advantage of eliminating the residuals common to crude oil refining and thus avoided the costly cat-cracking step. The Carstairs plant was conveniently located to supply the Bowden refinery with condensate. A four-inch pipeline ran from Carstairs to the main highway between Calgary and Edmonton. Here, tank trucks picked up the condensate and drove it to Bowden, one truck every one hundred minutes.

These were interesting features but, looking back, Kevin Milne believes the original producers' agreement may have been the most important aspect of the Carstairs plant. Home Oil, one of the largest Canadian independent oil and gas companies but not a large company by international standards, had proven that the smaller companies could get together and run a plant as a cooperative. "It was an idea whose day had come", and it swiftly became a more popular way of processing than to pay a processing charge at a plant operated by one of the majors in the field. Home Oil joined Dome and Goliad as a true pioneer of joint-venture processing in Canada.

*   *   *

The other plants coming on stream in 1960 were smaller than Carstairs (5-25 MMCF/day), and most served the TCPL system. Eleven were solid dessicant adsorption plants. Another feature of the plants of 1960 was that most had backed off from LPG production and extracted only pentanes plus. Because the LPG market had not kept up to the growing natural gas market, propanes and butanes were reinjected, flared or left in the residue gas. Of the 1960 plants, only the small compression-refrigeration plant at Nottingham, Saskatchewan, extracted LPGs. Nottingham's other claim to fame was the first attempt in Canada to sweeten gas by hot potassium carbonate adsorption. The overall success of this "hot pot" process is probably best summed up by the fact that only three natural gas processing plants in Canada ever used it.

RIMBEY — "THE LARGEST PLANT IN CANADA"

With supply to A & S scheduled to commence on New Year's, 1962, plant construction rose to a peak in the spring and summer of 1961. The largest of these plants was B.A.'s facility at Rimbey. Contributing to the size of the Rimbey plant was the costly experience of B.A., California Standard and Home Oil when they failed to reach agreement on one plant for the processing of Nevis gas two years earlier. All parties learned a costly lesson there and, when it came to Homeglen-Rimbey, B.A. was determined to see the gas processed by joint-venture. Such was the joint-venturing spirit that another large field, Westerose South, was added to the kitty so that twenty-eight different companies co-owned the Rimbey plant that B.A. was to operate. The largest co-owner was none other than California Standard which held a percentage slightly larger than that of B.A.

Various publications celebrating the birth of B.A. Rimbey in 1961 dubbed it "the largest processing plant ever built in Canada". However, by the usual measure of size, raw gas capacity, it ranked second. Rimbey's initial capacity was 326 million a day and the Taylor plant near Ft. St. John still topped that at 350 million. Rimbey certainly was the largest plant of any in liquids capacity. The sour gas at Rimbey was so rich in liquid hydrocarbons that its propane and butane facilities were sized at 2300 and 3000 barrels a day respectively (compared to 800 and 1050 at Taylor). Rimbey was the only 1961 plant to have LPG facilities. B.A. Rimbey also extracted sulphur but the percentage of H_2S in its gas was not high enough to give the plant sulphur production comparable to that of B.A. Pincher Creek or Texas Gulf Okotoks.

The first superintendent at Rimbey was John Beddome. Beddome, a native of B.C. educated at U.B.C., started in the oil and gas business with Canadian Gulf at Stettler. More recently he had worked as plant engineer for B.A. at Pincher Creek under the tutelage of Martin Bretz. He took over from Elmer Berlie when Berlie moved to Texas Gulf Okotoks. B.A.'s great advantage over many other companies was that it could call on men like John Beddome, who had extensive experience at Nevis and Pincher Creek, to see a new plant through its teething stage. Later arrivals in Canada seldom had that luxury.

John Beddome; superintendent of B.A. Rimbey in 1961; president of Dome Petroleum in 1984.

The design of the Rimbey plant came largely from B.A.'s meticulous chief engineer Charles Buskel. After all the hydrating problems at the first California-designed plants, and the pendulum swing to total housing, Buskel sent the pendulum back the other way by designed Rimbey as an outdoor plant. He believed the industry had over-reacted to the early catastrophes and that, with a bit of thought, safe and cheap outdoor plants could be operated successfully.

B.A. Rimbey, like several plants before it, used aerial coolers and in the summer they were beset by a curious problem. Rimbey lies nestled in the aspen parkland belt, all very scenic and enjoyable except during the poplar *fluff* season when the men would be out with high pressure hoses trying to keep the screens from plugging up. If they failed to keep pace, the amine system lost efficiency and H_2S would turn up in the gas at the AGTL metering station.

Another unique design aspect of the Rimbey plant was its total independence from outside utilities. Turbogenerators supplied electricity and gas-fired boilers fed steam to steam turbines, driving all major pumps, compressors and blowers. This preserved Rimbey from utility company failures but, as John Beddome remembers, it did not preserve Rimbey from its own power failures. So independent was the plant that when it went down, there was not a light in the place to start up by.

As his final stamp on B.A. Rimbey, Charles Buskel left a detailed method of calculating revenues. Faced with the new problem (new for B.A.) of how to divide the spoils amongst twenty-eight unequal interest holders, Buskel "went to the ultimate". The operators were kept on the run for years sampling the various streams several times a day and conveying the numbers to the accountants for application to the different owner percentages. Good reason existed for this beyond just a mania for accounting. So huge was Rimbey's production that one percent point difference in any calculation represented a great deal of money. Buskel had simply made sure that everyone got their due.

Looking back from the president's chair at Dome to his days as superintendent at Rimbey, John Beddome feels fairly certain that everyone did well out of the plant. He recalls Rimbey as one of the most profitable plants ever. Its cost of construction (by Poole-Pritchard Canadian Ltd.) seems absurdly low by present-day standards and, consequently, the plant paid out rapidly and has kept on paying for a long time. Shortly after its completion, B.A. Rimbey's capacity stretched to 426 million cubic feet a day which *did* make it the largest plant in Canada by all the usual means of measurement.

B.A. Rimbey, on stream in 1961; supplying natural gas to both TCPL and Alberta and Southern.

THE CANADIAN CONTENT OF B.A. RIMBEY

Between 1957 and 1962, a dramatic shift took place toward purchasing plant construction materials in Canada. When B.A. completed its Rimbey plant in 1961, it was able to boast that 83% of the equipment and materials for the plant (by dollar value) had been purchased in Canada, from Canadian fabricators. At the opening ceremony at Rimbey, B.A. president E. D. Loughney said: "It could well be that no major plant of a like magnitude has ever been built in Canada with a higher content of Canadian produced materials and equipment." The only major equipment still not purchasable in this country were the large compressors, the aerial coolers and barrel-type pumps.

The pressure vessels at B.A. Rimbey had much to do with the conspicuously high Canadian content percentage. Most of the plant's pressure vessels were built in British Columbia by Victoria Machinery Depot Ltd. In 1961, this company already enjoyed a hundred year history as shipbuilders and engineers, with major contracts for destroyer escorts and commercial passenger ships.

In the October 10, 1960, issue of *Oil in Canada*, a reporter enthused that "the successful execution of this fabrication contract shows that Canadian fabricators are quite able to take care of the country's burgeoning natural gas industry." He was correct in spirit if not in detail. It has to be admitted that this particular fabrication contract owed a great deal to the fact that Rimbey's design did not call for exotic metallurgy. B.A. and other companies had begun to understand that mild steel was more resistant to corrosion than high-strength alloys. The fact remains that B.A. did go to a Canadian company for the vessels and that the Victoria company lived up to the contract. Nor was this Victoria Machinery Depot's debut as a manufacturer of vessels for the gas processing industry. The company had supplied eighteen storage vessels to Goliad Oil and Gas for its processing project in Pembina in 1958. In 1959, V.M.D. built all the stainless steel clad vessels at Texas Gulf Okotoks. In 1961, it supplied two immense pressure vessels to the West Whitecourt plant. These latter vessels were fifty-five feet long and weighed 170 tons apiece. They were sent by depressed railcar from Edmonton to Vancouver and by special, heavy-duty trucks from there along the tortuous road to remote Whitecourt.

MORE PLANTS IN 1961

Other major plants besides Rimbey were built in 1961. Several of the plants backstopping the A & S system were of a good size. Canadian Delhi finally entered the processing business after all its years of successful exploration with a fifty-five million cubic foot per day plant at Buck Lake. The plant processed gas from the Minnehik-Buck Lake field Canadian Delhi had discovered years earlier on a farm-in from Great Plains. In the long wait for market, Canadian Delhi tried to sell its share of the field. Measuring the benefits that eventually accrued when the Minnehik-Buck Lake field eventually fed into the A & S pipeline, former Canadian Delhi president Smiley Raborn counts it a lucky thing they could not find a buyer. Like many sour gas plants of the era, Buck Lake did not initially make sulphur from the acid gases. It began sulphur production in 1967 after completing an expansion to seventy million cubic feet a day.

The foothills near Cochrane, home to Shell Jumping Pound, sprouted their second gas plant in 1961 when several companies joint-ventured on a forty million cubic foot plant called Wildcat Hills. The residue gas from the Canadian Fina Oil Ltd. operation sold to A & S. Albertan Bernie Coady served as Canadian Fina's project engineer at Wildcat Hills. He remembers the design as a happy medium between the wide-openness of a plant like Rimbey or Jumping Pound (at which he had worked) and the totally enclosed variety such as Taylor. Most of the vessels were outside, but their controls and gauge glasses were inside. The gas was sour but lean enough that the owners were able to go with a relatively inexpensive solid dessicant plant, catching the hydrocarbons and water in the molecular pores of Sorbeads (a Mobil patent).

Canadian Fina's president, Trajan Nitescu, made a great contribution to the Wildcat Hills facility by recommending a costly but incredibly reliable system of hot water tracing along the field gas gathering lines. So successful was this system that the Wildcat Hills gathering system has never been plugged off by gas hydrates in all of its twenty-plus years of operation. *(For more detail, see Chapter Eight.)*

Canadian Fina Oil Ltd. enjoyed a reputation as a source of innovation in the Canadian gas processing industry, particularly through its operations at Windfall and Wildcat Hills. The company originated in 1950 when Petrofina S.A. of Belgium sent Trajan Nitescu to Canada to organize and run a subsidiary. Nitescu was Rumanian by birth and worked with Petrofina's Rumanian subsidiary from 1926 until the end of World War II. At that time, he resigned his post as General Manager of the Oil Department because the company, like the country, was being taken over by the communists. For this and other reasons, he was soon an enemy of the Rumanian state, forced into hiding. After six months of flight from the secret police, he and his wife swam the Danube River at night to the relative safety of Yugoslavia. They were still prisoners under Tito's regime, but eventually were allowed to leave because of high level, indirect pressure from the United States and Belgium.

Canadian Fina's first president, Trajan Nitescu.

Nitescu took up employment with his old company Petrofina after the War and came to Canada. Under Nitescu's guidance, Canadian Fina grew rapidly through takeovers. In a short time, it absorbed Western Leaseholds Ltd. (a public company with large land holdings controlled by Eric Harvie) and Calvan Consolidated.

Canadian Fina's contribution to the understanding of sour gas begins with its involvement in the Whitecourt region, specifically with its interest in the Windfall cycling plant. Two of the key people involved at Windfall were, like Nitescu, Eastern Europeans who had suffered under communist rule. Dr. Alexander Petrunic, a Croatian scientist jailed by Tito after the War for his socialist involvements, escaped to Canada with Nitescu's help and was quickly employed by Fina. Nitescu knew Petrunic both as an established industrial scientist and a professor of considerable stature.

When a bright young Hungarian student by the name of Joe Lukacs made his escape to Canada after Hungary's quickly repressed revolt of 1956, Nitescu snapped him up as well, offering Lukacs a scholarship to complete his studies at the University of Alberta, then hiring him in the summers and after his degree to work for Fina. Lukacs' Master's Degree Thesis on the water content in sour gas was based largely on his working experience at Windfall.

All this is not to suggest that Canadian Fina and Trajan Nitescu were missing out on talent available in Canada and the United States. Harold Noyes who shares the patent for the hot water tracing system with N. R. Towie and Nitescu, graduated in chemical engineering from the University of Alberta in 1954. Bernie Coady, project engineer at Wildcat Hills, came from Cardston, Alberta, before his university education in the U.S. He is now president of Delta Projects, a Calgary-based gas plant engineering and construction firm.

Bernie Coady left Canadian Fina to start Delta Projects Limited in 1965.

American know-how was well represented on the Canadian Fina team by elder statesman Wally Palmer. After the construction of B.A. Nevis, Palmer had gone to work at Windfall. Palmer held the distinction of being one of the first ten professional engineers ever licensed in the State of Texas.

When Canadian Fina was purchased from Petrofina by Petro-Canada in 1981, Trajan Nitescu was enraged. He felt betrayed that the company he had worked so hard to establish had been nationalized through purchase by a state company. He also deeply resented what he regarded as a bloated price paid by Canadian taxpayers to the company's Belgian owners. On March 31, 1981, Nitescu took out a full page in the *Calgary Herald*, at his own personal expense, to make his views known.

WATERTON AND WHITECOURT

Two of the processing cornerstones in the A & S plan to supply Alberta gas to California came on stream in 1962. These were the Shell plant at Waterton and the Whitecourt plant operated by Pan American Petroleum Corporation on behalf of its partners Canadian Fina and Hudson's Bay Oil and Gas.

The Whitecourt plant had the longer history of the two. Canadian Fina obtained a million acre reservation in the Whitecourt area in 1951 and invited HBOG and Pan Am to join in the exploration taking equal 41⅔% shares (Fina held the 16⅔% balance). Whitecourt is a boreal forest landscape, rugged country with a summer floor of muskeg. The three companies waded in together and discovered the Windfall field in 1955, twenty miles from the village of Whitecourt, a sour wet gas accumulation in the Woodbend D-3 limestone reef. The partners discovered two more fields in the area; Beaver Creek in 1957 and Pine Creek in 1958.

Processing of the gas began in 1959 with a pilot plant in the Windfall field, the least sour of the three fields at 15.5% H_2S. The pilot plant stripped condensate for sale and recycled the *sour* gas (something which had not yet been attempted). The owners were hoping to gain enough knowledge about their sour gas at the pilot plant stage to prepare them for the building of a full scale plant later on. Canadian Fina operated the facilities on behalf of the partners.

The operators cycled the gas at Windfall because the reservoir was subject to retrograde condensation. Ordinarily gas liquids will flash or turn to gas as pressure is lowered, but, under certain temperature and pressure conditions, some gas mixtures will exhibit exactly the opposite behaviour: the gas will turn to liquid as the pressure drops. These conditions existed at Windfall. To achieve reasonable recovery from a retrograde condensation field, it is necessary to maintain the pressure of the reservoir. Otherwise liquids will form in the reservoir, adhering to the rock, and most of those liquids will be lost. The Windfall cycling plant proved that such pressure maintenance was possible in the Windfall reservoir, setting the stage for more elaborate sour gas cycling schemes later on.

The full scale plant known as West Whitecourt came on stream in April of 1962, operated by Pan American Petroleum Corporation. At 204 million cubic feet a day, it rated as one of the largest plants then in existence in Canada and an important link in the A & S chain of supply. Brown and Root built the plant (Stearns-Roger had built the pilot plant and wellhead units). Because the three partners in the Whitecourt area did not have any major marketing organization for sulphur, the sulphur facilities at West

Pan American Petroleum Corporation's West Whitecourt plant; on stream in 1962.

Whitecourt were eventually sold to Texas Gulf, an experienced marketer of the commodity.

The full scale plant and gathering system were revolutionary in many ways based on the lessons learned at the pilot stage. The scheme now consisted of gathering the extremely sour Pine Creek gas (23.5% H_2S) and reinjecting it into the Windfall reservoir. This ensured a much higher recovery of the less sour Windfall reserves due to the sweeping action and the prevention of retrograde condensation.

In the Pine Creek field and at the West Whitecourt plant, operating difficulties abounded. But most important in the long run, Pan Am and its field partners succeeded in pipelining, compressing and cycling high pressure sour gas. They designed a plant and cycling system without good data with which to predict the behaviour of the sour gas in this retrograde condensation reservoir. In future, the data for predicting sour gas behaviour would improve. It improved because of research and improved analytical techniques, much of which was based on trial and error experiences like those at Whitecourt.

As one informant put it, Pan Am's first crew at the West Whitecourt plant deserves mention not just for its ability but for the fact that the group stuck it out. Constant operational difficulties combined with a remote location at the end of an almost impassable road spelled challenge. The nucleus of the crew that met that challenge included area superintendent Errol Wagner, a man who had come up through the American ranks of

Stanolind like Martin Bretz of B.A. Pincher Creek. Wagner's plant superintendent was Bob Loffland. Process foreman was Fred Atkinson and
maintenance foreman was René Coutéréte. The area engineer was Jamey
Morrow, leading an engineering staff that included Tony Neidermayer and
Ed Baraniuk.

*West Whitecourt area superintendent Errol Wagner (l) and plant superintendent Bob Loffland talk over their
plant.*

The Shell Waterton play had a more recent origin. The field had been
discovered in 1958. Otherwise, in timing, market and frontiersmanship,
Shell Waterton had much in common with Whitecourt. It too served as a
cornerstone of A & S gas supply and it came on stream within a month of

West Whitecourt in the spring of 1962. Its capacity at start-up was 180 million cubic feet of raw gas a day.

In other ways, Shell Waterton cannot be compared to any other plant. The plant enjoys a magnificent site, snuggled up to the foot of the Rocky Mountains ten miles due west of B.A. Pincher Creek. The roads that serve its wells snake through the mountains and jackknife up the mountain walls.

Shell Waterton; a location of great beauty.

Ordinarily, when plants move into new territory and build new roads, the improvement of access is a positive factor in local public relations. In northern Alberta, for example, the building of roads by gas processors signalled the beginning of agriculture in the area and general economic growth. But, at Shell Waterton, many of the plant's nearest neighbours were mountain men and women who had little interest in improved communication with the outside world. One particular gentleman was so on the fight about this invasion of his domain that Shell frequently sent representatives down to visit him, hoping to make peace. Each time a company visitor arrived, the man would haul out his bottle and they would drink. Hours later, the Shell man would totter off full of spirits convinced he had made great progress. Nonetheless, the next piece of news that came into the plant about this neighbour would be that he was madder than ever. It took quite a while for Shell to figure out that the man's readiness with a bottle had nothing to do with good will; his wife simply wouldn't let him drink unless he had company.

The Bechtel Corporation won the contract to build the plant and Bill Fisher and Bill Roman of Shell went to San Francisco to consult with Bechtel on the design. As usual, the design had to be completed in a hurry, and Bechtel demanded that Shell give its emissaries full authority to make decisions so things would not be held up going through channels. Fisher's and Roman's boss, John Dillon, consented.

This was only the beginning of the gambles taken by Shell at Waterton. Shell Development, then located outside San Francisco at Emeryville, currently had in the works a method for removing H_2S by liquefying it at low temperature. This Low Temperature Flashing process had never been attempted at plant scale. If it worked, 85% of the H_2S could be flashed off and the remainder cleaned up by amine wash. Only three months remained before construction at Waterton so clearly there was no time to go to a pilot plant. John Dillon took his second risk, deciding to go from test tube to plant.

But the biggest risk of all at Shell Waterton had to be Shell's decision to own the Waterton sulphur plant and market its own sulphur. The capacity of the gas plant and the sourness of the gas meant large quantities of sulphur production every day. Other companies in this position (e.g., Pan Am at West Whitecourt) had chosen to let an established sulphur company (like Texas Gulf) take over the sulphur end of the operation. Such companies had world-wide sulphur markets on which to place the new production. Because of their privileged position, the sulphur companies drove a hard bargain for their services. When Shell approached Texas Gulf about running the sulphur facilities at Waterton, the deal offered was so disadvantageous that Shell decided — with great trepidation — to go it alone. Used to marketing 88 long tons of sulphur a day from Jumping Pound, Shell now had to find a home for another 1000 long tons a day from Waterton.

When Shell Waterton started up, it did have trouble with the Low Temperature Flashing unit but not the anticipated kind. The move from test tube to plant scale would have been a reasonable success if the acid gas had not attacked the flange bolts in the building causing a dangerous spill of liquid H_2S. From that point forward, Shell Waterton's operators learned what life had been like for their B.A. neighbours to the east. Despite a great deal of preparation to avoid the problems that had beset plants like B.A. Pincher Creek, Shell Waterton found itself with metal failure problems of its own. Also like B.A. Pincher Creek, efforts by Shell to solve its Waterton problems had a beneficial effect on the entire industry.

CALGARY AND COLEMAN

Westcoast Transmission's share of the gas passing into the Alberta Natural Gas (ANG) line that cut the corner of British Columbia to Idaho was supplied by two plants: The Petrogas Processing Ltd. plant at Balzac north of Calgary and the Saratoga Processing Ltd. plant at Coleman in the Crowsnest Pass.

The Crossfield and Elkton fields, with reserves estimated at 1.5 TCF, were the basis for the gas processing plant at Balzac. The agreement struck by the field owners represented the first *complete* unitization in Canada. Jefferson Lake Petrochemicals Limited owned 53% of the reserves, but the company that owned and operated the field was the new unitization company, Petrogas Processing Ltd. Ralph M. Parsons constructed the plant for Petrogas. Jim Leeper, who had successfully operated the Jefferson Lake sulphur plant at Fort St. John, accepted the position of superintendent at Balzac.

The Petrogas plant had the distinction of being the second out of three plants to use the *hot pot* process in Canada. The choice of process stems from the analysis of the D-1 Wabamun gas. Texas Gulf at Okotoks had already processed sour gas from this reef and had suffered high chemical losses in its MEA sweetening units. Petrogas sought to escape this problem by going to another process. The current choices were hot potassium carbonate adsorption which had been tried with virtually no success at Nottingham, Saskatchewan, and the diethanolamine or DEA process, which had proven successful in refineries. As Jim Leeper puts it, DEA was "even more of a black art" than hot potassium, so they opted for the latter.

Despite its very limited use in Canada, *hot pot* proved a satisfactory process at Balzac. Jim Leeper feels that it did what it was supposed to do: the chemical losses associated with it were low; it hydrolized the carbonyl sulphide and carbon disulphide in the gas; and it kept corrosion to a minimum. Leeper adds, though, that the plant was always on the verge of "going sour".

Many of Petrogas' greater problems occurred downhole in the field. Changes in temperature and pressure would cause sulphur to drop out of the sour gas in the wells, plugging them. Jim Leeper tried breaking up the blockages by pouring carbon disulphide down the hole. The first time he tried it, his president Harold Manley was dead against the idea. Consequently, Leeper used ten barrels, many times the amount actually needed. He "had to make it work", and indeed it did.

The rest of Westcoast Transmission's gas needs for the ANG line to Kingsgate were to be supplied from the Savanna Creek field deep in the

Rocky Mountains north of the Crowsnest Pass. Husky Oil owned most of this field and operated its wells. From the wellhead in, Saratoga Processing Limited, a wholly-owned subsidiary of Westcoast Transmission, operated all facilities. The Saratoga plant, a cost-of-service operation, was located in Coleman, Alberta.

The Coleman location had caused a certain amount of controversy. After their long years of experience with various kinds of coal-related pollution, residents in the Crowsnest Pass did not like the sounds of being downwind and downriver from a sour gas plant. On the other hand, because of economic depression in the area, some like Mr. Abousfafy, the Mayor of Coleman, badly wanted the plant. After an industry spokesman had spent a great deal of effort at one of the hearings explaining the safeguards of the proposed plant, Mayor Abousfafy jumped up and said, "Would you rather die quickly from H_2S or slowly from starvation?"

Fortunately, those were not the only options. Eventually the plant received the necessary approvals and was built by Bechtel. Tony Storcer, Saratoga's superintendent at Coleman, rigourously tested the plant with the help of Bechtel. The result was what Storcer calls "the sweetest start-up I ever went through." The plant had two leaks; they were found and fixed within two hours. This had to be quite a relief for Storcer who, as maintenance superintendent at Taylor, had lived through the lingering troubles that had beset that plant in its first year.

Still, as if there were some kind of Newtonian law at work insisting that each success be balanced off by an equivalent disaster, trouble came to Coleman from the Savanna Creek field. The six wells at Savanna Creek, two in the alpine zone high atop Plateau Mountain, tested out at a total of around 75 million cubic feet a day, which corresponded neatly to the capacity of the plant. The system had barely started producing, however, when well production collapsed. This happened so suddenly that the producers assumed they were victims of sulphur plugging downhole. But when carbon disulphide treatment helped only marginally, a more disastrous truth had to be faced. The problem lay in the reservoir rock itself and production was not likely to improve.

Tony Storcer's "nice little plant" at Coleman became troublesome. It was not receiving enough gas. In the early years, it seldom ran on more than fourteen million cubic feet of gas a day. When Storcer left Coleman in 1964, he was replaced by an operator who had moved to Coleman from B.A. Pincher Creek. Bob Krystoff, who had lived almost at the foot of Pincher Creek's frequently used emergency flare, became the second superintendent at Coleman.

WIND

Southern Alberta wind verges on the legendary. Local folklore abounds with characters who developed a westward lean and would fall flat if transplanted to other climates. The gas industry also has a folklore and, in the tales of those who have worked at B.A. Pincher Creek and Shell Waterton, the wind is a dominant player.

When the walls of the office building at B.A. Pincher Creek were erected, the wind huffed and puffed and blew one of them down. Elmer Berlie became acquainted with that same wind watching sheets of ¾" plywood flip off a pile like playing cards off a deck. They catapulted through the plant site miraculously killing no one.

Only one person at B.A. Pincher Creek claims not to have been astounded by the wind and that is Martin Bretz. John Beddome says of his former superintendent, "There isn't much in life Martin Bretz hasn't seen," so perhaps he must be believed when he describes Pincher Creek as the *second* windiest place on earth — next to Casper, Wyoming. The wind and the fact that Shell Waterton was built a few miles straight west of B.A. Pincher Creek also gave Martin Bretz a tongue-in-cheek answer when it came to pollution complaints: "Talk to Shell; they're upwind."

Bechtel, the construction contractor at Shell Waterton, built an airstrip west of the plant site. Many people have since studied the peculiar wave action that the wind achieves bounding over the mountains, but Bechtel's pilots learned about it the hard way, scaring themselves so entirely that the airstrip was abandoned.

Also discovered in the Waterton construction phase was the fact that a westward facing door is a useless thing on many days of every year. Little box entrances had to be built to shield these doors and still you could not get them open half the time. Six times in Shell Waterton's first fall the wind eclipsed the 100 mile per hour mark.

Perhaps the worst miscalculation with respect to Pincher Creek wind belongs to Bechtel. While building Shell Waterton, that company made the unfortunate decision to put its disposal field upwind from its camp.

Having said all of this it must be added that some who have worked at the Saratoga plant at Coleman in the Crowsnest Pass argue that Pincher Creek and Waterton wind isn't a patch on their own; that the wind is positively enfeebled by the time it gets all the way down to Pincher. The Saratoga plant was designed for 200 mile an hour wind and clocked a wind of 135 per mile in its early years of operation. Saratoga's ex-superintendent Don Duguid contends that the Coleman plant could not really cause a local pollution problem. Thanks to the wind, Saratoga effluent did not even hit the ground until it was beyond the last range of mountains — and then it could be blamed on Shell or Gulf.

WHERE TO AFTER '62

When Canada made its big surge into the sour gas processing industry, there were not any strong international precedents to rely upon and borrow from. Problems like hydrogen sulphide corrosion, hydrogen embrittlement and stress corrosion cracking had been around since Turner Valley, but still had not been satisfactorily solved. As the pressure of the gas and the percentages of H_2S and CO_2 increased, the situation became critical. What Canadian processors did in that circumstance remains an amazing feat, or series of feats. During the late '50's, and particularly in the '60's, epic battles were fought with hydrogen sulphide in Western Canada's plants — and eventually those battles were won. They were won because of personal dedication and ingenuity, and because of communication and cooperation between companies. They were won so convincingly that the Canadian industry became and remains the acknowledged world leader in the processing of sour gas.

FORT NELSON

The processing news of 1963 included Westcoast Transmission's processing plant at Fort Nelson, British Columbia. If Taylor had been a northerly plant project, Fort Nelson was two hundred and fifty miles farther up the Alaska Highway. Most of the men superintendent Gordie McKenzie took with him to Fort Nelson for the plant's first winter were looking for a challenge. Says McKenzie: "They found it too."

For various financial reasons, the plant was built one year too soon. When the construction season ended, the plant was operational but the pipeline south to Westcoast's transmission line wasn't. As Gordie McKenzie puts it: "It had a big hole in the middle." This meant that the plant had to run on a miniscule throughput of two million cubic feet of gas a day; just enough to run the plant's own boilers. This made the plant tough to run. Gordie McKenzie counted nineteen shutdowns during the first winter. With temperatures plunging below $-40°F$, the danger of freezing up was extreme. However, the crew managed to start the plant back up every time before such a freeze-up could occur. The crew became "quite good at it, in fact," says McKenzie. "At the first flickering of the lights, the men got into their parkas and ran to their battle stations." Adding urgency to the drill was the fact that the staff housing at the plant site depended on the plant for heat; that and the fact that the crew's families had been moved into that housing two weeks before Christmas. By the second winter, the pipeline was connected and, if necessary, gas could be backed up the line from Taylor. But, in the frosty seclusion of the first winter, the men at Fort Nelson were literally surviving on their skill as engineers and operators.

Despite the tensions and privations of that first winter, the entire crew signed on for a second season. The plant itself grew through a series of expansions to be one of the largest in Canada.

SOUR GAS PROCESSING: THE CANADIAN CONTRIBUTION

8

When the Canadian gas processing industry began its life in Turner Valley, it did so with American technology and, in many cases, with second-hand American equipment. To go with the American hardware came American know-how: engineers and experienced operators sent north by parent companies to show the local boys what to do.

Times change. In the 1950's, the Canadian industry began to grow. Several plants were built. But, more importantly, the kind of gas encountered this side of the border differed from the processed in most parts of the world. A generation of green engineers, mainly from Canadian universities, had to work on the problems of high-pressure sour gas processing without the safety net of American or world precedents. At the same time, a generation of operators, often recruited off the local farms or lured away from other industries, had to man plants that were quite experimental. They were as safe as the knowledge of the time could make them, which is to say unsafe by the standards of today.

In hindsight, it is probably fortunate that the Canadian situation was so different. The sourness of our gas and the coldness of our climate were factors forcing the industry to innovate. Dangerous and inconvenient as the new problems were, they created an opportunity for separate evolution and separate identity.

SOUR GAS PROCESSING: THE STATE OF THE ART IN 1950

The year 1950 may not seem like ancient history to most, but to people in the gas processing industry, it has the flavour of prehistory. The general concept is that, before 1950, you shoved the gas into the front end of the plant and hoped for the best. As for the problems associated with sour gas, they must have seemed as inevitable and unalterable as the weather.

Those involved with the Canadian industry in 1950 will not altogether deny such allegations, but they probably would rebel against the notion that science and technology had made *no* progress in dealing with these difficulties. Many of the complications that the Canadian industry has gained respect by solving were fairly well understood by 1950; and a few workable solutions had been found.

One feature of Turner Valley processing that slowed the pace of discovery was the gradual way that problems appeared. The gas was sour; but not very. The overnight corrosion and embrittlement catastrophes that jolted '50's operators into action simply did not happen in the Valley. There, the crises were often years in the making, and more years in the solving.

Norman Lukes, an engineering graduate from Queen's, became Royalite's first corrosion man. When Lukes arrived in 1937, he was put on the *bull gang*, digging ditches and tarring pipes; put to those tasks along with a lot of other men Royalite didn't want to lose but couldn't afford to pay as tradesmen or engineers. As things improved, Royalite brought Norman Lukes into the engineering office and gave him the task of inspecting vessels for corrosion. He found lots of it, "like raindrops on a sidewalk, only turned round the other way."

Royalite's operators, engineers and labmen believed the corrosion culprit to be hydrogen sulphide. Later, when Royalite switched over from Seaboard sweetening to MEA, they found that carbonic acid could be just as destructive a factor. The worst corrosion Norman Lukes ever saw in Turner Valley was inside locomotive-type boilers on the well sites. In the early years before sweetened gas became available to the leases as fuel, the boilers operated on raw, sour gas. Operating at only fifteen pounds pressure, the boilers were ideal sulphuric acid plants. When the rapidly cooling flue gas ascended the stack and mingled with the moisture there, it converted into a shower of acid. The smoke boxes became so badly corroded, Lukes found he could push his fingers through them.

Every year, Norman Lukes lent assistance to the inspectors from the Boilers Branch of the Department of Labour, and he found his next job with that Branch. Lukes went to work for the Boilers Branch as an Inspector of Unfired Pressure Vessels, a career that lasted thirty-five years. Up until the mid-'40s, the Boilers Branch restricted its inspections to the actual steam boilers at gas processing plants, but the work Norman Lukes took on included the inspection of all pressure vessels. This broadening of inspections turned up a series of corrosion problems in the vessels of Turner Valley's naphtha plants and inspired the first efforts to solve them.

In a manual entitled "Corrosion in the Petroleum Industry", written by Norman Lukes in 1950, he neatly encapsulates the knowledge available to the industry as of that year. One problem discovered in the late '40's at B.A. Longview was hydrogen blistering. On the outside of tanks used to store sour naphtha, operators and inspectors were finding blisters. Bubbles were forming within laminations in the steel, pushing the layers apart. Lukes describes the problem:

> The formation of blisters is based on the theory that the existence of hydrogen sulphide in a fluid or gas well causes an acid corrosion on the carbon steel in which atomic hydrogen is liberated and ferrous sulphide is formed as a black scale on the shell.
>
> The atomic hydrogen has a tendency to diffuse into the steel and under certain favourable conditions may collect in blow holes, slag inclusions, laminations or any defect in the steel. The hydrogen in doing this changes from atomic hydrogen to molecular hydrogen and is unable to escape by diffusion and remains in the steel. Over a period of time sufficient pressure may be built up by the molecular hydrogen to form a bubble or blister which will gradually increase in size until its rupture allows the hydrogen to escape.

The explanation continues:

> In addition to causing blisters, excessive hydrogen diffusion will reduce the ductility of the steel and cause hydrogen embrittlement. High temperatures and pressure will increase hydrogen diffusion in carbon steel and cause it to fail under stress.

A modern explanation of the same problem would not differ greatly.

Many placed the blame for hydrogen blistering on the steel mills, for the poor quality of their post-war product. Too much slag was left in the steel when it was rolled and the atomic hydrogen migrated to these discontinuities in the metal. The usual solution was to drill a hole in the blister, letting the gas out; then to hammer the metal down and weld it. This method continued in use right into the '60's. When Colin Duncan joined Pacific Petroleums at Taylor in the early '60's as corrosion engineer, he recalls that the safety man, Fred Dunn, loved drilling hydrogen blisters. One day they found a large one inside a tower and, as it looked to Dunn like "a boomer", he suggested Duncan take refuge down a tray or two. From that vantage, Colin Duncan heard the sound of the drill, an explosion and a shout from Fred Dunn in rapid succession. When he reached the safety man, Duncan found Dunn unhurt, but minus his eyebrows.

Weight loss corrosion had also been found and measured by 1950, in the vessels of the Seaboard and Girbotol sweetening units at Turner Valley Royalite. R. S. Phillips of Royalite wrote an article that year on "Corrosion Problems in Gas Scrubbing Plants" which again shows the quite detailed knowledge engineers of this era possessed:

> The gas as received by this plant contains from 700 to 1200 grains of hydrogen sulphide per 100 SCF* and from 2.0 to 2.5% carbon dioxide

---

*Standard cubic feet.

. . . It is readily seen that with this relatively high concentration of corrosive gases in the gas stream, various forms of corrosion will appear throughout the plant.

The Seaboard unit had corroded at the bottom of the scrubbing tower where the sour sodium carbonate solution departed, and in the bubble caps and trays where the corrosion product accumulated. This product was correctly identified as iron sulphide.

In the reactifier or stripper, "the foul sodium carbonate released its load of carbon dioxide and hydrogen sulphide in the presence of air and water — ideal conditions for corrosive attack on iron and steel."

Over in the Girbotol plant (the ancestor of all amine sweetening units), the worst of the corrosion problems were solved after the first nine months of operation in 1941. Before that, they were attempting to sweeten the gas (with monoethanolamine, or MEA) and to dehydrate it (with diethylene glycol), all in a single step. Severe corrosion started immediately. They tried raising the concentration of MEA and succeeded in moving the corrosion zone slightly. They added a flash tank and immediately corrosion of the heat-exchangers decreased — and the consumption of MEA increased sevenfold!

About this time the Girdler Corporation of Louisville which owned the Girbotol patent announced tests showing that MEA solutions containing more than ten percent diethylene glycol were corrosive in the presence of carbon dioxide. As R. S. Phillips puts it: "This left one practical answer to the problem and that was to separate the desulphurization and the dehydration section." The plant was arranged that way and, not only did the corrosion in the heat exchangers decrease, but the temperature necessary to reactivate the MEA solution also dropped by 100 degrees F.

Generally, Royalite had one solution for weight loss corrosion and that was gunite — lots and lots of gunite. Gunite is a mixture of "Portland cement, high silica sand and water", a strong, non-porous, non-corrosive cement which the company simply placed between the corrosive attacker and the carbon steel victim. Norman Lukes describes Turner Valley Royalite as being "full of gunite", and wonders with a smile if the company wasn't partly owned by Canada Cement.

The usual process was to wait for corrosion to thin the vessel down to the minimum. Metal studs were then tack-welded to the vessel's inner wall. Chicken wire was spread over the studs and the gunite mixture was shot onto this reinforcement to a thickness of an inch and a half. It may sound too simple to work but it did. The mixture was so hard you could hit it with a hammer. It was also awkward and had the habit of flaking off and floating into pumps, which explains why plants sought an alternative. It is interesting, however, that in a 1968 paper on the Wildcat Hills plant, Dr. Alexander Petrunic still listed gunite as a method for dealing with the problem.

Stress corrosion cracking had also been identified before 1950. R. S. Phillips, in his 1950 article, described "what was believed to be a form of stress corrosion" in and around the weld metal of the Royalite Girbotol plant as early as 1946. A test program was embarked upon and, though it did not exactly define the problem, the affinity of the cracks for welded metal was further established. The technology of stress-relieving* with uniform heat had been around for some time already and the decision was made to try this at Royalite. Norman Lukes and others were fairly sure this would prove to be the answer. Lukes also put in a plug for proper welding procedures as a preventative:

> If the welding is not done by efficient workmen, weld defects such as under-cut, poor penetration and buildup, slag inclusions, gas pockets, and improper fitting will result and these are ideal places for the beginning of corrosion, erosion and stress cracks.

Hydrogen embrittlement cracks in a carbon steel flange.

---

*Heating metal uniformly to a very high temperature relieves stress that builds up in the metal from being exposed to temperatures that are unequal (welding one spot in a vessel, for example, may create a stress point or point of weakness).

The arsenal of defenses against corrosive sour gas is not entirely different today. Stress relieving and proper welding procedure are still recognized methods of protecting against stress cracks; and, though gunite is somewhat out of favour, the principle of putting a barrier between the corrosive agent and the steel remains. What has changed, and dramatically, is the ability of the industry to control corrosion through chemistry and metallurgy. The industry was driven to those improvements by the sheer potential for catastrophe that attended the processing of high pressure, accumulations of Alberta sour gas.

Fighting the corrosive enemy within; the support rings on the inside of this fractionator at the Gas and Oil Products Limited gas plant at Hartell were made of stainless steel to resist the attack of hydrogen sulphide (1950).

The Madison Natural Gas Co. scrubbing plant, Turner Valley, in 1944. In the left bank of towers are the Seaboard and Girbotol scrubbing vessels and the Girbotol reactivator; to the right are the vessels in which the Seaboard solution was regenerated and the stacks through which the H$_2$S went to atmosphere.

ICE THAT BURNS

Gas hydrates are crystalline compounds formed by the chemical combination of gas and water. They look somewhat like snow and what makes them a formidable headache for the gas industry is the fact that, under the right circumstances, they will form well above the freezing point of water. Gas hydrates have the power to plug wells, pipelines and plant vessels and they plagued the industry long before anyone knew what they were.

Being temperature related, the gas hydrate problem is naturally worse in Canada than in the United States. All operators of Turner Valley vintage remember lines freezing off and having to be thawed by steam. Occasionally, thawing was effected by direct flame which led to some accidents, and probably to a lot of confusion. R. K. Graves remembers cutting a frozen section out of a pipeline and bringing it inside the B.A. Longview plant for a bit of experimentation. When they applied a flame to the ice, it caught fire! — and burned quietly down to nothing. The question of what kind of ice burns probably occupied their thoughts for a while thereafter.

Believing the gas hydrates to be ice, operators attacked them with heat and anti-freezes and got some relief. Anti-freeze was pumped into lines upstream of problem areas, and line-heaters were placed along lines to keep them above the freezing point. Bill Sage remembers that the flames in Royalite's line-heaters in Turner Valley had a tendency to blow out and that, as soon as one did, a "pipeline freeze-up" was sure to occur. Gas hydrates had enough in common with ice to perpetuate the confusion between them: they melted when heat was applied; they would not form in the absence of water.

Though it took a while to penetrate to the industrial level, the breakthrough in understanding of gas hydrates was made by E. G. Hammerschmidt in 1934. In a gas cooling plant at Fritch, Texas, he observed the freezing of lines at 40 degrees F, with no throttling. After considerable research he tumbled to the reason why. In his paper explaining that the blockages were gas hydrates rather than water-ice, Hammerschmidt noted that gas hydrates were not exactly new to human understanding. Humphrey Davy had found and explained one in 1810, a chlorine-water hydrate; and various other kinds had been isolated throughout the 19th century.

After Hammerschmidt's discovery, a body of knowledge began to accumulate that was quite useful to natural gas producers and processors. Based on the observation that the hydrate temperature varied with the pressure of the gas, a set of curves was developed predicting that relation-

A Turner Valley line-heater retired to the Western Decalta office yard.

ship. Important from a Canadian perspective is the fact that early curves, developed in the U.S., the land of sweet gas, were based exclusively on sweet gas streams, with no reference to sour gas at all.

One item explained nicely by the studies was the tendency for the hydrating problem to be worse when the temperature was beginning to rise. R. K. Graves and Tommy Grisdale often noticed at Turner Valley that the hydrates multiplied come spring. Studies showed that gas hydrate crystals would fall off the inner walls of pipelines when the weather improved, floating along until they reached *log-jam* proportions and froze off the line.

With these maps of gas hydrate behaviour in hand, the U.S. industry was able to work on solutions. Heating the gas hydrate was still one way of making it dissolve, but not a particularly good way when the hydrate plug was a mile long and in the middle of nowhere. A better method was to depressure the line. High pressure promoted gas hydrates; low pressure encouraged them to break down. Line heating has probably been the most lasting method of prevention, but the idea of dehydrating the gas to prevent hydrates has always had appeal as well. The popular dehydration methods developed in the U.S. included absorbents* and solid adsorbents*.

The Canadian industry was probably quite content with its imported knowledge of gas hydrates and with its imported means for preventing them, at least until the production companies began drilling into the really sour Canadian formations. Hydrates occurring downhole in these exceptionally sour fields brought about a gradual realization that the sourness of gas influences the hydrate temperature, somewhat in the same way that pressure does.

Probably the first set of sour gas hydrate curves were produced by Joe Labuda in 1952, based on test data from Shell's early wells at Okotoks. Dr. Donald Katz, the eminent American researcher from the University of Michigan, had already made some theoretical suggestions about sour gas but had no data on which to establish K-values and curves. Chemical engineer Vince Milo came to Shell in 1953 and joined Labuda in this enterprise. Milo recalls how they would theorize where the hydrate points might be and then would run a trial with the well's heat circulating string. He remarks that the first guesses were seldom good, but that eventually they came up with reliable curves showing gas hydrate temperatures ten to fifteen degrees F above those for comparable mixtures of sweet gas. The companies already committed to processing high pressure, highly sour gas must have felt a great unease over these revelations. They could only proceed in hopes that some of the old technologies would work.

To gather gas of this description, without hydrates, the operators at

---

*An absorbent makes the water molecule part of itself through a chemical reaction. An adsorbent attracts the water molecule to its surface where it adheres.

Pincher Creek, Fort St. John and Okotoks first tried to remove the water from the gas at the wellhead. If there was no water, there could be no hydrates: This is and always will be true. They went with the popular system of the day, glycol dehydration, but ran into problems because of the high solubility of the hydrogen sulphide in the glycol. When the glycol regenerated, it released the dissolved H_2S to into the atmosphere creating a serious pollution problem. Some companies tried complex glycol systems designed to counteract the problem, but these were generally too expensive and cumbersome and they fell swiftly from favour.

The first sour gas hydrate curves had stampeded many operators away from the tried-and-true method of line-heating. The significantly higher hydrate temperatures presented the slightly ludicrous vision of having to heat the gas to tropical temperatures and keep it that way over several miles of gathering system. When the glycol dehydration systems ran into difficulty, line-heating slowly inched its way back into respectability. People were suddenly more inclined to think of the successful applications of line-heating such as at Jumping Pound, where sour gas had been line-heated into the plant for years without any insurmountable mishaps.

For a period in the early '60's, most new plants were built with line-heated gathering systems; California Standard at North Nevis, Home Carstairs, B.A. Rimbey and Shell Waterton being a few notable examples. Other early fields such as Devon-Palmer's Okotoks operation exchanged their expensive glycol experiments for line-heaters.

At Windfall, Bob Cunningham of Canadian Fina worked on one of the ill-fated glycol dehydration experiments that was eventually converted to line heat. When he was transferred to Fina's new Wildcat Hills project in 1962 and put in charge of the gathering system, Cunningham not surprisingly came up with a design calling for line-heaters. What is surprising is that Fina's president Trajan Nitescu stepped in at this point with a totally different idea for gathering the gas. Nitescu's scheme also relied on the concept of line heat, but his way of accomplishing it was new and extremely costly to boot.

In his engineering days in Rumania, Nitescu had observed how gas, heated by compression, would warm the ground through which it passed. The earth is an excellent heat bank: a poor conductor of heat and, therefore, an excellent insulator. What he proposed for Wildcat Hills was an underground hot-water tracing system; a circulating line full of hot water running alongside the gas main that would keep the gas above the gas hydrate temperature.

The general feeling among Fina engineers was that the idea was ridiculous, but Trajan Nitescu had an uncompromising nature and those who believed the idea to be a passing fancy were proven wrong. Ted Baugh was Fina's senior engineer at the time and his importance to Fina extended beyond engineering to linguistics in that he was one of the few people who could always understand Mr. Nitescu's heavily accented English. Logically, it became Baugh's job to interpret Nitescu's hot water-tracing scheme to the people who would design and build it. Baugh put Harold Noyes in charge and, with much trepidation, Noyes went ahead, studying the idea theoretically while Joe Lukacs built models of the system. The team also included Herman Leith and Ed Wichert.

Eventually, the hot-water tracing system went into the ground and, though hard to defend economically, it worked like a charm. Most everyone who has worked at Wildcat Hills speaks of it kindly. Clayton Edgelow, a man quite familiar with gas hydrates thanks to his years at Fort St. John, still cannot understand why more people did not choose to install it — expense or no expense. George Brown, an operator at the plant during start-up and still with the plant today, is obviously proud of a system that can control temperature into the plant within half a degree. It's hard to knock a sour gas gathering system that has never had a gas hydrate in all its years of operation.

Not all of those dissatisfied with glycol dehydration opted for line heat. Many continued to experiment with methods of dehydration. As mentioned, glycol dehydration was tried in the Windfall field after the start-up of the Windfall pilot plant in 1959. Canadian Fina (on behalf of its partners, HBOG and Pan Am) cycled sour gas in the Windfall field, stripping it of its condensate before reinjection. Eventually Fina switched over from glycol dehydration to line heat.

Later, in 1963, when the West Whitecourt plant was built to process gas from another field in the region, Pine Creek, field operator Hudson's Bay Oil and Gas decided once again to attempt wellhead dehydration. The Pine Creek gas was very sour (25% H_2S) and the gas would be travelling through the pipeline at over 2000 psi, both of which would contribute to an extremely high hydrate temperature. The other reason for using de-hydration rather than line heat was the potential corrosiveness of the sour gas if the water was left in it. For these reasons, HBOG erected dry dessicant towers at the wellheads. The adsorbent selected initially did not do the job, however. Bob Smith of Travis Chemicals remembers that the Mobil Sorbead dessicant he supplied to HBOG was defeated at Pine Creek by its affinity for hydrocarbons. It did not have enough room for both the hydrocarbons and the water.

The slow elimination of things that would not work led finally to something that would. As Aki Masuda, HBOG's project engineer at the

Pine Creek project, remarks, "it was getting close to a write-off situation" when the silica gel-type dessicants were finally set aside in favour of molecular sieves. Linde had developed the AW 500 acid-resistant molecular sieve whose controlled pore size captured the water while letting the hydrocarbons pass. A means had finally been found that would dehydrate gas of this pressure and sourness without giving rise to any serious, unwanted side effects.

Inlet facilities at Pan Am West Whitecourt.

PIGGING THE LINE

Gathering liquids-rich gas into a plant is attended by other problems having nothing to do with gas hydrates. The gas and liquids are either separated at the wellhead and sent to the plant in two lines or, as has become common, they are sent together as a two-phase flow. In either case, a tendency exists for the liquids to hang up in low spots creating an irregular flow of gas and liquids into the plant. The word the industry has coined for such a plant-upsetting surge is "slug"; and the record for the most dramatic liquids slug in Canadian processing history belongs, without contest, to the Taylor plant at Fort St. John.

In the first spring of operation at Taylor, the operators became concerned that liquids were sitting in the line and cutting the flow. A decision was taken to *pig* the line; that is, to run a contraption through it that would drive the liquids into the plant.

What may have tipped the operators off to a greater than expected problem was the fact that liquids began pushing into the plant when the pig was still miles away. Gradually the horrible truth dawned: the pig was where the pig was supposed to be and, ahead of it, moved a twenty-four-inch, solid sausage of condensate two miles long.

There was no way on earth to handle this in a controlled manner. Terry Smith, plant superintendent at the time, remembers how they threw everything open and wondered if it would be enough, or if they were destined to go sky high. The earth shook, tanks overflowed, the emergency flare belched the flaming con densate down its sides so the stack was lit top-to-bottom like a massive Roman candle. And the operators waited in an atmosphere of futility and fear for an explosion that did not come.

Big problems need big solutions, and what the pigging accident at Taylor gave rise to was one of the more elaborate slug-catchers in the world of processing. Whereas most companies make do with a vessel of some sort, Taylor has a pipeline on the end of its pipeline, a slug-catcher one mile long.

WHEN STRONG STEEL IS WEAK

As seen earlier, corrosion in sour gas processing was a well recognized problem in 1950; in fact, it seemed to be problem reasonably well in hand. Stress relieving for stress corrosion and some form of strong, non-porous coating for weight loss corrosion seemed to be workable if not perfect solutions. In the early '50's, engineers at Jumping Pound came up with an alternative to the bulky gunite coating by *cladding* the worst corrosion trouble-spots with stainless steel. Most of the Jumping Pound vessels were also built with a corrosion allowance of extra thickness. Engineers called for all welds to be stress-relieved, and it was only after accidentally missing a couple of welds and finding that no harm resulted that they began considering the atmosphere the weld inhabited before going to this step.

In many ways, Jumping Pound can be called the *sour gas laboratory* of its day. It provided a confident basis of operation for all plants dealing with low percentages of H_2S and CO_2 at low pressure. However, dramatic events in the field kept Shell and other companies operating in the early '50's from becoming too confident of their ability to control sour gas operations.

In a *Canadian Petroleum* article, Vince Milo tersely reviews the disasters that led Shell and other companies into two decades of research into sour gas resistant metallurgy: "Gulf (at Pincher Creek) ran an alloy tubing string that fell apart and we (Shell at Jumping Pound) ran a standard high-strength tubing string that fell apart." The companies were shocked. On the Gulf Coast in the U.S., these materials had stood up well; in fact, the nickel tubing string that failed at Pincher Creek was considered one of the best anti-corrosion devices in the industry. Shell and Gulf embarked on separate bouts of research trying to find materials that would withstand these special conditions.

Over the next ten years, one essential conclusion asserted and reasserted itself and no one person or event can really be credited with its original disclosure. As everyone pondered stress-cracking and rapid metal failure, they always came back to the seeming contradiction that Turner Valley wells and plants had never had these drastic problems, even though they had done almost nothing in terms of special metallurgy to avoid them. The next step in the process of learning was accidental: the replacement of a stress-cracked, high-strength steel part with a soft, low-carbon steel part and the discovery that the replacement seemed to last longer. Typical of that step was a discovery made by Gordon Barnes at B.A. Nevis. Floating heads on the plant's heat exchangers were bolted on with very strong, high-carbon steel studs. Nonetheless, all the bolts began to stress crack and when one gave, the added stress caused the others to go in sequence, like bullets from a Gatling gun. In those days, it took a long time to replace exotic parts like high-tensile studs and superintendent Barnes wanted to avoid any lengthy shut-down. He went to a local machine shop and asked the proprietor to build him some B-7 studs. All the machinist had to make the studs from was cold-rolled steel, but Barnes told him to go ahead. Barnes had them installed and watched with some wonder as they far out-lasted their predecessors. Gradually, events like these spread the word that high carbon steels should be avoided in sour service.

Unfortunately, the full realization of this came after many plants had been built. Faced with higher pressures than those for which carbon steels were recommended, some of the companies had *played it safe*. They had gone for stronger, high-carbon steels, and paid the price when these steels rapidly stress-cracked.

B.A. Pincher Creek had the questionable fortune of being the first of the high pressure sour gas plants in Canada, a kind of guinea pig for the industry. Its gas contained 11% H_2S and 6% CO_2 and the plant was designed to operate at 1500 pounds per square inch of pressure. When Martin Bretz arrived from Texas on New Year's Eve, 1956, the day gas was turned into the Stage I plant, a highly dangerous circus began. Murray Wright came to B.A. Pincher Creek as an operator with H_2S experience gained at the Canadian Chemicals Ltd. petrochemical plant near Edmonton, but it is unlikely that he ever lived through anything comparable to those first days at Pincher Creek. One night Wright entered the inlet separator building to close a valve and it came off in his hand. In the next few weeks of operation, small valves failed all over the plant, some popping off without even being touched.

The majority of these problems were traced to the same cause, in fact to the same type of valve. Scattered through the plant were 158 welded lip-seal valves. The metal around the welds, between the valve body and bonnet, cracked and failed for the simple reason that the welds had not been stress-relieved. B.A. had relatively good specifications for equipment and operating procedures, but new circumstances forced them to evolve new, even stricter measures. Elmer Berlie, who was plant engineer at Pincher Creek, recalls the procedures they developed for battling welding problems. They learned to limit the hardness of the steel they used and to control its carbon-manganese ratio. They also got tough on welding procedure: no cold starts, no slag inclusions. They stress-relieved and they radiographed "100% on sour service". And, if a weld was not perfect, they cut it out and did it again.

The one place where corrosion had been expected and did not appear was in the gathering lines. Gradually it was appreciated that when H_2S is present in greater percentages than CO_2, the hydrogen sulphide reacts with steel to form a hard coating of iron sulphide that inhibits corrosion by carbon dioxide. It was another essential observation and one made in several places at approximately the same time.

When Elmer Berlie left Pincher Creek to work on Texas Gulf's 1959 plant at Okotoks, he was as well prepared as anyone to deal with the high-pressure, highly sour gas from the D-1 Wabamun formation. Some people still refer to the Okotoks plant as "Elmer Berlie's stainless steel plant". As Berlie himself put it in a 1960 *Oilweek* article:

> Since the (Okotoks) plant was designed with somewhat higher solution loadings than is normal, the problem of corrosion was approached using detailed specifications respecting metallurgy and fabrication techniques. Considerably more stainless steel has been used in the sour gas and sour amine systems than is normal both in equipment and piping. After one year of operation, there has been no evidence of serious corrosion.

After twenty-five years, some of the original reboiler bundles at Okotoks have never had to be replaced.

At the Petrogas Processing Ltd. plant north of Calgary which started up in 1961, superintendent Jim Leeper had another sour gas materials crisis, and contributed to the growing arsenal of defensive weapons in dealing with it. Visiting his inlet building one day he noticed a 1¾" stud that looked a bit askew. He was able to pick it apart with his fingers. Over the next twenty-four hours, he had every bolt in the plant "changed out". He put the same B-7 alloy studs back in, but "having read somewhere that it didn't happen if you didn't stress them too far", he had the new bolts torqued down to no more than 75% of their yield strength. It worked.

In 1962, when Shell started up its huge Waterton plant, it seemed doomed to repeat at least part of the Pincher Creek scenario. Early on in the plant's operation, a small leak developed in a valve in the Low Temperature Flashing building. The Nordstrom valve had a top and bottom flange and, when the H_2S got to the bolts, it swiftly caused them to stress-crack and fail. The valve fell off and liquid hydrogen sulphide poured out on the floor. Plant engineer Bill Roman gives great credit to the operators on shift. They donned their masks and waded into the area, shutting it in without casualties. It was still a fearful situation, with the liquid rapidly vapourizing and a cloud of H_2S floating out across the plant.

Nobody at Shell really knew at this point what to do to put the plant right again. The metallurgy at Shell Waterton was the product of the company's research since the failures in the Jumping Pound and Okotoks fields. It was supposed to work. Now that it had not worked, the plant had to be left largely shut in until the problem was isolated and solved, and the plant made safe.

At the Calgary office, gas manager John Dillon put Bill Roman in charge of finding out the answers. It was a heavy burden for Roman in that millions of cubic feet of production were being lost every day the plant remained on low flow. He quickly called upon Treceder and Swanson at Shell's research centre in Emeryville, California. He had met them during the design phase for Waterton and knew them to be two of the top metallurgical engineers in the world.

In a one-week evaluation of the plant, Treceder and Swanson isolated the problem: the material specifications for the plant were not at fault; the problem was that the bolts which had failed had not been manufactured according to that specification.

The problem can be viewed as a relief and a potential disaster all at once. According to Bill Roman, there were as many as half a million of these bolts in the plant. The possibility existed that all would have to be changed. An inspection team was pulled together and it went through the plant, bolt by bolt, piece by piece. Like Jim Leeper at Petrogas, the team developed a system of bolt-torquing that limited the stress on the replacements.

The process took ten months and, when it was complete, Bill Roman phoned John Dillon and "with great pleasure" announced that the plant was safe. How do we know it's safe, asked Dillon? The proof, said Roman, would be that when Dillon came down to the plant he would find Roman sitting in the centre of the LTF building without a gas mask.

Bill Roman, Shell's engineer in charge of making Shell Waterton safe again after a dangerous liquid H$_2$S spill in the LTF building.

Within the companies most afflicted by these corrosion disasters, a movement was forming which would eventually control them. During the '50's, the research staff of various companies, men like Vince Milo at Shell and Jack Stamberg and Roy Carlson at B.A., with some assistance from the research departments of their U.S. parent companies, developed material specifications for sour gas. With sour gas being such a Canadian dilemma, goods made of these materials were not readily available from the largely American-based suppliers. They had to be specially constructed, and that meant expense, delay and some lack of reliability (as the Waterton case shows). The situation was made worse by the fact that each company's materials specifications differed. Suppliers were being driven mad by the demand that they stock a host of special trim equipment for each company.

Standardization of material specifications had obviously become a pressing need, and in May of 1959 (that year of cooperation in which the CGPA and CGPSA were formed), a group of Calgary corrosion engineers from several companies met with the specific purpose of seeing if they could agree on a standard specification for one item: a wellhead master valve. Included in this informal group were Vince Milo from Shell, Jack Stamberg and Roy Carlson from B.A., Noel Cleland from HBOG, Joe Messenger from Mobil, and Glenn Mainland from Imperial.

Vince Milo, described by many as one of the top corrosion engineers in North America.

It was not a simple task. Beyond having to agree amongst themselves, they had to find a supplier, respected by the industry, who either had a valve that met their specification or who would build one. Just finding out the exact metallurgy of the existing valves presented a major problem, but they also had to convince most of the industry research groups in North America that their specification was the right one. It took two years to develop the general specification for the wellhead valve and, by that time, the informal group had become "formal subcommittee TIB of the National Association of Corrosion Engineers (NACE)". This new affiliation gained the committee the respect enjoyed by NACE and helped spread the word about the sour gas specification quickly through the industry.

From valves, the committee spread its umbrella wide, developing specifications for more and more equipment prone to stress-cracking in Western Canada. Eventually, the NACE standards were accepted by the Canadian Standards Association, and, in 1978, NACE Committee TIB published a standards catalogue (MRO1 75) covering every aspect of sour gas service.

It had been a long haul, but few if any developments in the Canadian gas industry have had more wide-ranging benefits. The guesswork on materials was gone, and the safety conditions for those working in the plants and fields had thus been improved dramatically. For suppliers, it was also a boon. No longer having to stock special assortments of high-priced equipment for each plant, they could meet orders quickly and be confident that the equipment supplied would not fail.

It is interesting that the Canadian industry, publicly recognized as competitive, has made so many of its greatest strides through cooperation. Like the evolution of joint-venturing, the development of reliable sour service materials allowed improvements in the industry that would have taken much longer had the companies chosen to seek those improvements alone.

THE GENTLE ART OF SWEETENING

Because of the quantities of sour gas found in Canada, it stands to reason that the art of sweetening natural gas should have had much of its evolution in this country. Such has indeed been the case. The Koppers or Seaboard method of removing H_2S had been frequently used in the U.S. before it was first used in Canada, but Canada holds the distinction of being the first to sweeten *natural* gas by this method. The American precedents had taken place in manufactured gas plants.

But perhaps the most unusual thing about Canada's first sweetening plant is that it *was not in Turner Valley*. A person becomes accustomed to saying that everything in the industry started in Turner Valley, but the first sweetening plant was actually built at Port Alma, Ontario, in 1924 by Union Gas. Turner Valley was not far behind. Sam Coultis built a Seaboard scrubbing plant in the Valley in 1925.

Construction of Canada's second gas purification plant in Turner Valley (1925).

In response to the gas needs of wartime, a Girbotol sweetening unit was added to the Seaboard unit at Turner Valley Royalite in 1941. The absorbing agent in this process was monoethanolamine, or MEA, and thanks to its capacity for both H_2S and CO_2, and its relative ease of regeneration by steam heat, Girbotol and its MEA descendents dominated gas sweetening in Western Canada for about the next twenty-two years.

One of the early discoveries for what *not* to do with MEA was that mentioned in R. S. Phillips' article on Turner Valley Royalite's corrosion problems. Combining MEA and diethylene glycol to get sweetening and drying in one step was strictly a no-no, with violently corrosive results. The same lesson had to be learned again at Jumping Pound. When Kevin Milne started his career with Shell at Jumping Pound, his first assignments included trying to stop the corrosion in the treating system and keep the amine solution clean. Milne credits John Flynn, chief gas engineer for Shell in Calgary, with sticking his neck out and saying that the glycol-MEA mixture was at fault. They separated the two and found that corrosion decreased. They also found that the solution was no longer dirty and that the sulphur plant operated more efficiently.

Discovering the relationship between efficient operation of the amine unit and the efficiency of the sulphur plant was a big step forward. Adding glycol to MEA gave the solution an affinity for heavy hydrocarbons. These hydrocarbons were separated from the amine along with the acid gases and entered the sulphur plant where they fouled the catalysts.

The foaming problem in MEA plants never entirely went away though various methods evolved for counteracting it. One of the earlier methods used in Canada came from Texaco's pioneer conservation plant at

Bonnie Glen. Frustrations with foamy solution led to the insertion of a carbon filter that continuously cleansed a portion of the amine solution. At B.A. Pincher Creek, investigations into the amine tower foaming problem led to the discovery that, at times, the towers in which the amine contacted the gas were operating below the hydrocarbon dew point of the gas. The resulting condensation caused the contactors and the regenerators to *puke*.

As the various processors of sour gas got to know their MEA units, Shell was considering what sweetening alternative to use on its much sourer Okotoks field. Faced with gas that was 35% hydrogen sulphide, the company decided on an experiment in bulk H_2S removal. On the advice of someone in its research department, Shell constructed a pilot plant at Okotoks to evaluate the water wash process.

Dr. Martin Winning worked on this pilot project for Shell and his recollection of water wash is that, while it did work for bulk removal of hydrogen sulphide, the amount of H_2S removed was not sufficient to meet the specifications of the pipeline and utility companies.

Dr. Martin Winning began his career at Shell Jumping Pound in 1952.

The unsatisfactory results of this experiment, difficulties in unitizing the field, the high costs of operating an MEA plant and the quite reasonable fear of processing extremely sour gas — all these factors finally drove Shell to sell the Okotoks field rather than attempt to process the gas. The purchaser was Devon-Palmer Oils Limited. Morris Palmer (the Palmer in Devon-Palmer) succeeded in unitizing the majority of the Okotoks field and, for a time, was determined to both produce and process the sour gas. He investigated this proposition from all angles, and made liberal use of his experienced Texan cousin Dan T. McDonald as an advisor. McDonald was still living in Texas at this time (he later moved to Canada himself) and he recalls being wakened up in the middle of almost every night by his cousin Morris with more queries about Okotoks. The central theme in the advice McDonald gave him was that he should not take on the processing and marketing of so much sulphur. The sulphur marketers were few and formidable and it would be a far better idea, said McDonald, to invite one of them in on the deal. Morris Palmer finally took his advice, bringing Texas Gulf into the picture as owner and operator of the sulphur plant. Behind these dealings, Shell had retained 15% of the operation through a contract that enabled the company to increase its holdings to a maximum of 25% over the next several years.

Before leaving the subject of Shell's water wash experiment at Okotoks entirely behind, it should also be mentioned that this was not the end for the process. Ralph M. Parsons became quite interested in water wash, and eventually tried the process for sweetening sour gas at a plant in Lacq, France.

With all its faults, MEA remained the major method of sweetening gas until the early '60's. At B.A. Pincher Creek, the problems of the MEA system were gradually erased through trial and error, but the process of improvement started from a point of dismal failure in the early years. The trace sulphur compounds in the gas, yet unrecognized, gave rise to phenomenal solution loss. To use superintendent Martin Bretz' words, "They ate our lunch for two years."

With time, B.A. began to appreciate the part the trace sulphur compounds, carbonyl sulphide (COS) and carbon disulphide (CS_2), were playing in the loss of MEA solution. The MEA and the trace compounds were reacting together to form salts that would not regenerate. Martin Bretz and his men gained some interim relief by adding soda ash to the amine, possibly as a result of experimental work being done at Okotoks.

When Texas Gulf built its Okotoks plant in 1959, the company had been joined by Elmer Berlie, fresh from two exciting years at Pincher Creek. Berlie found it quite a switch to suddenly be with a company which had lengthy experience in sour gas processing. Texas Gulf had been operating a sulphur plant at Worland, Wyoming, for ten years and it made a considerable difference. The choice of sweetening system at Okotoks was nothing unusual; they went with the MEA process that was being used at most plants. What was unusual was that much of the amine plant was clad in stainless steel. Another innovation was that Okotoks employed a split stream amine process, meaning that bulk removal of the acid gases was accomplished with one amine stream, followed by cleanup in a second, leaner stream.

The one thing that the Worland experience could not prepare Texas Gulf for was the presence in much of Alberta's sour gas of the trace sulphur compounds, COS and CS_2. Just as at B.A. Pincher Creek, the losses of amine solution to the compounds at Okotoks was tremendous and costly. In a 1961 *Canadian Oil and Gas Industries* article, Elmer Berlie wrote:

> Since COS is present or likely to be present in the great reserves of sour gas found in Western Canada, the major suppliers of amine have been conducting vigorous research programs in an effort to solve the problem. As yet, no proven economical method has been found.

Experimentation to fill that gap, done at Okotoks, produced the method of injecting potassium hydroxide into the amine solution. Elmer Berlie says that this treatment of the stream decreased the solution losses by 50%, from forty-four pounds per million cubic feet of raw gas processed to twenty-two pounds per million cubic feet processed.

While some companies worked on MEA to reduce its problems, other companies were in a mood to try something completely new. The second such experiment, after Shell's attempt to wash the gas sweet with water at Okotoks, belonged to Imperial. In 1960, Imperial installed a hot potassium carbonate adsorption sweetening system at its Nottingham plant in Saskatchewan. *Hot Pot*, as the process was nicknamed, got off to such a bad start it is a wonder it was ever used again. To put it simply, the plant would not work at all. Veteran Imperial engineer Jim Haliburton says that Imperial did not give up easily on *hot pot* at Nottingham and was even, at one stage, injecting carbon dioxide into the raw gas in a vain effort to make the sweetening process function. But, sadly for Imperial, very little specification gas ever left Nottingham until the hot pot train was trashed and an amine plant installed.

Given those circumstances, it took something very like courage for Petrogas Processing Ltd. to choose hot potassium as the sweetening process for its Balzac plant northeast of Calgary in 1961. Jim Leeper was first superintendent at Balzac and he suggests that the main reason for the choice was economy. The gas at Balzac was from the same reef system as Okotoks gas and the high amine solution losses at Okotoks had warned Petrogas off the MEA process. As well, the Elkton portion of the gas that

Petrogas would process had the high Co_2/H_2S ratio that hot pot was designed for. Petrogas went ahead with the hot potassium carbonate process, albeit with an amine unit for cleanup.

As far as Jim Leeper is concerned, it was a success. While others grumble of hot pot's messiness and difficulty to contain, Leeper sees it as having done the job it was supposed to do at Balzac. It saved money, and gave rise to no unbeatable process problems. Nevertheless, hot pot did not catch on with the industry. The only other plant in Canada ever to try it was Westcoast Transmission's 1963 plant at Fort Nelson. The gas in that far-off, northeastern British Columbia locale again had the right ratio of acid gases to make the process work, and it is still working on two of the trains at Fort Nelson today.

The search for an alternative method of sweetening continued. In the early '60's much attention focussed on the *di*ethanolamine, or DEA process. Although diethanolamine was a familiar process in the refining industry, the natural gas sweetening application of the amine had been patented by SNPA, the French state energy company. It had developed the patent process at its sour gas processing plants at Lacq, France, the only major sour gas area outside Canada being exploited at the time. The claims made on behalf of DEA were expansive: it used less energy than MEA; it was less corrosive;* it was more stable.

Not surprisingly, given the grief it had suffered at Pincher Creek with MEA, B.A. became the first Canadian operator to use the new DEA process. Charles Buskel, whose name comes up so often in the stories of this bons. The choice of Sulfinol, like the choice of most processes, depended on the type of gas in the field. It was ideal for gas that was both sour and dry.

The first Sulfinol plant in Canada was built in 1965 by Pritchard Canadian Ltd. for Pan American at East Crossfield. A year later, Fluor built the second Sulfinol plant for Canadian Superior at Harmattan. Canadian Superior had been operating an MEA plant at Harmattan since 1960, but the company had recently drilled into the D-3 Leduc formation encountering gas that was 53% hydrogen sulphide. The gas was also lean in liquids and, consequently, made-to-order for Sulfinol. Shortly after this, Shell finally used its own Sulfinol process in Canada. The LTF sweetening plant at Waterton was being phased out as the hydrogen sulphide percentage of Waterton gas dropped and a new Sulfinol plant was phased in. The MEA

---

*Widely held for years was the opinion that MEA itself was corrosive. In fact, amine solutions are not themselves corrosive at all. The corrosion they were blamed for in the 1950's was generally caused by uncontrolled flashing of the acid gases.

era, went to France for B.A. to investigate the DEA process. While there, he may have run into students of the process from other companies operating in Canada, most notably Shell. Waterton was currently on that company's drawing board, and it was still looking for an alternative to MEA.

Buskel decided in favour of DEA; Shell decided against. Several reasons existed for both decisions, but the main one was probably that the Pincher Creek plant for which B.A. wanted the new process already had an MEA system. The equipment for the two processes is compatible so that B.A. would incur little expense in making the switch. Shell, on the other hand, had yet to design Waterton so the switchover feature had no attraction.

By the time the DEA system went in at Pincher Creek, the operators there were not all that pleased about the change. They had all but conquered the problems associated with MEA using inhibitors and the prospect of a full set of new problems with a different amine did not overjoy them. To make matters worse, a great deal of secrecy attended the new patent process and it came from Europe with few instructions. Martin Bretz and company had to devise their own set of tests for it.

Still, when DEA was in and operating, Martin Bretz had to confess that it was better. DEA solution was not lost to chemical reactions with trace compounds the way MEA had been. Jim Richardson, whose company engineered so many plants in this era, cites this as having been the end for MEA. All the plants he did thereafter were based on DEA.

Because of its initial lack of enthusiasm for the DEA process, Shell went on to develop alternatives. When Bill Fisher and Bill Roman were in San Francisco, working with Bechtel on the design for Waterton, they decided that the best choice for sweetening was an all-new Shell process — still a test tube baby — called Low Temperature Flashing (LTF). LTF went from test tube to plant scale at Waterton, with no comforting pilot experiments in between. For the high hydrogen sulphide gas at Waterton (35% H_2S), the LTF system worked well. Unfortunately the gas analysis at Waterton changed. After a few years, the hydrogen sulphide in the field gas dropped off dramatically and at the lower concentrations LTF was not as efficient.

In the meantime, Shell Development Corporation had come up with yet another sweetening process called Sulfinol, based on a physical and a chemical solvent, operating together. The treating solution was expensive, but the plant itself could be more energy efficient than one based on DEA or MEA. The disadvantages also included a tendency to absorb hydrocar-

Pan Am East Crossfield, the first Canadian plant to sweeten gas by the sulfinol process, 1965.

cleanup unit that had backed up the LTF process was switched over to Sulfinol as well.

Prior to this latter switch from MEA to Sulfinol, the Waterton operators gave the MEA equipment a thorough cleaning. As soon as they introduced the Sulfinol, however, the solution became filthy. They had not reckoned on Sulfinol's extreme efficiency as a cleansing agent. What the Sulfinol had done was scrub off the film of iron sulphide laid down over the years by hydrogen sulphide on the vessel walls. According to Bill Roman, Shell was buying filters by the truckload for a while. The average life of a filter on the Sulfinol unit was fifteen minutes.

When Imperial built its sour gas plant at Quirk Creek in 1971, consulting engineer Jim Richardson, suggested the company go with Sulfinol. Because of the process' difficulty with liquids-rich gas, he suggested extracting a certain amount of those liquids ahead of the Sulfinol plant. The adjustment worked so well that Shell eventually used this adaptation at its Waterton plant.

The search for improvements in sweetening continued and continues still. A recent story shows how many of the problems are still around. HBOG, at its massive Kaybob plants, had over the years tried about everything to get stable operation without corrosion. The company had always experimented in search of answers by altering one variable while leaving the others constant. Al Kiernan, with HBOG at the time, credits Richard Jagodzinski with putting an end to the vain pursuit. The Polish-born, British-educated chemical engineer recognized that at least five variables were involved in the problem, not just one, and that all five would have to be controlled if they were ever going to win. A half million dollars were spent and, finally, the problem was conquered. The year was 1980.

As for the future of gas sweetening, many companies are banking on the use of permeable membranes, a process that separates acid gases from raw natural gas by a means not unlike that which selects oxygen in the human lung. The battle is currently being joined on both sides of the Canada-U.S. border to see who will succeed in spreading the innovation throughout the industry.

AN UNPLEASANT ODOUR IN CALIFORNIA

In the early '60's, a shake-up occurred in the Canadian sour gas processing industry which originated in sunny California. It seemed that since Canadian gas had arrived on that State's market from the Alberta and Southern line, consumer complaints had shot up to an alarming extent. The single grain of hydrogen sulphide allowed in every 100 standard cubic feet by the A & S contract with Canadian producers was not wholly pleasing to the denizens of that State. The result was that Canadian processors along the sour foothills trend were told they must further sweeten their gas down to a quarter grain of H_2S per 100 SCF of gas. This sent more than a ripple through the Canadian gas processing industry as everyone wondered if they could possibly sweeten their gas that efficiently. The processors went to work and found that they could. Some operators found that low temperature chilling of the sales gas stream extracted sulphur as well as liquids and assisted them in meeting the *¼ grain spec.* *

* A grain of H_2S is roughly equivalent to 17 parts per million.

COMPRESSION

Almost as old as gas processing is the use of compression in that industry. Initially it was a matter of moving gas. If the pressure was lacking at the wellhead, it had to be supplied to get the gas to the plants; if pressure was lacking at the plant exit, it had to be supplied to move the gas to market. Originally, the power for compression was supplied by steam, but gradually the efficiency and availability of natural gas urged a switch to natural gas-fueled engines, a change-over that was more or less complete by 1920.

In the U.S., the C & G Cooper Co. was a leader in building natural gas internal combustion engines. It cemented its relationship with the pipeline transmission business in 1909 by building the first engine-compressor combination.

At the processing end, an early method of getting natural gasoline from raw gas was to *squeeze* it and the leader in building small engines for that purpose was the Bessemer Gas Engine Co. of Grove City, Pennsylvania. The accompanying compressors were often supplied by Ingersoll-Rand. In 1929, Cooper and Bessemer merged to form the Cooper-Bessemer Corporation, a powerful combination for plant and pipeline.

Installation of Clark Bros. Co. compressors at the Bow Island repressuring plant (June 25, 1930).

In Canada, some of the earliest compressors in the natural gas industry were those used to inject Turner Valley gas into the Bow Island reservoir beginning in 1929. At the Turner Valley plants, Royalite had Cooper-Bessemer compressors installed, while B.A. Longview went with Clark compressors for its pressure boosting needs. R. K. Graves remembers the installation of the Clark compressors well because he "fell in love with those big engines". B.A. had sent Graves to Olean, New York, where the Clarks were built and he liked them so much he eventually joined the company. Around 1950, Dresser Clark came to Canada looking for a representative and Bob Graves took the job. He stayed with the company for thirty years.

After World War II, industry attention focussed on the industrial frontiers, one of which was Western Canada. The Cooper-Bessemer philosophy was expressed by C-B representative Bob Jones this way: "Before a remote area can blossom from mining, or oil, or lumber, it has to have power so we always are among the first into the underdeveloped places." That philosophy led Jones to Western Canada shortly after the war to beef up Cooper-Bessemer's presence there. A subsidiary, Cooper-Bessemer of Canada Ltd., was formed for that purpose.

The move looked brilliant when oil was discovered at Leduc in 1947. Bill Sage moved from Turner Valley to the Imperial Devon plant near Leduc in 1949. The last compressors installed at Turner Valley Royalite were Cooper-Bessemers and Sage says that "they worked so well and the service was so good, we bought four more for the Leduc plant." Familiarity with the Cooper-Bessemer product led to quite a lot of work for the company after Leduc and Bob Jones was joined by engineer Ted Van Fossen. In 1956, another engineer with a diesel background, Harry Neuman, came to work for C-B in Canada.

At Redwater, Imperial again installed some Cooper-Bessemer compressors, but "not wanting to put all (its) eggs in one basket", the company bought Ingersoll-Rand compressors as well. At Swan Hills/Judy Creek Imperial further spread itself across the supply industry by purchasing several Clark compressors.

As for the technological development of compressors to their modern state, the story has been well and often told. They grew in power and they grew again, with one company leap-frogging another in the number of horsepower its unit could generate. The rapid expansion of natural gas reserves on both sides of the border and the building of massive pipelines devoured that increased horsepower as soon as it was available. The move from reciprocating to centrifugal compressors and on to jet engine turbine systems (the jump from hundreds of horsepower to 25 to 30 thousand horsepower) seemed to happen swiftly, a symbol of the spiralling technological ability that has characterized our society since the War.

In Canadian processing, however, the tremendous capacity of the new compressors was not always the answer. Harry Neuman remembers that the trend in Canada in the early '60's was not to larger but to smaller, separate compressors. The high speed separables were more versatile and "a hell of a lot cheaper" than the big integral units.

Probably the most important thing to Canadian processors about compressors was the time it took to get them fixed. High pressure sour gas was devouring compressor parts in the early '60's and, when a breakdown took place, a part of the plant was often shut down for months while the American supplier built a replacement.

Charles Cooper, export manager for Cooper-Bessemer, said a mouthful in 1957 when he told his employees that "the company with the best record for field service, repair parts service and operating performance will be the most successful in getting business in Canada." Gordon Barnes, who was superintendent of B.A. Nevis at that time, concedes that Cooper-Bessemer was a good supplier, but its closest service shop was still in Seattle. Rather than wait months for a new cylinder or piston, Barnes found a company in Ponca City, Oklahoma, that would work round-the-clock to fix such an item. To get it there and back, Barnes instituted a system of *hot-shot trucking*, two drivers going day and night. Often he could get a compressor back in business within a week.

Finally Barnes concluded that if he had a problem getting replacement parts, so did everyone else and that meant that plenty of horsepower was sitting idle. Together with Jack Leary of Barber Engineering, Jim Cruickshank and John Young, Gordon Barnes incorporated Midwestern Compressor Supplies. They built their first plant in 1963 and began fixing equipment "in competition with the biggies". They were not terribly popular with the equipment manufacturers who dubbed them "the pirates of the parts industry", but they were popular with the processing companies and plant personnel for whom they were doing field overhauls and saving time and money. This company and its subsidiaries "grew like mad". "We were selling service, that's all," says Barnes, "appreciating our clients' losses, and frankly, we smartened up the compressor suppliers. They started building their own shops and warehouses. They realized we were eating their lunch."

The compressor manufacturers and the corrosion experts who put together sour service specifications for compressors both deserve tremendous credit for eventually building compressors that could contain and withstand Canada's high pressure sour gas.

HOW TO CHOP DOWN A CONCRETE TREE

Canadian Oil Companies Limited operated a gas plant at Bowden for a seventeen company unit in the Bowden/Innisfail area. The plant started up in 1960. In the majority of the plant, corrosion seemed to be well under control, but the sulphur stack proved to be a different story. Wisps of vapour puffing out of several points in the upper part of the 250 foot stack led to an inspection and, though the inspection did not show much, the minor repairs that followed did. While grouting holes in the upper stack, workmen found that they could pound a wedge through the cement with two average hammer blows. Acid gas had been getting between the internal firebrick and the outer concrete of the stack. Combined with moisture, the gas had formed sulphuric acid which had severely corroded the concrete to the extent that the entire structure was unsafe to leave standing.

Herb Bagnall of Canadian Oil Companies (who began his career with the Conservation Board in Turner Valley in the early '40's) was forced into the timber business for a couple of days. A notch was chopped in the concrete tree and thick fir posts were set into the notch so that the whole weight of the stack rested on them. A couple of well placed sticks of dynamite blew the posts out of the notch and it was TIMBER!

A sulphur train in the Rocky Mountains.

SULPHUR RECOVERY: THE CANADIAN CONTRIBUTION

9

Sulphur is part of the chemistry of a great many things used by modern man and woman — so much so that sulphur consumed per capita is a reliable indicator of a nation's standard of living. The amount of sulphur and its compounds in the atmosphere is also a fairly reliable indicator of environmental pollution. Add to that the fact that Western Canadian gas has in it great quantities of the sulphur compound hydrogen sulphide and you have all the basic reasons why sulphur has become one of Canada's most important industrial products.

Canada has the capacity to produce about eight million tonnes of recovered sulphur per year*, placing it second to the United States in sulphur production in all forms for the free world. Canada is the world's largest exporter of elemental sulphur. To give an idea how recent that status is, we can look back to 1959 when the Canadian processing industry was just completing its first growth spurt. That year, Canada's total production of recovered sulphur was 291,000 long tons, 3.5% of free world production. By 1968, the totals were up to 3.1 million long tons and 19%. By 1976, the total had surpassed seven million.

Sales seldom kept pace with this production and much of Canada's sulphur went into pretty yellow blocks at the plant site. Unlike most businesses, sulphur recovery from natural gas shows little relationship between production and sales. When natural gas production grows, as it did in Canada in the '60's, sulphur production grows alongside, regardless of the potential for sales. When the natural gas market stagnated in the early '80's, the stockpiles began to shrink into a sulphur market that was still strong.

ORIGINS OF THE SULPHUR INDUSTRY

Sulphur has enjoyed a rather long life as a commodity useful to man. A mention of its use as a bleaching agent for linen has been found in a four thousand year old record. In the early 19th century sulphur was much in

---

*Because of gas market constraints, Canadian recovered sulphur production is down to six million tonnes per year. To meet the market demand, sulphur stockpiles are being drawn down by 1.5 to 2.0 million tonnes per year.

demand by makers of sulphuric acid, and by far the major source of sulphur was the brimstone mines of Sicily. The Sicilian sulphur merchants were notoriously unreliable, changing the price almost daily. Finally, the acid makers switched to the roasting of pyrites in search of a stable supply.

Toward the end of the 19th century, two names — Frasch and Claus — became connected with the sulphur industry. They have remained so ever since. In 1884, Herman Frasch came to southern Ontario from Germany and worked for Imperial Oil. While in Canada, he patented a process for removing sulphur from refined products. He also became involved with Ontario's solution salt mines and, when sulphur was discovered in the salt domes of Louisiana and Texas, Frasch took his know-how to those States and developed the technique for the solution mining of sulphur that still bears his name. By the 1920's, U.S. Frasch sulphur was available in large and reliable quantities and most of the world's sulphuric acid-makers had switched over to it.

In 1959, Frasch sulphur dominated the world supply of elemental sulphur to the tune of 70%; But shortly thereafter, sulphur recovered from natural gas began to make rapid inroads on that market control. Recovered sulphur was already approaching parity with Frasch sulphur by 1968 and had slightly eclipsed it by 1976, with Canadian sulphur playing a major part in the change.

Claus, the second name to become enmeshed with the sulphur industry, belonged to Carl Friederich Claus, a chemist working in London in the late 19th century. He gave his name to a process patented in 1883 for recovering sulphur from the production of soda. After making H_2S, Claus mixed it with oxygen and passed it through a preheated catalyst bed to make sulphur. It was this second step that gave Claus his household name status in the sulphur recovery business.

In 1938, I. G. Farbenindustrie A-G of Germany modified the Claus process. In this modification, part of a stream of H_2S was oxidized to SO_2 in a boiler and useful steam was generated with the heat from the reaction. Next, the remainder of the H_2S stream was reacted over a catalyst with the SO_2 forming elemental sulphur. This *modified* Claus process remains the basis of sulphur recovery today.

THE CANADIAN SULPHUR FRONTIER

Modified Claus sulphur recovery made its Canadian debut at the Jumping Pound and Madison gas plants in 1952, thanks to a sulphur shortage in the West Coast pulp and paper industry. After watching sulphur forming spontaneously in boilers fired with sour gas, Turner Valley

The Madison Natural Gas Company's sulphur unit at Turner Valley, 1952.

operators must have been surprised to find out how difficult it is to make the substance where and when you want it. First came the realization that the sulphur process requires a stable and narrow range of temperature, just above the dewpoint of sulphur. Given too low a temperature, sulphur condenses on the catalyst instead of in the condenser. Terry Smith, first superintendent at Jumping Pound, tells of "plugging up" the catalyst and having to have a "burn out" to get his sulphur back. Too high a temperature in the catalyst converter and the catalyst cannot efficiently convert the H_2S and SO_2 to sulphur. Gingerly, the operators tried to stay within the narrow range.

But most of the crises in the early sulphur plants were inherited from mishaps in the amine treating sections of the adjacent plants. When amine towers foamed — which they often did — hydrocarbons and amine travelled with the acid gas to the sulphur plant, causing the deactivation of bauxite catalyst.

The big difference between the first two Canadian sulphur plants was that the Madison sulphur facility in Turner Valley was single stage (one catalyst bed), whereas Jumping Pound was two stage (two catalyst beds). On a good day, Jumping Pound got the better sulphur recovery of the two. Operators and engineers at these early plants generally concede that recovery was in the 80-85% range.

The early sulphur plants were small. Madison and Jumping Pound weighed in at 30 long tons of sulphur per day each. Imperial's first sulphur plant at Redwater made thirteen long tons a day (recovering 80% of the sulphur in the gas). In the 1956-57 period, the average size of plants leaped tenfold with the construction of the Taylor plant near Fort St. John and the first stage of B.A. Pincher Creek. The Taylor sulphur plant, owned by Jefferson Lake Petrochemicals of Canada, could make 300 long tons a day and Stage I at Pincher Creek was capable of producing 225 long tons a day.

Jim Leeper, who superintended the Taylor facility, had operated a sulphur plant for Jefferson Lake in Wyoming before coming to Canada. Leeper's main problem at Taylor was the hydrocarbons Pacific was sending over from its amine unit; that and the fact that the gas plant was "up and down like a yo-yo".

Elmer Berlie, as second plant engineer at Pincher Creek, freely admits that they did not know a great deal about their sulphur plant at the beginning. Ralph M. Parsons Co. built the plant and gave them crude control tests to run, but for the most part, says Berlie, "we put the gas in the front end and took what we got out the back."

But the late '50's award for *winging it* has to go to the first sulphur unit at Dome's Steelman plant in Saskatchewan. Jim Richardson flew out to Steelman with Dome's Don Wolcott and Jack Gallagher to have a look at this facility and he recalls his amazement at the sulphur plant he saw there. A Mr. Joe Packer had built the plant out of scrap, setting two used oilfield boilers back to back, "donkey-style". He called one his reactor and the other his condenser. As for instrumentation and fine-tuning of process, Evan Bodrug and Jim Hartley, the men attempting to run the plant for Dome, adjusted the gas and air flow manually until the "flame looked about the right colour". Then, you made sulphur, at the startling rate of four long tons per day.

There was so much sulphur left in the tail gas at Steelman that a mushroom of the stuff used to grow at the top of the stack. Jim Hartley's remedy was to blast away at the yellow dome with his shotgun. This need for good aim as a prerequisite for the successful operation of gas plants has probably been overlooked. Another example of its necessity can be found in the early sagas of the Taylor plant. There, the sour gas flare was wont to blow out, and the auto-igniters seldom auto-ignited. Superintendent

Smith and his men found remedies both in the bible and in the Hollywood western. First, David and Goliath-style, they slung rocks wrapped in burning rags at the gas. Next, they advanced to the technology of the bow and arrow, firing flaming shafts through the escaping gas.

The Texas Gulf Sulphur Company's sulphur plant at Okotoks, built in 1959, was the next of the large sulphur plants to be built in Canada (370 long tons/day). While its configuration of two catalyst beds, a wash tower and an incinerator stack was generally the same as that at the Jumping Pound plant, Okotoks was unique in that it processed a natural gas stream that had an exceptionally high hydrogen sulphide content (35%). Texas Gulf expected to make 85% of its revenue at Okotoks from sulphur. It was definitely the first Canadian facility to be a sulphur plant first and a gas plant second.

Raising sulphur forms at Texas Gulf Okotoks.

In designing and running the sulphur recovery plant at Okotoks, Texas Gulf drew heavily on its experience at Worland, Wyoming. The man in overall charge at Okotoks was James Estep, a Worland veteran and one of the top sulphur recovery experts on the continent. Plant manager Fred Ronicker also came to Okotoks via Worland. Before that, he had worked in Texas on the Frasch sulphur mines. According to Texas Gulf's original intention, there would have been many more Worland veterans working at Okotoks. After ten years, the Worland plant had lost its feed stream from the adjacent refinery and was faced with closure. Texas Gulf hoped to transplant its crew to Canada and thereby avoid laying off such experienced men. However, Canadian immigration law would only allow this if individuals capable of doing the work could not be found in Canada. An indication of how far Canadian processing had already progressed, Texas Gulf was able to find most of the necessary manpower north of the border and the transplantation of the Worland crew did not take place. Among the Canadians who arrived on the scene were assistant plant manager Elmer Berlie and process foreman and steam engineer Karl Balzun.

Because of the Worland precedent it might be assumed that the Okotoks plant was nothing new, that it simply duplicated the proven technology of the Wyoming plant. In fact, thanks to the research acumen of Jim Estep, Okotoks differed in several key ways from Worland and a great deal of research was done at the Okotoks plant to bring about additional improvements. The more stringent Alberta environmental regulations also necessitated certain changes. To reach the sulphur recovery standard demanded by the Alberta Conservation Board, Okotoks was built with a second catalyst bed that enabled it to reach 95% sulphur recovery. A 250′ stack reduced ground level concentrations of sulphur dioxide to the level accepted by Alberta's Department of Health. Later, Okotoks added a third catalyst bed, upping recovery of sulphur another few points.

REGULATION: THE MOTHER OF INVENTION

The approval of gas export to the United States in 1961 meant the processing of much more sour gas in Canada. The sheer volume of sulphur turned out by these new plants and the tons of sulphur compounds released to atmosphere through their stacks focussed attention squarely on the sulphur recovery process: its efficiency and its means for dealing with waste by-products.

In 1960, Alberta's Department of Health acquired an Air Pollution Branch. In the following year, that branch, in conjunction with the Alberta Conservation Board, produced new and significantly tougher regulations for the control of sulphur emissions from natural gas processing plants. The plants had five years in which to comply.

There were two ways of attacking the problem: the plants could build taller stacks with greater exit velocities, or they could improve their sulphur recovery by making the process more efficient. Dr. George Govier, chairman of the Conservation Board, was a strong advocate of the second approach. He was so sure that the pollution problem could be controlled at the source through better efficiency that he doubted the need for government bodies beyond the Board to battle it. Throughout the '60's, the Board lent its encouragement to all forms of research in pursuit of higher sulphur recovery.

Many suppliers with products they believed were superior to those in use also promoted better sulphur plant efficiency. For example, Eric Baker, representing the Linde Gases Division of Union Carbide, presented a paper to the CNGPA in which he argued that better catalysts and thus better sulphur efficiency was the way to solve the sulphur emissions problem, rather than by building enormous stacks. He reminded the members that every percentage point increase in sulphur recovery meant a decrease in sulphur compounds emitted to atmosphere of 100 tons. The slogan of all those who shared this view became:

"The solution to pollution is NOT dilution!"

Many groups and many individuals spearheaded the move toward greater sulphur recovery efficiency. The CNGPA and the CNGPSMA played a basic role by providing a forum for discussion and exchange of technical information, a cross-fertilization that certainly quickened the pace of discovery. This also had the effect of raising the confidence of the industry as a whole. Those not directly involved in research were made to feel part of an overall industry movement which was shifting the boundaries of world knowledge on the subject of sulphur recovery from natural gas.

In the early '60's, Canadian sulphur research and development acquired a powerful asset when Dr. J. B. Hyne decided to make Calgary his career home. Dr. Hyne was originally from Scotland, educated at the University of Edinburgh. His early work in Canada included a stint in the

Dr. J. B. Hyne of Alberta Sulphur Research Ltd.

Arctic with the Canadian Department of Defence. At some point, he made the observation that Canada, a large scale producer of sulphur, was doing no basic research of consequence on the subject of sulphur. He decided that he would make it his business to fill that gap and chose the young University of Calgary, right at the heart of the industry, as the place from which to launch this research.

Most people in Dr. Hyne's position, as he set up shop at the University of Calgary, would have gone immediately in pursuit of public funds. Jim Hyne is not of that philosophical bent. He went instead to the companies producing sulphur in Canada and asked them to become involved in his research out of self-interest. John Dillon of Shell was one of Dr. Hyne's original backers and, together, in 1964, they gathered the support of several companies in an enterprise called Alberta Sulphur Research Limited (ASR). (ASR recently celebrated its 20th anniversary.)

One of the first practical problems attacked by Dr. Hyne on behalf of the industry was sulphur deposition in wells. It had been proven in the field that the problem could be attacked successfully with carbon disulphide, but CS_2 is flammable, so much so that it can be touched off by contact with a light bulb. Consequently, people in the industry were looking for other approaches. What Dr. Hyne did was establish a *formula* for sulphur deposition. With this tool, the industry could devise operating procedures that kept the problem to a minimum.

Another individual who contributed enormously to the understanding of sulphur recovery was Dr. Alexander Petrunic, a Croatian engineer who went to work for Canadian Fina after his escape from Tito's Yugoslavia. So many people remember Dr. Petrunic fondly and with admiration that it is hard to know whom to quote in that regard. It is probably enough to say that almost everyone who has made important contributions to sulphur research cites Dr. Petrunic as an important influence and friend. Dr. Petrunic's first work with Fina took place at the Windfall pilot plant. Trajan Nitescu believed that all his employees must experience the industry at first hand; consequently, the middle-aged ex-professor Petrunic found himself wading through the muskeg of Whitecourt along with the other men.

Always the teacher, Dr. Petrunic offered to run a school for the twenty or so men working at Windfall. Most of his superiors thought such a thing would fizzle out after a day or two, but they allowed him to go ahead. The real problem turned out to be that everyone wanted to attend and that interest *did not wane*. It was hard to run the operation with all hands in school. It was an example of Dr. Petrunic's powers as a teacher, his ability to inspire people with the desire to improve their knowledge.

One of those encouraged by Dr. Petrunic at Windfall was young Joe Lukacs, who had escaped from Hungary in 1957 and had finished his science degree at the University of Alberta on a Fina scholarship. After working at Windfall, running lab tests often at Dr. Petrunic's request, Lukacs returned to university to do his Master's under the tutelage of another respected Alberta researcher, Dr. Don Robinson. The subject of his thesis was water content in high pressure sour gas, a problem which had devilled the Windfall project, and which Dr. Petrunic had suggested he investigate. Lukacs' thesis broke new ground for the industry, adding to the basis of information needed to solve various sour gas design problems.

In the 1960's, Dr. Petrunic went to Fina's Wildcat Hills plant where he again worked with Joe Lukacs. It was there that Dr. Petrunic did his pioneering studies on the modified Claus process. He went through the plant, step by step, analyzing all aspects of performance and raising necessary questions. Could the catalyst be improved? What would the features of an improved catalyst be? Could they cycle the acid gases to get at the entrained sulphur?

Dr. Petrunic's work is summed up in a paper on Wildcat Hills delivered to the CNGPA in the year of his tragic death. The major problem at Wildcat Hills was that it was required by the Conservation Board and the Department of Health to achieve a 93% recovery of sulphur and that it was not doing it. In his paper, Dr. Petrunic also explained why the industry was now eager to improve sulphur recovery. "When the plant was built", he wrote, "sulphur production was not economically attractive. Since then the situation has changed entirely, so that at the present time it could be said that the sweet gas is a welcome by-product, and producers are happy to have a high concentration of H_2S in the raw gas."

The difficultly in achieving high sulphur recovery at Wildcat Hills (common to many plants) was that the raw gas contained more carbon dioxide than it did hydrogen sulphide, making the acid gas mixture almost incombustible. Dr. Petrunic remedied the problem with a series of adjustments to the front combustion chamber. Among other things, he made it longer, creating more time for the difficult combustion reactions to take place.

Perhaps the most important of the many other refinements Dr. Petrunic made at Wildcat Hills was his work on catalysts. The bauxite used at Fina, when he came, seemed to break down readily, and the bauxite fines were hampering the rest of the process. He used the plant's two identical sulphur trains to compare different catalysts and found that activated alumina did dramatically better than either granular or pelletized bauxite.

Although Dr. Petrunic's actual contributions helped the industry immensely, Joe Lukacs suggests it was only the beginning of what he could have done had he been designing plants rather than improving on existing ones. For Lukacs, Dr. Petrunic's greatest contribution was the spirit of analytical inquiry that he instilled in those with whom he worked. He proved that a working plant could be a highly effective laboratory, and that engineers working in Canada could be — indeed had to be — innovators in sour gas chemistry and engineering.

In 1969, the year of Dr. Petrunic's death in an Air France crash in the Bay of Caracas, the CNGPA initiated its Research Fund. One of the biggest projects ever promoted by the CNGPA Research Fund was a pilot plant situated inside an actual gas plant (first at Petrogas and then at Gulf Nevis) to study catalysts. It was a project after Dr. Petrunic's own heart, one in which he might have been involved had he lived.* The CNGPA also honoured Dr. Petrunic's memory by creating a University of Calgary engineering scholarship in his name.

Another venture that would have likely pleased Dr. Petrunic was that carried out by his one-time field apprentice, Joe Lukacs. In 1965, Lukacs left Fina to start a company called Western Research and Development in conjunction with Rod McDaniel. Computers were just beginning to make their debut in the oil and gas industry and the original aim of Western R & D was to take an active part in the introduction of this new tool. They quickly realized, however, that the move into computers would not happen swiftly enough to provide them with a living.

Joe Lukacs studied the modified Claus process from the ground up through his company Western Research and Development.

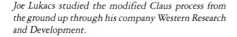

---

*This pilot unit study of catalytic reactors is funded by four groups: the University of Alberta, the Canada-Alberta Energy Research Fund, Gulf Canada and the Canadian Gas Processors Research Fund to whom the pilot unit belongs. The researcher in charge of the project is Dr. I. G. Dalla Lana of the University of Alberta.

Joe Lukacs took a reading of the industry and forecast, correctly, that pollution controls on the gas industry were destined to become even stricter. Based on the work he had done with Dr. Petrunic at Wildcat Hills, he broadened the services offered by Western R & D to include the improvement of sulphur plant efficiency.

One of the plants the company served in this regard was HBOG Edson. A new plant, Edson was faced with shutdown if it could not improve its sulphur recovery. The Western R & D team spent three months working on the Edson sulphur plant. The methods devised to solve the plant's problems became the basis of Western's analytical techniques thereafter.

In 1971, Alberta's Department of the Environment came into being, Peter Lougheed's Conservatives came to power, and the Conservation Board (ERCB) made a prophet of Lukacs by instituting much stricter sulphur recovery standards on the province's processing industry. Part of this package of new rules was insistence that all plants install continuous emission-monitoring systems on their sulphur stacks.

In its new set of standards, the Conservation Board divided the sulphur plants into four categories. The first category consisted of plants in the 1000 to 4000 long tons per day range. Within three years, these plants were required to achieve recovery of from 97 to 99% of their sulphur. To give some idea of the recent boom in the sulphur industry, *six* plants fit into this category.

It must have been a frustrating circumstance for the companies that had made an honest effort to achieve high recovery and still did not comply with the new standards. Many plants had gone to a third catalyst bed and Chevron's newly completed Kaybob III plant (designed to produce 2850 long tons/day) had gone to a fourth bed to pick up an extra 0.5% of the sulphur. But, no dice; Chevron Kaybob III was one of the five plants in category one that did not make the grade. *

The only one of the category-one plants which did meet the standard was Aquitaine's soon-to-be-opened Ram River plant. After tremendous success at Rainbow Lake, on the coat-tails of tiny Banff Oil (the outstanding exploration company started by John Rudolph) Aquitaine had made several discoveries in the Ricinus and Strachan fields west of Rocky Mountain House. Based on this gas, Aquitaine built the Ram River plant. Ram River was massive and up-to-date in every way. Aquitaine (which had by now swallowed the last vestiges of Banff Oil) was a subsidiary of SNPA,

---

*Eventually, through refinements of its process, Kaybob III did make the standard (98.5%) *without* going to tail gas cleanup: the fourth catalyst bed was enough.

the French state oil company. SNPA's plants at Lacq, France, were pioneers in the area of computerized process analysis and Aquitaine used this technology at Ram River to give the plant the most highly developed analysis system in North America to date. Each of its four 1000 long ton/day sulphur trains had its own closed-loop process analyzer, making continous gas/air adjustments at the front end. Stack emissions were also continuously analyzed by chromatograph. This system was part of what enabled Ram River to make the sulphur recovery standards when others could not, but a more important reason was the plant's tail gas sulphur unit, the first ever commercially installed in Canada.

The tail gas cleanup unit consisted of a Sulfreen system, another SNPA development, licensed in North America to the Ralph M. Parsons Co. In some ways. Sulfreen is reminiscent of the accidents that used to happen when temperature got too low in the early plants like Jumping Pound and sulphur adsorbed onto the catalyst. The *modus operandi* of a Sulfreen system is to adsorb sulphur on a catalyst, followed by catalyst regeneration with heat. Combined with a modified Claus plant, Sulfreen can give a sulphur recovery in the 98-99% range.

The second company in Canada to opt for tail gas cleanup was Chevron at its North nevis plant. It used the Institut Francais du Petrole (IFP) process which had its pilot run in Canada to HBOG's Lone Pine plant. From this point forward to the mid-'70's, much of the movement within the industry was geared toward tail gas cleanup — or resistance to same.

When Dr. George Govier came to address the CNGPA in the spring of 1972, he faced a group that was not entirely happy with his Board's new regulations on emissions. He began by complimenting the industry on its work to date. The 88% average recovery of sulphur during the '50's had been brought up to 95% by 1971; that was laudable. But now it was time to do better still. So much sulphur was being produced in Alberta that 95% recovery still translated into 900 long tons a day of waste — 900 long tons a day of sulphur compounds going up into the atmosphere.

When it was the audience's turn to speak, Ed Baraniuk of Amoco said what many were thinking. Tail gas cleanup was still new, and the processes available had not had time to be thoroughly tested under Canadian conditions. Problems were already cropping up in Chevron's IFP unit and problems would likely show up in the others, given time. With the price of sulphur looking bleak, the insistence on tail gas cleanup "gives encouragement only to the contractors" building them.

There were of course other points of view in the room. Bernie Coady was applying his Jumping Pound-Wildcat Hills experience with a Calgary-based contracting firm (Delta Projects Limited) and he argued that the price of adding these units was going to be much lower than the estimates that were currently being rumoured — in the vicinity of $34 million rather than the $60 million some people were suggesting.

Joe Lukacs, whose company was taking steps toward the development of process and emission analyzers, argued that the current systems for metering emissions were not capable of accuracy, and that it would be very hard to ascertain if someone was meeting the standard or not. Lukacs added that it would probably be cheaper to build a tail gas unit than it would be to construct an emission analyzer capable of showing that one was not needed.

Summing up, Dr. Govier said that the rules would be applied realistically, as Board rules always had been, and that the economic impact would be equalized as much as possible.

In the years between the 1971 change in regulations and the 1974 deadline for compliance, several tail gas units and stack and process analyzers went into Canadian plants. Petrogas at Calgary and the two HBOG Kaybob plants installed Sulfreen tail gas units. In 1975, Shell installed the SCOT process for tail gas cleanup in Waterton, far exceeding the guidelines with a recovery of up to 99.9%. Amoco* also developed an in-house process called Cold Bed Absorption (CBA) for use in its East Crossfield plant. Meanwhile, Dr. Hyne at Alberta Sulphur Research developed the ASR tail gas process which, in addition to handling the hydrogen sulphide also recouped the sulphur from COS and CS_2 created by the sulphur recovery process. †

Several other tail gas cleanup processes have been patented. It is interesting that, while the modified Claus process remains the standard way of getting the first 95 or so percent of the sulphur out of the gas, many processes have come along for cleaning up the last few percentage points of sulphur in the tail gas.

Still unsatisfied with the modified Claus process itself, Dr. Jim Hyne devoted part of his attention in the early '70's to improving the thermo-dynamics of the first stage of that process, the reactor furnace. Quite logically, he felt that the more sulphur that could be converted at this stage, the less that would need to be converted beyond it.

---

*The Pan American Petroleum Corporation became Amoco Canada Petroleum Company Ltd. in 1969. Prior to 1957, the company's Canadian operations went by the name Stanolind.

†The ASR tail gas process has not, to date, been used commercially.

The other method of improving sulphur process efficiency was process analysis. As mentioned earlier, process analyzers were a feature of the Ram River plant built by Aquitaine in 1972. These systems had been developed and used by Aquitaine's parent company, SNPA, in its French plants at Lacq. Process analysis had also been developing in North America in the late '60's. In a 1969 article written to celebrate the 10th anniversary of the CNGPA and CNGPSA, Jim Richardson spoke of the greater plant efficiencies "achieved by the use of chromatograph and sophisticated instrumentation to provide closer control of air and gas ratios." In 1971, at Quirk Creek, Imperial installed its own computer-controlled instrumentation system, which updated a variety of analytical data and accounted for all sulphur emissions from the stack.

Joe Lukacs, at Western R & D, was not satisfied, however, with the level of process analysis that was being achieved in Canada. In helping many plants to meet their recovery standards, he came to the conclusion that the modified Claus process was still not adequately understood. No really successful process analyzers could be built until a better knowledge of that process was achieved. In 1970, Lukacs approached Ottawa for funding of a study of the thermodynamics and kinetics of the sulphur recovery process. He was successful and, over the next ten years, the Western R & D team of Harold Paskall, Robin Rankine, Richard Kerr and Lukacs proceeded to do an in-depth analysis of modified Claus. The result was a definitive text on the process, a brand new computerized, closed-loop analyzer and a set of methods for testing the efficiency of sulphur plants. By 1977, the company was marketing its instuments to Canadian plants and, by 1978, it had gone to the international marketplace, selling both equipment and knowledge round the world. What had started as a pollution control device was now a world-class process controller, capable of analyzing plant efficiency and keeping it automatically at optimum.

The dramatic improvement of sulphur plant operation in Canada over the last two and one-half decades is a phenomenon that certainly cannot be laid at any one door. A major problem in describing the phenomenon is that so many people and companies contributed, it is difficult to mention them all. Researchers at universities and in the private sector contributed essential knowledge; chemical companies developed improved catalysts; and processing companies isolated the areas where improvements could occur. No matter where the innovations were developed, their ultimate test came in the day-to-day operation of the processing plants. In that sense, every engineer, operator and maintenance man in every sulphur plant in the country has played a part in the immense improvement of sulphur recovery science and technology.

DR. ALEXANDER PETRUNIC

When asked whom they would like to see given special recognition in this history, a great many informants suggested Dr. Alexander Petrunic. By deed and example, they felt Dr. Petrunic had improved Canadian processing as much as any single person.

Before he came to Canada from his native Yugoslavia in the mid-'50's, Dr. Petrunic achieved a great deal of respect in Europe as both a professor and a chemical engineer. He had also been a victim of that continent's realignments and political swings. Prior to World War II, Dr. Petrunic had been active as an advocate of socialism and that made him unpopular with the Nazis and just as unpopular with Tito's communists when they came to power. After the communist take-over in Yugoslavia, Dr. Petrunic was jailed.

Dr. Alexander Petrunic.

His salvation was his engineering acumen. Prior to being imprisoned, he had been teaching in the university at Zagreb and also serving as a technical director at a Yugoslavian carbon black plant. A disasterous explosion at that plant during Dr. Petrunic's imprisonment seems to have made the politicians recalculate the cost of keeping such a man in jail. He was released, given an apology and asked to resume his position at the plant.

Back in Yugoslavian society, Dr. Petrunic repeatedly refused requests that he join the communist party. His life became increasingly dangerous until, finally, he left Yugoslavia for Canada and employment with Trajan Nitescu's Canadian Fina.

Nitescu and Petrunic had met as engineers before the war, and again as victims of political repression after it. Nitescu had been pursued by the Rumanian communists, and had passed through Yugoslavia on his road to freedom. In many ways, the similarity between the men ends there. Nitescu was a free-enter-priser with no love for the Left, and the friendship between them must have been an interesting one, based on a common belief in the free expression of political views whatever they were and a common love for Canada.

Dr. Petrunic worked for Canadian Fina from his arrival in Canada until his untimely death in 1969. In Fina's plants, he set about improving the efficiency of various processes. His interest and ability as a teacher never left him and he informed his co-workers on subjects from chemistry and engineering to personal conduct and the presentation of technical papers. In his private life, he was renowned for his sense of humour, his concern for Canada and his assistance to Yugoslavian immigrants making their adjustment to Canada. Dr. Petrunic and his greatly respected wife Dragga were killed in an Air France crash in the Bay of Caracas in 1969.

SULPHUR HANDLING

Once sulphur is made, it has to be moved to market. Often, given the nature of the commodity, that movement is across thousands of miles of land and water. Also, given the topsy-turvy nature of the sulphur market and the industry's inability to control the production rate, sulphur must be stored for lengthy periods. The procedures for this handling and storage of sulphur are another area in which Canadians have played a leading role.

From the early '50's on, sulphur storage in Canada has been accomplished by building forms and pouring blocks. The lemon-coloured blocks are probably the most noticeable and most photographed aspect of the industry. Once the sulphur was in block form, a means had to be found to reduce it again to a portable form. Originally, that meant dynamite, which in turn meant danger and pollution. Sulphur dust explodes easily when allowed to collect; when it carries on the wind, it may result in harm to

Slate sulphur travelling by conveyor at Aquitaine Ram River.

some soils. The industry soon tired of the Russian Roulette of sulphur handling by dynamite, but the new means found, mainly power shovels, were still dusty, hence, potentially explosive.

Various events conspired to change the methods of breaking up and shipping sulphur. Increasing pollution awareness soon translated into a demand that sulphur handling and shipping be conducted in some dust-free manner. This applied not only to the locale of the plants, but also to railway right-of-ways and off-loading points: the industrial cities and coastal harbours the sulphur was destined for. The key event forcing a change in sulphur handling was a sulphur dust explosion in a Vancouver terminal in 1971. The Vancouver port authority banned crushed sulphur and the industry went in search of other methods.

Though not always feasible for use, the most efficient method of transporting sulphur is in liquid form. Rail cars had long ago been developed in the U.S. for handling Frasch sulphur as a liquid. The liquid sulphur was loaded into insulated tank cars and at the other end of the voyage, the sulphur was heated within the car by steam coils until it returned to liquid form. This method was fine for immediate sales of produced sulphur destined for domestic and U.S. markets, but would not solve the handling problem when the sulphur had already been blocked and was destined for an overseas market.

In 1964, Vennard and Ellithorpe (V & E) patented the *slating* process. It had been developed at Shell Jumping Pound and was given its name by one of the first Australian customers to receive the product. The liquid sulphur was poured onto a long conveyor, on which it froze into a long continuous sheet. The conveyor rose up to a point above the storage area and, reaching the end, the slates broke off and fell onto a pile. It kept the dust down nicely, allowed the continued use of open rail cars, and was rapidly grabbed up by an industry in search of an answer. In 1969, Shell asked V & E to design a slating facility for Waterton capable of producing 500,000 long tons of slate sulphur per year. But V & E itself seemed to realize that slating was not the be-all and end-all of sulphur handling. The company patented another process in 1969 for producing sulphur in pelletized form.

A year earlier, a great deal of experimentation had been done into shipping sulphur in a slurry through a pipeline. The companies felt that the high cost of shipping by rail seriously hampered their ability to compete internationally. A number of engineers for various companies went to work on the slurry pipeline idea and, when it began to look as if someone might go through with it, the railways found a way to drop their rates.

In the early '70's, with the new emission guidelines in Alberta threatening to bring even more sulphur onto the market, Dr. Hyne and ASR entered the sulphur handling fray with the battle cry: "We don't even know what sulphur is!" It was Dr. Hyne's contention that, to know how to handle sulphur, you have to first understand the many crystalline forms it can take and how the speed and sequence of cooling influences those forms. Thanks largely to ASR, Calgary became the centre for research and testing

The prilling tower at Gulf Hanlan-Robb.

in this area during much of the 1970's. In that decade, pellets, popcorn, nuggets, granules, capsules and prills of sulphur all competed for recognition and a market share. All the forms relied to some extent on Dr. Hyne's basic research into the physical chemistry of sulphur.

Whether made into a slate, a pellet or a prill, the sulphur must enter the process as a liquid. When high demand necessitates dipping into the stockpile, this in turn requires that the stockpiled sulphur be melted.

Various methods were evolved for doing this. The Bowman melter, developed by Eric G. Bowman of Eagle Inspection Services of Calgary, works like a gigantic household iron. The Bowman melter sits atop the sulphur block and, by means of steam coils, melts eighteen foot square holes down through the block.

In the early '80's, most companies were using the Ellithorpe remelter

An Ellithorpe Remelter, thawing its way through Canada's sulphur stockpiles.

which attacked the block on its flank, heating by steam coil and pressing forward into the block at fifteen inches per hour pushed by hydraulic jacks.

It is a sign of the times that the great sulphur blocks are vanishing. In the early '80's, the sulphur market was buoyant, the gas market stagnant. Sulphur production was naturally down alongside that of natural gas and the companies had no choice but to melt their way into and through the sulphur they had stockpiled in the boom years. Sulphur inventory reached its peak of over twenty million tonnes in 1978. From 1979 to 1984, that inventory dropped to thirteen million tonnes.

SULPHUR SALES

Canadians have had to finesse and muscle their way into a tight and suspicious world market in order to reach their present status as the world's foremost sulphur exporters. Storage could only go on so long. Some of the

Pouring sulphur to the block at Shell Waterton.

companies like Texas Gulf, Jefferson Lake Sulphur and Pan Am (Amoco) were major world marketers already and were able to absorb their Canadian production into their established global networks. But, for other companies, new to the game, it was a struggle.

Ted Baugh, former president of Canadian Fina, remembers when his company made its first offshore sale of sulphur in the early '60's. "There was no sulphur market then," says Baugh. "It was just an idea in the newspapers." Fina did not have enough sulphur to make up the 8000 ton shipment to Australia, so it bought some from other producers. He recalls that the cost per ton to get the sulphur to the West Coast and aboard the ship was in the $12-14 range; the Australians were paying $8. Nor was the loss entirely accidental; Fina knew that it was going to have to crack that iron clad world market somehow, even if it meant giving the sulphur away at first.

Also in the early '60's, Chevron Standard* decided it could no longer market all the sulphur produced by the North Nevis plant it was operating. Chevron's markets were absorbing only the amount of sulphur Chevron itself was producing and its partners in the joint-venture plant were simply going to have to fend for themselves. According to Ian Drum of Home Oil, Chevron suggested that the other partners band together into a committee for that purpose. Gulf, Petrogas and others took Chevron's advice forming Cansulex Ltd. in 1962, an offshore company charged with the task of marketing sulphur on behalf of its member companies.

In 1980, five marketers accounted for 95% of Canada's sales offshore. They were Shell, Texas Gulf, Amoco, Canadian Superior and Cansulex. At that time, Cansulex was handling over half of Canada's export tonnage; 15% of the world export trade in sulphur.

Canada's success in the export market is outstanding for several reasons, not the least of which is the distance that our sulphur must travel to reach tidewater. Most Canadian sulphur is in Alberta, 1100 to 1500 kilometres from the ports of Vancouver. Two organizations have been important in overcoming that disadvantage. The Sulphur Development Institute of Canada (SUDIC) was created in 1973 to find alternate uses for sulphur and to help the industry solve various logistical problems including transportation. A 1973 Sulphur Task Force organized by SUDIC looked into the transportation problem and recommended the creation of a company that would concentrate on sulphur transport to the West Coast, in somewhat the same way that Cansulex focussed on offshore sales. The result

---

*Formerly California Standard.

was Sultran, a company owned by twenty companies, charged with transportation and terminal operation. Sultran is devoted to getting sulphur from Alberta and northeastern British Columbia onto the West Coast ships in the smoothest, most cost efficient way possible. Sultran was created in 1976 and, largely as a result of its efforts, Canadian sulphur unit trains and terminals are capable of moving six million tonnes of sulphur from the processing plants to the offshore market every year; double the capacity that existed prior to the incorporation of the company.

GROWTH

Canada's sulphur industry is a success story; few would argue with that. In a country often accused of letting others do it for us, the advances behind that success have to a healthy degree been pioneered in Canada. When the government is looking for examples of Canada's technological prowess and maturity, its ability to market expertise, it can point to the sour gas processing industry in general, to the sulphur part of that industry in particular.

What is more, as Jim Hyne pointed out in a 1977 address to the Canadian Chemical Engineering Conference in Calgary: "It is highly unlikely that Canada's interest in sulphur as a natural resource will be short-lived." When we have finally exhausted our considerable reserves of sour gas, there will still be the tar sands to exploit for sulphur and the estimates are that those sands contain perhaps hundreds of years of supply.

If the relationship between sulphur consumption and standard of living maintains, our economy should remain strong for a long time.

Construction at HBOG Kaybob #1. The Kaybob name honoured R. E. "Bob" Allen and his wife Kay. As Alberta Conservation Board chairman in 1940-41 Allen set aside large provincial oil and gas reserves. The giant, liquids rich Kaybob field was found on one of them.

DEEP CUT: HOW THE HISTORY DUG DEEPER AND SOLD MORE

10

A theme in these pages is that natural gas was long regarded as the oil industry's poor relation. By that token, the propane and butane by-products of natural gas were the poor relation's orphan children. The pentanes plus or condensates were more highly regarded because they could be sold to the oil refineries for the making of motor fuel. Known as *naphtha* to the refiners and *natural gasoline* to the gas processors, the pentanes plus were in fact the reason why natural gas was processed for liquids at all in the early years. The Liquified Petroleum Gases or LPGs were another matter. Propane and butane sold for a paltry price through most of the industry's history and were only extracted from the gas to the extent necessary to meet the *hydrocarbon dew point specification* of the sales gas. The principle reason for a hydrocarbon dew point specification was to prevent condensation of hydrocarbon liquids in transmission lines. This specification determined the amount of propane and butane Canadian processors removed from their gas.

In the absence of a reliable market for propane and butane, a large quantity of these products went up the stack to flare; particularly in summer when the demand would drop to a quarter of what it was in winter. Alberta's Conservation Board always meant to put out these flares but held to a policy that it would only demand as much conservation as was economic.

GAS BEYOND THE GAS MAINS

Propane, or *bottled gas*, came on the Canadian scene as a retail commodity in the late 1940's. Almost no propane was being extracted in Canada and no steel cylinders or propane appliances were built here. Consequently it began as an import business. Canadian retail dealers rapidly entered the business because it seemed to fit the facts of Canadian life so well. Propane was hailed as *gas beyond the gas mains* and most of Canada qualified as being beyond the gas mains. Every farm in the West was a potential customer and most of the nation's towns and cities were likewise unconnected to a source of natural gas.

The U.S. propane industry had several years head start on Canada's, and the first Canadian dealers found themselves competing vigorously with their American counterparts for the American-made cylinders. They purchased Wyoming and Oklahoma propane through dealers in places like Cutbank, Montana, and Minot, North Dakota. Among the pioneer Canadian companies were Hugh Gas Ltd., Northland Bottle Gas Ltd., Canadian Propane, Sturdie Propane, Regas, Rock Gas, Stewart Petroleums and Alberta Gas Services. There was just enough money in it to attract many keen, usually undercapitalized entrepreneurs and, while they used every dodge and wile to compete with each other, they were all at pains to keep relations with U.S. suppliers cordial.

It was at that point that James Barber stepped onto the scene with his Western Propane Limited venture in Turner Valley. As pointed out in Chapter Four, Barber planned to do everything for the Canadian propane industry that was currently being done in the States; Western Propane would supply the product and Barber Engineering would build the cylinders. Decades ahead of his time, Jim Barber's true intention included ethane extraction to provide feedstock for the manufacture of ethylene.

A Sturdie Propane truck fills up at the Turner Valley Madison plant in the early 1950s.

Barber hoped to use the propane business as a means to finance this even grander venture.

Western Propane's distributor in Alberta was John Johanson's Sturdie Propane, operating out of Lethbridge. This was a successful venture, but, as Western Propane's general manager Morris Pryde points out, the B.C. and Saskatchewan distribution efforts were not so surefooted. Spence Pepper, who literally grew up with the propane business, collided headlong with one of Western's would-be distributors while working for Regas in Regina. An acquaintance of Pepper's took to frequently dropping by his office. The alleged reason for the visits was to warn Pepper that he should get out of the propane business fast because Saskatchewan's socialist Premier Tommy Douglas meant to put the business under state control.

Tommy Douglas happened to be a friend of Pepper's and, smelling a rat, Pepper went straight to the Premier's office to find out. Douglas found Pepper's news surprising. If socialization of the propane business was on the province's agenda, no one had informed the Premier. Douglas handed Pepper on to Provincial Treasurer C. M. Fines and there the mystery was solved. The acquaintance who had been helpfully warning Pepper turned out to be a prospective distributor for Western Propane who had been making a sales pitch to the Saskatchewan Government to form a provincial propane monopoly. C. M. Fines did not care for the man's methods and Spence Pepper's Regas wound up with the government contracts instead.

Spence Pepper always preferred this way of dealing with government. If you've got a problem, go straight to the top. The tandem of Tommy Douglas and Charlie Fines seemed to get a kick out of it. Pepper's recollection of Tommy Douglas in his days as Premier is that he always remembered your name and the business you were in. Meeting you at a party, he would say: "Propane. If I was going into business, that's the business I'd go into." So much for the socialist bogey.

The early propane companies suffered as a rule from a shortage of capital. In search of funds to operate on, Spence Pepper next went into business with oil man Leon Plotkins. It was an attempt to amalgamate the oil and propane businesses which, Pepper says, never works and did not work in this case either. Still, he remembers his association with Plotkins fondly. Leon Plotkins had one finger severed at the joint and when he wanted to make a point, he would spit in his hand and smack the finger-stub into his wet palm. When people came to him complaining about the lack of security in their business, Plotkins would call for Pepper. "Look at Pepper," he would say. "He never comes in here and asks what his security is. You know why? He *knows* what his security is. Hard work, hard work, hard work!" Spit. Smack.

A major change came to the propane business when Alberta's Conservation Board demanded that the associated gas in the Leduc oilfields be conserved. The first such plant, Imperial Devon, was equipped to extract LPGs. This gush of 3¢ propane was the death-knell for Western Propane which up to that time had been selling at the Oklahoma price plus transportation. For the sellers of propane, the cheap propane meant an opportunity to break into the Canadian space-heating market.

The bulk delivery truck also made its debut about this time putting an end to the bottled gas business. Customers could now be outfitted with a tank in their yard to be filled up when necessary from the roving tank truck. A. W. Hugh, who had started Hugh Gas in Regina in 1947, watched the bulk trucks rolling in from the States and did not care for what he saw. He called up one of his competitors, Ted Doyle at Northland Bottle Gas, and said, "Ted, I understand you have a bulk truck." Doyle said yes, he did. The U.S. trucks invading his territory had made it necessary. "OK," said Hugh, "I'm selling out."

Sellouts and takeovers proved to be the next trend in the propane industry, a predictable one perhaps for such a young industry. In 1953, International Utilities Ltd. moved into the propane business, buying up not only Hugh Gas, but Ted Doyle's Northland Bottle Gas and Sturdie Propane as well. That lasted until 1956 when Canadian Hydrocarbons Ltd. in turn bought the International Utilities' propane holdings for its growing propane empire.

Spence Pepper, an accomplished LPG marketer, plant builder and violinist.

Spence Pepper also found himself under a succession of managements. First, his company was taken over by Stewart Petroleums and then Stewart was absorbed by New York-based Progas of Canada Inc. Progas Ltd. was the holding company's producing entity in Canada and the marketing branch retained the Stewart name. Spence Pepper was attached to Progas and sent by engineer-in-charge Gus van Wielingin to Ardmore, Oklahoma, to learn how to build and operate a gas plant. The type of plant was the Grimes Portable Gas Plant and, after a six month crash course, Pepper returned to Alberta to build one at Big Valley in the winter of 1954. In 1955 he built another plant for Progas at Acheson.

Pepper liked setting the plants up and training the local farm boys to run them, but once they were running, he didn't care for the work of operation; "waiting for something to break down." He went back into the marketing end with Stewart. Not long after this, the president of Progas, Brigadier McCarthy, left the company. When all was said and done, Pepper found himself president of both Progas and Stewart.

As president of Progas, Spence Pepper created an opportunity to do something quite unique in Canadian gas conservation and that was to buy gas for nothing. Progas was not a money making concern at this time. The Conservation Board's new oil prorationing scheme had cut the Acheson plant's throughput in half. (The Big Valley plant was doing badly as well and had to shut down in 1956 when it lost its gas supply to the new B. A. Nevis plant.) Not able to change things on the selling end, Pepper decided he would change the terms of purchase with the producers.

In this pursuit, Spence Pepper had an excellent coach, his old friend Don Wolcott. With Canadian Gulf at Stettler, Wolcott had figured out that since the oil companies *had* to conserve the gas (they were obliged to by the Conservation Board) they couldn't as a rule afford to hardline the company that was processing their gas. To Wolcott that was a lever to buy the producers' gas cheaply. He shared this insight with Spence Pepper and Pepper went to his principal supplier, California Standard, asking to renegotiate the purchase price of raw gas to zero. California Standard needed the plant to stay in operation but did not want to set the precedent of giving the gas away. Still, they agreed to play ball Pepper's way if he could get them a break on the royalties they were paying to government. Pepper headed to Edmonton, forthwith.

It has to be a record of some sort that Spence Pepper was able to wring these royalty concessions out of not one but two government offices *in a single day*! Part of the gas was taken from Indian lands so he had to talk to both Indian Affairs and the Alberta Department of Lands and Mines. He left Edmonton, concessions in hand, by four p.m. the same day.

Back at California Standard, the negotiators were ready to stand by their word. But, at the last minute, because California Standard had dealt with him so fairly, Pepper softened. He offered to pay them a cent an MCF, just so the free gas precedent would not be set. "And that", says Pepper, telling the story three decades later, "is better than a boot in the rear with a frozen mukluk."

In the end, Spence Pepper's propane producing and marketing companies fell to the sweep of takeovers. Having taken over the International Utilities group of propane retailers in 1956, Canadian Hydrocarbons Ltd. added Stewart and Progas to its holdings in 1961. It says a lot about the rivalrous nature of the propane business that Canadian Hydrocarbons was, at times, more successful in getting the companies than it was in getting the people who worked for the companies. Back in 1956, a number of the Sturdie, Hugh Gas and Northland employees had refused to go to work for their old rivals at Canadian Propane (Canadian Hydrocarbons' main marketing company). Many quit the business instead. Several others (George Hefter, Tiny Thompson, Bob Watson, Elwood Percy and Ted Doyle) banded together to form Prairie Gas Ltd. in Regina in 1957. When Spence

Ted Doyle, travelled the take-over trail from Northland Bottle Gas to Prairie Gas Ltd. to CIGAS.

Pepper was asked to join Canadian Propane in 1961, he also refused. He had been competing against that company for most of his working life and wasn't about to join them now. He found new employment with Petrolane Gas Services which was affiliated with Maurice Strong's company, Canadian Industrial Gas. Strong wanted into the propane business and proceeded with a string of acquisitions of his own, including the takeover of Prairie

Gas Ltd. in 1962. This time, most of the men went with the new company. To strengthen the identification between Petrolane and its parent, Canadian Industrial Gas (CIG), the former's name was changed in 1962 to CIGAS George Hefter was the first president and Spence Pepper was vice-president.

LPG PRODUCTION AT CANADA'S CONSERVATION PLANTS

In the 1950's, a great deal of propane and butane continued to burn up in plant and well flares. At times, in summer, you could not give it away. The irony was that in the bitterest cold of winter, not *enough* propane could be found and the shortfall had to be made up from the U.S.

At Imperial Devon, Canada's first conservation plant, a concerted effort was made to market the LPGs. Imperial constructed three products pipelines into Edmonton in 1954; one for propane, one for butane and one for pentanes plus. The lines led to Imperial's Edmonton refineries which took care of the pentanes plus and most of the butane, utilizing these liquids in the making of motor fuels. Nearby, Imperial built a loading facility where the propane bulk delivery trucks could fill up. Some of the remaining propane and butane was pipelined to nearby Clover Bar, where Canadian Chemical Company Ltd. had recently opened a petrochemical plant. The plant oxidized propane and butane to produce a lengthy list of chemicals some of which went into the synthesis of fabrics and yarns. This was a definite breakthrough in LPG marketing, and an omen of things to come. In future, Canada's petrochemical industry would soak up increasing quantities of hydrocarbon by-products as feedstock.

In 1956, Canadian Gulf brought its Nevis conservation plant on stream. Nevis collected liquids from two satellite plants for fractionation into products including propane and butane. Nevis LPG production, at a few hundred barrels per day, was low by modern standards, but was more than enough to upset the small applecart of the day. Earl Scott, who began his career at this Stettler Area Gas Conservation Project, remembers that Canadian Propane was the plant's biggest customer and it could not begin to take all the product. The winter/summer swing in demand still resulted in winter shortages and summer glut. Even Devon, with its products pipelines and petrochemical outlet had to have a Conservation Board permit allowing it to flare the summer surplus.

If a few hundred barrels of LPGs a day could plug the market, what would a few thousand do? The Canadian processing industry was about to find out. Several of the plants coming on stream in the boom year of 1958 were equipped to recover LPGs. Total Canadian production doubled that year. What's more, that doubling of production was achieved without any great effort on the part of producers to maximize recovery. Most producers had moved from the ambient temperature oil absorption process used in Turner Valley to refrigeration processes which boosted LPG recovery some-what, but propane recoveries remained in the 60% range. The name of the gas was hydrocarbon dew point control, *not* high LPG recovery, and what Imperial process engineer Jim Haliburton calls "simple chill and flash plants" were good enough for that.

Of the 1958 plants with LPG facilities, the largest was Goliad's gas conservation operation at Pembina which had a capacity of 7000 barrels of liquid products per day. The seventy-six producers that took part in the Pembina conservation agreement retained ownership of their residue gas. Goliad, as operator, had to make a go of it by the sale of liquids and the operating fees it received from producers. Goliad's advantage in this agreement was the term of the contract; twenty years allowed plenty of time for prices to improve. Initially, Goliad was able to sell most of the pentanes plus to the usual oil refinery market, but the LPGs were much harder to move. Earl Scott came to Goliad from Gulf at the commencement of the Pembina project and he says that the propane/butane glut was such that the products were often sold for the price of injection water. They were injected back into the reservoir so that some of the liquids could be produced in the future when better prices and marketing conditions would hopefully exist.

The irony of Goliad's struggles in the late '50's is that the industry as a

Dan T. McDonald, a leader in the struggle to forge a viable Canadian LPG industry.

whole eventually benefited from them. Companies like Texaco, Gulf, or Imperial were not likely to go out of business because they could not sell their Alberta LPGs. A company like Goliad, on the other hand, had no other source of income and had to sell the *nuisance* products. Goaded by necessity, Goliad's chief Dan T. McDonald and his men worked hard on the problems facing the LPG industry. They joined the retail distributors in promoting propane and in looking for new applications for propane and butane, applications such as fuel for lumber drying kilns in B.C. and for orchard heaters in Washington State. Jumbo tank cars were brought into Canada for rail transportation of LPGs and freight rates were negotiated down to a level where Canadian LPGs became competitive in places as far away as California and Georgia. Finally, they worked to balance the teeter-totter of glut and shortage that LPG producers and retailers currently rode with the seasons.

Another company with a big stake in LPGs was Dome. Like Goliad, Dome was small and looking for gaps in the petroleum industry that it could profitably fill. In charge of the gas end of Dome's business was Don Wolcott who had recently moved over from Gulf. In 1958, Wolcott created Steelman Gas Ltd., a Dome subsidiary, to process solution gas from the oilfields of southeast Saskatchewan. Dome had been farming-in successfully in the Steelman fields and now would try to make more money by processing the solution gas and garnering the by-products.

Using the techniques he had taught Spence Pepper, Wolcott succeeded in getting Steelman gas for ¼¢ per MCF. He could have sold the residue gas to TCPL but was forced to sell it to the Saskatchewan Power Corporation instead for 4¢ per MCF less — a bitter pill for a dealer to swallow. With the residue gas bought and sold, Wolcott went shopping for a market for the Steelman LPGs. Like others in the industry, he had concluded that Canada's market would not be large enough to absorb the new levels of LPG production and he headed south to find a customer.

Looking back on the deal he hammered out with Anchor Petroleum of Tulsa, Oklahoma, Don Wolcott shakes his head and says, "I learned a valuable lesson from that. Never make a deal the other guy can't live with." Anchor simply could not perform under the terms of the contract and, in the end, Wolcott had to pay to have the contract torn up.

With that deal fallen through, Don Wolcott started to think in terms of storage. Rather than burn the summer surplus of LPGs, he would try to store it, then sell it on the more buoyant winter market. While on Gulf's training program in the U.S., Wolcott had seen men working for a Sid Richardson oil company storing LPGs in an underground salt cavern in New Mexico. The idea was to find a salt layer covered by a cap of impermeable rock and to leach out a cavern with injected water. Surplus LPGs can be pumped into the cavern and held there with little leakage until the peak sales season when the brine is used to displace the LPGs to the surface. Don Wolcott went in search of strategically located underground salt and found it near Melville, Saskatchewan.

At virtually the same time, the fall of 1958, George Murray, another individual familiar with the Sid Richardson storage schemes in the U.S., started bringing interested parties together to launch an underground LPG storage project in Alberta. B.A., Canadian Propane and Goliad created a company, Alberta Underground Storage Ltd., and began leaching salt caverns at Hughenden, Alberta. Product was injected into both the Melville and Hughenden caverns in 1959.

None of this was new in the technological sense. Salt storage had been going on for some time in the U.S. and the Sid Richardson interests had patented the concept in the late '40's. In 1960, fifty U.S. companies got together and paid $1.5 million to the Richardson Estate to free salt storage from any future patent charges.

In Canada, the entire Sarnia, Ontario, area is underlain by salt. In the early '50's, Dow Chemical of Canada leached out salt caverns at Sarnia in which to store the company's surplus ethylene.

Having created storage for the Steelman LPGs, Dome's Don Wolcott still had to sell the stuff. To that end, he made more forays into the United States. He had been renting planes and hiring pilots for these trips, but finally decided it was a foolish expense given that he was a pilot with two years wartime experience. Consequently, when he set out for Minneapolis to see if he could sell some propane there, he was at the controls himself.

With Wolcott on this journey was a young lawyer from Manitoba by the name of Bill Richards. Richards had recently joined the company's legal department. Together, they negotiated a propane deal with a Minnesota farmers' union — "a good one for Dome" — and then took to the air again headed for Brandon, Manitoba. Halfway between Fargo and Grand Forks, the engine blew up. Wolcott turned the plane around and aimed for Fargo. "My airforce training took over," he says, and he managed to put the powerless plane down safely on a U.S. airforce landing strip in amongst a squadron of fighter planes. A lieutenant trotted out to congratulate him on the best emergency landing he had ever seen.

Wolcott had had enough for one day. He decided he would repair to a local hotel for the night. But the young lawyer Richards declined to join him. He booked a seat on the next commercial flight out, "so that he could keep dealing."

Don Wolcott, architect of the Dome Petroleum gas liquids empire.

EXPORTING NGLs BY PIPELINE

The doubling of LPG production in 1958 set in motion a number of trends; some based on the idea that 1958 was the beginning of a great surge of growth for the LPG industry, others predicting that LPG extraction would not be profitable for a long time.

The LPG retailers saw 1958 as a time of unparalleled opportunity. LPG production was up and underground storage was putting an end to the shortfalls of winter. That meant a stable supply. The sellers could, with confidence, attempt to push their sales frontiers farther into the hinterland and deeper into the industrial fuel and feedstock marketplace. That it could be done was not in doubt because it had already been done south of the border. In some states bordering Canada, per capita propane use was fifteen times higher than in the province a few miles to the north. An atmosphere of optimism stimulated and characterized the 1958 formation of the Western Division of the Liquefied Petroleum Gas Association of Canada.

The only cloud on the distributors' horizon was a rumour of plans to export Canada's natural gas liquids surplus to the United States. If that happened, the Canadian retailers might not get a shot at the LPGs between the Canadian producers and the American vendors. This did not change the retailers' strategy but it did add an urgency to their sales pitch. The best way to fight export pipelines was to rapidly broaden the domestic market, thereby proving that no surplus existed.

In the same post-1958 time frame, the processors of gas liquids held an almost opposite view. The marketing problems of companies like Goliad had left the impression that, for the time being, LPGs were best left in the gas. This was not an entirely profitless alternative to extraction in that TCPL was paying a bonus for gas above 1050 BTUs per cubic foot of heating value. Alberta and Southern, the company that was currently trying to get permission to remove Alberta natural gas to California, was offering a similar *BTU bonus* on its contracts. Consequently, of the thirty-eight plants built in 1959, 1960 and 1961, only two were equipped to extract propane and butane. The others were content to leave the LPGs alone and cop the BTU bonus from the transmission company.

For the companies in Canada producing LPGs already, Socony Mobil Oil of Canada provided badly needed relief in 1961 by opting for a miscible flood in its section of the Pembina reservoir. Over the next several years, Socony Mobil bought $6 million worth of propane and butane (much of it from nearby Goliad) and pumped it into the Pembina reservoir in banks to push the oil from the tight reservoir rock. It took a long time to determine that the miscible flood was most often bypassing the reservoir rock through more permeable strata. Mobil finally stopped the flood in 1967. Meanwhile, it had been a great help to those with LPG surpluses and cash deficits. It was not a total loss for Mobil either in that the injected LPGs were to a large extent recovered at a later date.

The other people with a compelling interest in natural gas liquids at the end of the 1950's were the pipeline entrepreneurs who were hoping to do for NGLs what Alberta Gas Trunk Line, Trans Canada Pipe Line, Westcoast and A & S had done for natural gas; that is, gather the NGLs for transport to faraway places. These promoters were banking on the approval of the A & S natural gas export to California which would bring the liquids-rich, foothills sour gas reservoirs into production. The flood of liquids that this would bring onto the already strained Canadian market would create a surplus the pipeliners could gallantly offer to remove. The Alberta regulations at the time were such that propane could depart the province without permit if it made the trip by rail or truck. If it was to be pipelined, a permit had to be granted. Therefore the plans of the entrepreneurs were soon proposals before the Alberta Conservation Board with the usual array of counterproposals and interventions.

In 1958, the Mannix group of companies proposed, through subsidiaries of its Pembina Pipeline Ltd., a 1300 mile products pipeline from Alberta to the Chicago area, and a 900 mile gathering grid within Alberta. The companies founded for that purpose were Westalta Products Pipeline Ltd., Foothills Pipe Lines Ltd. and Dakota-Eastern Pipe Lines Ltd. It was a corporate configuration similar to that used by Alberta and Southern to get gas to California with the difference that Mannix would use its own company to gather liquids in Alberta rather than depending on an AGTL-like government company to do the job.

Several other proposals were added to the Foothills-Westalta one. Two of the plans featured the *batching* of hydrocarbon liquids through crude oil pipelines. Cities Service and Shell had shown this to be feasible in the United States and Interprovincial Pipe Line Ltd. had sent an experimental batch of liquids to Eastern Canada through its oil pipeline with some success. No one was quite certain yet if you could handle the lighter LPG liquids this way.

One of the batching proposals belonged to Provincial Producers' Pipeline Limited, an Eldon Tanner company. This plan stressed that Alberta consumers would be served first and that only the surplus would be exported from the province. The surplus would be batched between crude oil consignments through the Interprovincial Pipe Line (IPPL) system to the east and through Trans Mountain Pipe Line to the west.

Canadian Hydrocarbons Ltd., "the largest LPG distributor in Western Canada", was proposing to store the liquids underground at Hughenden. It would then market most of them in Western Canada and export only the surplus through the IPPL line to the east.

The Mid-America Pipe Line Co. surprised a lot of people by announcing it had an arrangement with both Provincial Producers and Canadian Hydrocarbons such that, whichever one got the right to ship through IPPL, would sell into a Mid-America line starting in Wisconsin and terminating in Chicago. Later, Interprovincial announced intentions of building a Superior-Chicago line of its own.

All these major proposals finally brought Trans-Canada Pipe Lines into the fray. It has been mentioned that TCPL was buying natural gas by the BTU; it had a problem in that it was not selling the gas the same way. TCPL gas sold by volume and the consumers were getting more than they paid for. The answer, the company felt, was to built plants that "straddled" the main line removing the hydrocarbon products that the upstream processors were leaving in the gas. TCPL's argument at the Conservation Board hearings was that it was already exporting the so-called surplus liquids and could export more gas providing it was allowed to build these *straddle plants*.

Besides the self-interested objections of one proposer against another, several other parties intervened at the Conservation Board hearings against these various projects. Canadian Industries Limited, representing the Alberta petrochemical industry, argued that cheap and plentiful LPGs were the only reason to locate a petrochemical plant near the source rather than near the market. If the pipeliners interfered with that situation, all hope of a petrochemical industry in Alberta would disappear. The LPG retailers pleaded the fast growing Western Canadian market and the fallacy that a surplus existed.

By mid-1961, the Conservation Board was ready to make its recommendations. It rejected every one of the large projects: Foothills-Westalta, Provincial Producers' and Canadian Hydrocarbons. Recommended for approval were the smaller schemes for removing specific supplies to specific destinations. These included a Hudson's Bay Oil and Gas project to export Pincher Creek and Waterton condensate through a small line to Montana, a Britamoil Pipe Line Ltd. (B.A. Oil) proposal to deliver Rimbey condensate to Edmonton refineries, and a Royalite request to move condensate from fields west of Calgary into Calgary. Of key importance is the fact that all the approved schemes involved condensate and not LPGs. For the present, the Conservation Board would not support large scale export of LPGs and suggested that the producers with surplus reinject that surplus or try to broaden their markets served by the traditional means of rail and truck. The reasoning behind this may have been that the LPGs could be left in the gas to earn the BTU bonus whereas the condensate, if produced, had to be sold. Not that selling condensate was that difficult — more and more Canadian refineries were using condensate as a feedstock instead of crude oil. The condensate approach avoided some nuisance by-products of crude oil refining and, since Alberta refineries were close to such excellent and abundant sources of condensate, they were natural candidates for such a switch.

A sad side-effect of the changeover to condensate as a refinery feedstock was that the pioneer refinery-gas plant at Hartell had to close. In Turner Valley, where natural gas had once dripped with naphtha, no local source of condensate now existed for the Hartell refinery. Uncompetitive without condensate, Hartell was closed in 1961.

The historic gas plant and refinery at Hartell in Turner Valley; on stream in 1934; forced to close in 1961.

B. A. RIMBEY

During the 1950's, British American had been one of the foremost producers of LPGs. Its B.A. Pincher Creek operation added LPG facilities in 1958 capable of producing propane and butane at the respective rates of 600 and 900 barrels per day. B.A. Nevis produced propane and butane at 580 and 480 barrels per day.

Between 1959 and 1961, when all other companies were following the conventional wisdom that LPGs should be left in the gas, B.A. stemmed the tide by building a plant at Rimbey capable of extracting more liquids than any other plant in Canada. The plant's daily throughput of 400 million cubic feet of raw gas surrendered in the vicinity of 30,000 barrels of liquids. The pentanes plus from B.A. Rimbey went into the Britamoil pipeline for transport to Edmonton's refineries. The propane went out in tank cars and trucks. Rimbey's butane was sent to refineries as far away as Puget Sound and Clarkson, Ontario. If these markets failed to take all the Rimbey output, the liquids were reinjected.

STRADDLING THE LINE

The TCPL application to the Conservation Board to retain LPGs in its line for possible extraction downstream caused a few ears to perk up. With the market for LPGs improving slowly but steadily, the idea of harvesting the bounty of products left in the TCPL line was enticing to some.

Don Wolcott on behalf of Dome was interested and he envisioned a plant on the frontier between AGTL and TCPL (that is, at Empress on the Alberta-Saskatchewan border). Dome's proposal to TCPL, according to Wolcott, was to give the pipeline company "a million bucks" for the right to build the plant. One of TCPL's major shareholders stepped in at this point with doubts about Dome's ability to market so much product. Dome was, after all, still a small company. The result was that Pacific Petroleums, controlled by Phillips Petroleum the biggest marketer of LPG in North America, got the nod to build the plant instead.*

Wolcott and Dome did not give up the idea of harvesting products from a pipeline company's gas. Their gaze merely shifted to Edmonton where Northwestern Utilities (NUL) had a gas stream entering the city from the west which was heavily laden with liquids. That NUL would be amenable to such a proposal was perhaps forecast by the means it had devised years earlier for dealing with Leduc oilfield gas. Leduc gas had been too rich for customer use, even after having been processed once at Imperial's Devon plant, and NUL had built a modification plant to mix the gas with air. Dome had done exactly the same thing at Steelman to lower the BTU rating of the gas it was selling on an MCF basis to the Saskatchewan Power Corporation.

What Dome subsidiary Steelman Gas Ltd. proposed for Edmonton was a straddle plant that would *double-squeeze* the NUL gas coming in from the Pembina, Lobstick, Bonnie Glen, Wizard Lake and Glen Park fields. (It had already been processed once at the Texaco Bonnie Glen and Goliad Pembina plants upstream.) Don Wolcott had a market lined up for the products. He would store them at Melville and then would ship them in season to the towns of northern Manitoba. The International Nickel Company (INCO) was mining at Thompson, Manitoba, and Wolcott foresaw an LPG system serving that swiftly growing community as well as other industrial towns in the region. Another customer in Minnesota was willing to take the surplus.

When this application was heard by the Conservation Board, the

---

*TCPL was given a 50% share of the Pacific Empress straddle plant, a share that Petro-Canada inherited when it took over Pacific.

upstream producers *objected strenuously* (that wonderful, bureaucratic euphemism for noisy collisions among competing interests). The producers contended that the double-squeezing plant violated their contracts with NUL. They had the right to remove from the gas "any of its constituent parts other than methane". Goliad, as a liquids producer, pleaded that there was already a surplus of products on the market and that the Edmonton plant would only make the situation worse.

The Board's solicitor handled the first objection by saying that nothing whatsoever prohibited a second round of processing if those who had the right to process the gas the first time chose to leave certain products in it. Don Wolcott parried the second thrust saying that his markets were in northern Manitoba and Minnesota and therefore did not affect marketing conditions in Alberta. As Wolcott puts it, Dome "was so skinny then" one witness had to answer to everything.

In the end, the Edmonton straddle plant was approved over the cries of protest. It made sense that the Conservation Board would favour it in that the Board had often told producers that it wanted high rates of LPG recovery and would demand them as soon as they were economical. Dome's application was consistent with that goal. Dome moved so quickly on the Edmonton straddle plant that the plant was on stream and squeezing gas in 1962, long before Pacific's giant Empress plant was constructed.

The Pacific Petroleums straddle plant at Empress was not officially proposed to the Conservation Board until mid-1962. The plant that Pacific laid out before the Board was the largest plant (by gas throughput) in Canada. At a billion cubic feet a day, it was, in fact, double the size of the second largest plant. The project also included a 580 mile, six-inch LPG pipeline from Empress to Winnipeg, a line that Pacific president John Getgood predicted would spread LPG use and stimulate a petrochemical industry in Western Canada. The Conservation Board approved the plant with little delay, and, by February, 1963, the NEB had given the approving nod to the Empress-Winnipeg products pipeline as well.

Though certainly out-done in size by the Empress project, Dome showed that it was not to be outdone in ideas. Dome soon proposed its own products pipeline to the NEB. Dome acquired Cochin Pipe Line Ltd. from the Banister pipeline construction company and applied through this subsidiary to build a line to carry products from Regina's refineries to the Melville caverns and from Melville to the northern town of The Pas, Manitoba. Telling the story, Don Wolcott says, "We fought like hell to get that line approved and, when we did, the railway promptly dropped the rate into Thompson." The tariff on the pipeline was now above that charged

The Edmonton Liquid Gas plant built by Dome in 1962 to double-squeeze Pembina region gas.

by the railway company and the northern leg of this first Cochin pipeline died on the drafting table. *

There is an unmistakable satisfaction in Don Wolcott's voice as he tells his story, however. A blond giant with a shy delivery, Wolcott is a bit pleased to see those who doubted him proved wrong. TCPL started out as one of those doubters, squeezing him out at Empress because some of the shareholders did not think he could sell the liquids. He hints that they

---

* A three-inch pipeline was built from Pacific's pipeline at Grenfell to the Melville Caverns (about 90 miles).

might have had second thoughts when they saw the success of Dome's northern Manitoba and U.S. distribution networks. As for the Edmonton straddle plant, Wolcott's former boss at Dome, Jack Gallagher, describes it as "not a money-maker on its own" but more of a "lottery ticket", a way for Dome to get into the LPG business in anticipation of market growth in the Edmonton area. In fact, the Edmonton plant lost money for Dome, initially, and might have been sold if the right buyer could have been found. The plant became more profitable when Amoco joined Dome in the venture and the fractionation facilities were expanded.

LPGS — ORPHANS NO LONGER

The Empress and Edmonton straddle plants and the products pipelines east opened up large new territories to LPG distribution. From the Fort White terminal near Winnipeg, tank trucks could more economically serve Ontario and Quebec while others went south and found new American customers. The introduction of 30,000 gallon jumbo tank cars on the railways had reduced transportation costs and made it possible to export to most parts of the continent. At Empress, Pacific and TCPL had made a pact that TCPL would create a market for the plant's huge LPG output by converting the compressors along the TCPL mainline from natural gas to propane or butane. A sign of how swiftly the LPG market grew after Empress, the conversions were never carried beyond a testing stage. Behind this market growth was a vigorous sales campaign by individual companies and by the Liquefied Petroleum Gas Association on behalf of all companies.

One of the industry leaders was Maurice Strong. His new LPG subsidiary CIGAS was steadily extending itself across Western Canada through a series of propane company acquisitions. When it came to thinking up new applications for the LPG fuels, CIGAS vice-president Spence Pepper was a one man army. First he tackled the portable asphalt plants used in highway construction. "They were practically giving butane away at the time", says Pepper, so he set out to devise a way of fuelling the asphalt plants with it. Perfecting the burner orifice turned out to be a problem and Pepper finally went to a Phillips Petroleum man who had written an article on the subject. The Phillips employee conceded that Pepper was on the right track and helped him to redesign the burner. In the following three years, Pepper estimates he converted 90% of all asphalt plants in Western Canada. That done, he and others went after the lumber drying market. Over the next few years, many lumber kilns were changed over from the burning of oil to the burning of propane or butane.

When the town of Thompson bought an asphalt plant, Don Wolcott convinced them to convert it to LPG and said he had just the guy to do the converting (Spence Pepper). Wolcott flew Pepper to Thompson in his Comanche and after Pepper had readied the asphalt plant for start-up, Wolcott gathered a few town dignitaries to witness the actual event. To quote Pepper, starting up one of these plants is "about the noisiest thing in the world." He got the Thompson plant running, "ironed out a few problems", and then looked round. He was alone. "They must have thought, if this guy's crazy enough to blow himself up, that's fine, but we're not going to stick around and get blown up with him."

A Steelgas storage tank on the Canadian Shield at Thompson, Manitoba. Dome put engineer Gail Stitt in charge of selling this LPG distribution system and, unable to find buyers, Stitt bought it himself, operating the system under the company name, Sittco Ltd.

Another encouraging note for the LPG industry was the building of a peak-shaving plant by the Greater Winnipeg Gas Company. Propane from the Empress products pipeline could be mixed with air at the plant and used to supplement natural gas during periods of peak demand. This was economical because natural gas fetched an extremely high price when it had to be bought on a spot market during a cold snap. The plant was built by Mon-Max, engineered by T. E. Morimoto.

At the 1964 annual meeting of the Western Division of the Liquefied Petroleum Gas Association, the talk was of a "rising flood of liquids"; of LPG output that had quadrupled in six years and was headed upward still. The Association had also undergone a rising tide of membership during that six year period. From sixty delegates at the first annual meeting, attendance had risen to 400 at this, the sixth annual meeting. A decision was made to merge the eastern and western divisions into a single national body.

When the first annual meeting of the national Liquefied Petroleum Gas Association (LPGA) took place the following year, the delegates debated a name change. "Our customers don't know what LPG is and they don't care," one man complained. Propane was their retail product and they reached the consensus that the Association's name and emphasis should change to reflect that fact. The following year, the LPGA became the Propane Gas Association of Canada (PGAC).

The LPGA (then the PGAC) was responsible for various changes in government regulation and several large scale promotions. It succeeded in having the sales tax on propane tanks eliminated and in promoting safety in the installation of LPG equipment. Goaded by statistics that said U.S. use of LPG was still considerably higher than ours, the Association sent demonstration teams to small towns to promote the use of its fuels. Mac McCaffery was one of the Association's star performers. Arriving in a town, Mac would contact a ladies' organization to tee up a cooking exhibition. McCaffery always wore a scrupulously clean white shirt and, after he had performed the amazing feat of baking an edible cake in a frying pan over a propane burner, he would take the pan and rub its bottom on his shirt — no mark, no stain! The cake was handed out to the audience for eating.

Other promoters were touring the farm machinery agencies putting on demonstrations of propane carburetion. One estimate had it that over 300,000 farm tractors were working across Western Canada; the PGAC and the individual propane retailers aimed to convert every one.

TAKING THE DEEP CUT

The retailers could speak of a "rising flood of liquids" only because of a change in attitude among processors regarding the viability of LPG extraction. That change was partly due to LPG marketing breakthroughs and partly because the Conservation Board was demanding a 60% recovery of propane.

While Dome and Pacific were planning and building their straddle plants, several companies battled for the right to process the rich gas from the new Swan Hills area oil fields. Federated Processing Limited, a subsidiary of both Home and Texaco, was after the gas and so was Imperial. Both parties proposed to build 40 million cubic foot capacity plants in the area.

Pan Am and B.A. entered the competition next, making a team proposal to build a producer-owned, joint-venture plant. Imperial first insisted that it needed no partner, being practically the sole owner of the Judy Creek field. Then, in a surprise move that may have clinched the competition, Imperial threw in with the Pan Am-B.A. team. Maurice

Strong also got into the race on behalf of Canadian Industrial Gas. Predicting that NUL would not be able to handle the vast quantity of gas that would come from Swan Hills, he proposed to take a portion of that gas for sale to *new* industrial users in the Edmonton area.

The newly created Gas Utilities Board was in charge of making the decision of who would get the project and the choice the Commission made was a bitter one for Federated. The combined project put forward by the Imperial-Pan Am-B.A. team won the derby. They were told they could go ahead providing they sold most of the gas to NUL and did not extract the ethane which was reserved for Canadian Industries Limited in Edmonton. Federated was excluded completely. Ian Drum, who worked with Home Oil during those years, says that it is a fact that vexes him still.

This decision was made in mid-1962. Imperial named Stu Mason project manager at Judy Creek and Mason recalls that Chuck Collyer, an Imperial refinery engineer from Sarnia, had much to do with the choice of refrigerated lean oil absorption for the new Swan Hills area plant. Imperial's previous plants at Redwater and Devon were strictly *dew point control* plants, or *chill-and-flash* plants as Imperial's veteran process engineer Jim Haliburton calls them. The new Judy Creek plant with its refrigerated lean oil absorption process was designed to take a *deeper cut*. It allowed a much

Chuck Collyer (centre) leads a tour around the Imperial Judy Creek construction site. Left to right, the people under the visitor's hard hats are: Herb Cooper, Jerry Drysdale, Bill Sage and Eric Snell.

higher recovery of propane and butane than did the chill and flash plants. Only the extraction of the liquids took place at Judy Creek; their fractionation was done at Devon. The liquids were pipelined as a mix to Devon, 115 miles away. There the mix was split into the different hydrocarbons and sent through the products pipeline to Edmonton.

Judy Creek was not the only refrigerated lean oil absorption plant built in this period. Both Dome's Edmonton and Pacific's Empress straddle plants were based on this process as well, as was the Rimbey "deep-cut" expansion which B.A. had proposed as soon as Pacific's straddle plant intentions became clear. B.A. had decided it would sooner extract the LPGs itself than leave them in the line for Pacific to harvest. Because of the richness of Rimbey gas and the degree of deep-cut the expansion plant allowed, this represented a considerable change in fortune for Pacific at Empress. Pacific intervened against B.A. at the Conservation Board hearing on the Rimbey expansion but the Board decided to let it go ahead. Essentially, upstream processors had the right to take out LPGs, even at a high rate of recovery, if they so wished. The Board allowed this and also that straddle plants should exist because there would always be enough products left in the gas to make them profitable. The gas from many fields was too lean to make *deep-cut* a viable proposition and the straddle plants would be able to feed off these fields.

The new deep-cut plant at Judy Creek and the addition of deep-cut facilities at Rimbey were precedents soon followed by other operators. In fact, from this time forward, most plants based on liquids-rich gas were equipped with high recovery LPG extraction facilities. Many of the existing plants which processed rich gas added deep-cut equipment. In 1964, Petrogas announced a $5 million LPG extraction facility to be added to its Calgary plant. Delta Engineering would build it. Canadian Superior at Harmattan doubled its capacity in 1964, adding propane and butane extraction facilities. In 1965, Canadian Superior was back before the Board applying for deep-cut facilities for the same plant. When Hudson's Bay Oil and Gas announced the design of its upcoming Edson plant the same year, *Oilweek* made special note of the fact that it was not equipped for LPG recovery although *Oilweek* believed that "future plant additions could provide deep-cut facilities."

In 1965 and 1966, Shell at Waterton, Texaco at Willesden Green, B.A. at Nevis and Socony Mobil at Carson Creek all joined the trend. Pacific was also given permission to boost its Empress throughput by one half with a consequent, though limited, increase in LPG production.

And so it continued. Canada Cities Service Petroleum Corporation's 1966 plant at Breton, though a compression-refrigeration type, did extract

LPGs. Home Oil at Carstairs, Amerada at Olds and Tenneco at Hussar all added LPG facilities to their plants in 1967. Canadian Industrial Gas and Oil added a refrigerated lean oil process to its St. Albert plant in 1968 as did Chevron Standard at Sylvan Lake and Shell at Jumping Pound.

Hudson's Bay Oil and Gas had an incredible building year in 1968 with a considerable impact on the LPG market. That year, HBOG opened its Caroline plant, removing LPGs by activated carbon adsorption, added LPG facilities to its Sylvan Lake plant and opened the gigantic Kaybob South plant at Fox Creek. South Kaybob's propane/butane capacity was 3690/3090 barrels per day. The Kaybob field expanded so rapidly that HBOG began building a second, nearly identical plant at Fox Creek before the first was fully constructed. Because it was a retrograde condensation reservoir, the plants were equipped for cycling the gas.

Seeing Double. The Kaybob field developed so quickly, Hudson's Bay Oil and Gas had to build a second, nearly identical Kaybob plant at the Fox Creek site, before the first was even completed.

The surge of total LPG production caused by all these new and expanded deep-cut plants was dramatic. In the years between 1955 and 1963, LPG production had posted small, unspectacular gains. After that, the curve for combined LPG production darted upward. From the beginning of 1964 to the end of the 1966, production climbed from 20,000 to

60,000 barrels a day. Even more impressive is the fact that the market kept up with the surge. Most of the product was being soaked up by the total North American market which could now be reached by jumbo tank car, but the first offshore sales were also being made. In 1965, Pacific sold a trial shipment of LPGs to Japan, 7.5 million gallons. The Japanese had been relying on the Middle East for most of their supply but political tensions in the region were causing them to search out alternatives. Later in the same year, B.A. announced a deal with the Japanese for 28.5 million barrels of propane over a period of ten years. B.A. was planning to move the propane from its own Alberta plants to Vancouver by jumbo rail car. B.A. had a refrigerated terminal built in Vancouver to prepare the product for shipment by refrigerated tanker across the Pacific.

Instead of drowning in a rising tide of liquids as most had predicted for the mid-'60's, the LPG distribution industry in Canada found itself conspicuously short of supply. The word shortage was bandied about and not idly. Goliad's top man in Canada, Dan T. McDonald, spoke in 1966 about the reasons for the shift: "When we had a surplus a few years ago, it stimulated the salesmen to push it out. Now we'll have to make more product to cover his sales." The message must have felt strange to the man who had struggled with surpluses of "nuisance" fuel only a few years earlier.

What McDonald was describing was the beginning peaks and valleys of a cycle that may always characterize the LPG industry. Jim Richardson summed it up in a 1969 article he wrote on the Canadian gas processing industry through the first ten years of the CNGPA:

> Periods of high demand (for LPGs) result in over-expansion of production facilities and therefore over-supply. The consequent fall in prices slows down the installation of extraction facilities, and eventually, under-supply, rising prices and a resumption of the cycle follow.

THE COCHRANE STRADDLE PLANT

The supply of Liquified Petroleum Gases is clearly proportional to the percentage recovery achieved by the processing companies. The deep cut of the late '60's added considerably to the total. But the other factor influencing supply is the total number of cubic feet of raw gas from which the processing companies are extracting LPGs. In the late 1960's the great triumvirate of tribunals (Alberta's Conservation Board, the National Energy Board and the U.S. Federal Power Commission) was once again deciding whether or not to allow that figure to increase. All the natural gas pipeline companies wanted to increase their export volumes and the proposals were working their way slowly through the various levels of jurisdiction.

Meanwhile schemes for moving the liquid by-products by pipeline continued to pop up and be slapped down. Canadian Hydrocarbons Ltd. had a plan to move liquids from Harmattan-Elkton to Sumas near Vancouver by a proposed pipeline owned by its subsidiary, Hydrocarbons Pipe Line Ltd. Permission was granted to remove the LPGs from Alberta, but the 597 mile pipeline was rejected by the NEB in March of 1966.

Home Oil had been planning to sell some of its Carstairs propane to Hydrocarbons Pipe Line Ltd., but when the pipeline was rejected, Home turned its face to the east. It proposed an LPG and condensate pipeline that would gather from several fields and deliver to a terminus at Hardisty, Alberta. There, the heavier liquids could be injected into the Interprovincial Pipe Line and the lighter ends could move out by tank car and truck. This proved to be a successful venture. Over the next few years, Hardisty Storage Ltd., owned jointly by Canadian Superior and Home Oil leached four underground salt caverns at Hardisty and installed a depropranizer and butane splitter at the same location.

In this rush to garner and transport LPGs, one major source remained untapped in 1966. The flow of gas from the rich foothills trend reservoirs was still loaded with liquids as it left the Province of Alberta destined for California. Alberta and Southern, the owner of the gas, was not anxious to perform any further squeezing of the stream because, unlike TCPL, A & S was selling on the basis of BTU as well as buying that way. At the same time, the American subsidiary of Pacific Gas and Electric was very conscious of the Alberta Conservation Board's policies with regard to LPG recovery in the province. In all permits issued by the Board, it was clearly stated that extraction of *any* substance other than methane could be ordered before the gas was allowed to leave Alberta. As early as 1962, the Board had suggested that the reprocessing of foothills trend gas was just a matter of time.

When Robert Blair became the first Canadian president of A & S in 1966, this reprocessing issue was one of the first he faced. A & S was approached by no less than twenty-seven companies with proposals for the reprocessing of its gas. Dr. Andy Younger was the architect of one of those twenty-seven on behalf of HBOG and, when his bid was rejected, he was told that HBOG finished second to a Dome-Pan Am proposal. Subsequently, he found out that all twenty-six of the unchosen had been told they finished second to Dome and Pan American.

Behind the winning Dome-Pan Am bid, the deal-maker Don Wolcott could once again be found. The proposal was to extract the liquids with a straddle plant on the AGTL Foothills Division pipeline, to pipeline the liquids to Edmonton and then batch them into the Interprovincial Pipe

Line to Sarnia (an idea not unlike those the Conservation Board had rejected back in 1961). The liquids would be batched as a mixture and fractionated at the Sarnia end in a new plant. Those factors made the Dome-Pan Am proposal economically viable for those companies, but the key to winning approval may have been the fact that A & S was asked to build and operate the straddle plant, thus giving the pipeline company a chance to partake in the project and its profits over the long term. A & S gave responsibility for the plant to its own subsidiary, Alberta Natural Gas (ANG).

Don Wolcott's team at Dome had originated the idea and Pan Am was asked to be an equal partner. One reason for a partnership was to avoid the problem that had frustrated Dome at Empress. Don Wolcott did not want Dome's size to be a negative factor in another decision. Pan Am was also a major supplier of gas to Alberta and Southern. Its participation would therefore lessen the chance of the straddle plant being *upstreamed*; that is, having the liquids removed upstream of the straddle plant.

The location chosen for the straddle plant on the AGTL Foothills line was near the town of Cochrane. Cochrane was chosen because gas entering the pipeline south of there to the B.C. border was fairly lean. Reprocessing that gas would not be worth the cost of the longer line. The Cochrane location was also close to the CPR.

Probably the most intriguing thing about the Dome-Pan Am proposal for the Cochrane liquids is that it was made without asking anyone at Interprovincial if they had an interest in the project. Planning for the proposal had been so *tight*, so secret, that no such overture could be made without risking that a competitor would hear of the scheme and duplicate it. The Dome proposal was handed to Bob Blair at the deadline and Don Wolcott raced for Toronto to try and convince IPPL to allow the proposed batching through its line.

Initially, Interprovincial was resistant to the idea, Don Wolcott admits, but he finally convinced the pipeline company to try it. The Alberta and federal regulatory bodies gave their consent and the plants, pipelines and other facilities went into construction. The Cochrane straddle plant was built for ANG by Stearns-Roger with Angus Leitch and Associates consulting on the design. Lean oil absorption was chosen to achieve 85% recovery of propane.

Dome's engineer in charge of construction and operation of the natural gas liquids transportation system was Gail Stitt, a graduate of the University of Oklahoma. Stitt was another in the group of engineers Dome had enticed away from B.A. The transportation system he helped design for Dome was necessarily complex. The Cochrane to Edmonton (Co-Ed) pipeline, built by Wonderly and Kershaw Construction Ltd., wandered the countryside in order to pass by the maximum number of plants that might one day be its customers. There was storage at either end of the Edmonton-Superior, Wisconsin, leg of the IPPL and salt storage at Sarnia. Also at Sarnia was the fractionation plant that would split the mixed liquid stream into its saleable components.

Finally in 1971, the NGL system was complete. Says Don Wolcott: "We got our plant in Sarnia all shiny and ready to go" and the first batches

Dome's fractionation plant at Sarnia, Ontario, received NGLs from Alberta through the Interprovincial Pipe Line.

were started down the line from Edmonton. During the thirty day trip east, the propane in the mixture showed an unfortunate liking for the crude oil at the interface between the two and reacted to form asphaltines. When the batch hit the Sarnia plant, the fractionation system plugged solid with the gluey substance. The worst part was that more fouled batches were on their way. In the long run, Dome's engineers found that a condensate buffer between the liquids mix and the crude oil prevented the reaction. In the short run, however, there was no answer other than to catch the guck and haul it away.

Quite a while before this NGL system was in full operation, Dome made another startling coup. In mid-1967, TCPL finally received all the permissions it needed to build the much warred over pipeline south of the Great Lakes to Sarnia. The higher volumes allowed by this expansion put TCPL in the market for a second straddle plant at Empress. Pacific may have believed that it would fall heir to the second plant by virtue of owning the first, but, in 1968, the project went out to bid. The successful bidder was Dome. Explaining the victory, Don Wolcott says: "We were very powerful NGL people now; we utilized our systems and we won." Offering a 50-50 partnership in the project to TCPL did not hurt either.

ETHANE TO ETHYLENE

The Dome Empress plant began its drawing-board life as a refrigerated lean oil absorption plant with an initial capacity of one billion cubic feet a day. With that process, it would recover 90% of the propane and 20% of the ethane. Its *ethane-rich* stream would be used as fuel in TCPL's compressors; the old trick of supplying a market for surplus products from within the partnership no doubt borrowed from the early agreements between Pacific and TCPL at Empress. But, before the plant was actually constructed in 1970, it had transformed into a turbo-expander plant in order to recover saleable ethane. Fluor, the contractor at Dome Empress, was trying to market turbo-expander plants in Canada, but credit for influencing the choice must also go to consulting engineer Glen Handwerk. Legend has it that Fluor was offering to put the expander in for an extra 10% of the cost for a lean oil absorption plant. Wolcott asked Handwerk what difference it would make and Handwerk said, "It's simple. If you want to make ethane, go turbo-expander." Wolcott replied, "We want ethane."

The first commercial production of ethane from natural gas in Canada by the turbo-expander process stems from that conversation, there is little doubt of that; but ethane *and* turbo-expanders both have histories in

Canada that precede Dome's Empress plant. Credit for recalling the earliest plan to extract ethane from Alberta gas must certainly go to Ian Drum, an ex-Home Oil engineer of long experience who recalls that Union Carbide promoted a project to utilize Turner Valley ethane in the production of ethylene way back in 1928. The project did not fly and neither did James Barber's scheme to capture ethane from the Madison Gas Plant's flare gas for the production of ethylene in 1949. Barber had to settle for the production of propane while the ethane was flared.

The first company to capture and use Alberta ethane was Canadian Industries Limited. In 1951, CIL became interested in polyethylene, a thermoplastic resin made by polymerizing ethylene. Ethane is a good feedstock for its manufacture. Although the company would have rather located in the East where the markets for the product were, feedstock was hard to come by there. Edmonton, though certainly far from markets, was close to some of the highest ethane-content gas in the world. Finally, CIL opted for the latter. A stream of Leduc-Woodbend gas (18% ethane) was diverted to the plant and divested of its ethane by deep refrigeration absorption before returning into the mains of Northwestern Utilities. The first customer shipments of polyethylene left the plant in early 1954.

As for the expander turbine technology, Jim Richardson of Partec Lavalin traces its origins to Russia. Dr. Swerengen of the Rotoflow Corporation in Los Angeles improved upon Russian technology to come up with the initial turbo-expander. It was first used for the extraction of helium. Then, in 1964, it was applied to natural gas to acquire a very high propane recovery at the Coastal States plant at San Antonio. The advantage of the turbo-expander is that it produces a much deeper chill than any of the other refrigeration-based processes. The first "cryogenic expander" plants could reach a chill of $-80°F$ to $-100°F$, and the latest ones can plunge the mercury to $-190°F$. This produces liquefaction of a higher percentage of the lighter components of natural gas (ethane and propane). Another advantage of the turbo-expander plant is that it is compact and generally requires less maintenance than other types of gas processing plants designed for similar purposes.

While still with Barry and Richardson, Jim Richardson proposed the use of turbo-expanders to several of his Canadian clients as a means of achieving high propane recovery. In fact, it was Barry and Richardson's studies into the feasibility of turbo-expander plants at Empress and Cochrane, done for Maurice Strong at Canadian Industrial Gas in 1966 and 1967, that launched the competitive bidding rally for the Cochrane straddle plant. As Jim Richardson puts it, the turbo-expander plant "went back on the shelf" when CIG failed to win that competition and was not taken off again until 1970 when Imperial chose it for high propane recovery at its third Judy Creek plant and Dome chose it for ethane recovery at Empress.

The turbo-expander process might have come in for slightly earlier use in Canada had Dr. Andy Younger had his way. After being aced out of the Cochrane straddle plant by Dome and Pan Am, Dr. Younger had been forced to admire what his competitors had done. The idea of batching the liquids down the IPPL crude oil line had been a good one. Younger and Gerry Maier, also of HBOG, were discussing the Dome-Pan Am scheme when Maier asked if HBOG might not be able to do something of the same sort through the Trans Mountain crude oil line to the West Coast. Dr. Younger went to work on the idea and came up with a project for gathering all the Kaybob liquids, including Chevron's, and moving them to the West Coast through Trans Mountain. He had also decided to extract ethane and had Dupont interested in building an ethylene plant in the Pacific Northwest based on this feedstock. The idea fell through, however, when Chevron decided it did not want its liquids on the West Coast. In May, 1967, a very short time after this project had collapsed, Andy Younger was approached by Don Wolcott and Bill Richards with a job offer from Dome. He took it. Earl Forgues who had worked with Andy Younger on the Trans Mountain concept at HBOG was also enticed to Dome where he continued to work for Younger. Forgues had worked in Union Carbide's ethylene plant in Montreal from 1960-1968, experience that fit in nicely with Dome's next set of entrepreneurial plans.

One of the people who had been anxious to hire Dr. Younger at Dome was Gail Stitt. Stitt was growing dizzy trying to keep up with the business schemes pouring from the fertile imaginations of Don Wolcott and Bill Richards. Dr. Younger was the top gas operations man Dome needed to translate those ventures into fact. By the time Andy Younger arrived at Dome, planning for the Cochrane-Edmonton-Sarnia NGLs system was more or less solid. The NGLs from Dome Empress could also be worked into this system without too great of difficulty; all that was needed was a short pipeline from Empress to a loading point on the IPPL. But the ethane from Empress was a challenge requiring considerable ground-up research and planning.

Ethane's industrial niche was still as a feedstock for the making of ethylene (en route to polyethylene). That had not changed a great deal since CIL first went into business in Edmonton in 1954. In fact, CIL's polyethylene plant still represented a significant portion of the total market for Alberta ethane in Western Canada. The Conservation Board had been forecasting since 1962 that Alberta ethane would be needed in future as a petrochemical feedstock and, technically, the Board was right. But, in 1970, that market was still unrealized.

What Dome's deal-makers did in the absence of a petrochemical market for their ethane was to unearth a *thermal market* for it in Green Springs, Ohio. Columbia Gas was willing to take Dome's ethane as a feedstock for the creation of synthetic natural gas! That's right; less than thirty years after natural gas had been left to burn in the oil field flare stacks of the continent, the same commodity had become precious enough to synthesize.

A new Cochin Pipeline project was proposed to the NEB to carry the ethane and other light hydrocarbons from Edmonton and Empress to Ohio. Dome once again showed its ability to attract top people by bringing John Beddome in to take charge of the Cochin project. Beddome was working for Gulf at the time, in his 19th year with the company and not unhappy there, but the challenge of working on something so entirely new for a company in the midst of a vigorous growth spurt won out. Beddome came to Dome.

The first Conservation Board hearing on ethane export from Alberta through a Cochin pipeline took place in July, 1971. Even CIL, Alberta's only petrochemical consumer of ethane, was hard pressed to argue against it. Under cross-examination, CIL had to admit that it was highly unlikely that other petrochemical plants in need of ethane would establish themselves in Alberta in the foreseeable future. The profitable place to be was in among all the other petrochemical plants that used ethylene, in places like Sarnia. This principle was the foundation of the Board's recommendation to the Alberta government that Dome be given the green light.

When the project arrived before the NEB, however, there was stiffer opposition. A total of 32 intervenors stood against Dome's plan, including the so-called SOAP group (Sarnia Olefins and Aromatics Project). SOAP included Dow, Dupont, Union Carbide, Polysar and Koch Oil and the companies were planning a joint-venture ethylene plant based on ethane from naphtha in the Sarnia area. They regarded Dome's plan as an intruder on theirs. In his usual conciliatory fashion, Dome president Jack Gallagher had met with the SOAP companies and asked them to support Dome's plans before the NEB, but most of the companies involved in SOAP turned him down.

One company from SOAP did choose to speak in favour of Dome's Cochin project before the NEB and that was Dow Chemical of Canada Ltd., a highly influential player in that it was the largest consumer of ethylene in Canada. Dow already had chlorine production facilities in Alberta and the company saw that, with a source of ethylene in that locale, it could go into the production of vinyl chloride. While retaining membership in SOAP,

Dow undertook a second study of ethylene and related petrochemical possibilities based on Alberta ethane. Most aspects of this were jointly undertaken with Dome.

Cliff Mort, Dow's vice-president of business development, moved from Sarnia into a Calgary apartment in 1972 to look after this proposed project for Dow. From then on, Mort became progressively more involved with the project until, finally, he achieved the unofficial title of *grandfather* of the ethylene industry in Alberta. During the early phases of the project, Cliff Mort was busily involved with Dome, with the Alberta Government, with the ethane producers and with the NEB. Each time the Cochin pipeline went before the NEB, Cliff Mort spoke as Dow's policy witness for the project.

In this general time frame, Dow and Dome planned ethylene facilities in Alberta that would serve both Alberta's and Eastern Canada's needs. The Cochin pipeline was revised into two pipelines, one for ethylene, the other for LPGs and ethane. Dome also went ahead with the eastern leg of the Cochin pipeline in order to meet its obligations to Columbia Gas. LPGs from the Interprovincial Pipe Line and ethane-plus purchased in the U.S. were pipelined to the synthetic natural gas plant in Green Springs, Ohio.

The various entrepreneurs involved in the Cochin project may have felt quite optimistic at this point that the Cochin pipeline and the Dow-Dome ethylene plants were on their way. If so, they were considerably mistaken. A series of delays, revisions and rejections were on the horizon and two of the major reasons, though they may seem unrelated, were the appointment at AGTL of a new president in 1970, and the election in Alberta of a new government in 1971.

The new president of AGTL was the old president of A & S; Robert Blair. A & S, though certainly a fine company, had turned out to be a bit too confining for Blair, a native Albertan with nationalist views and vast ambitions. A & S was "a gas buying subsidiary" for a big U.S. utility and Blair had found the San Francisco landlords fairly uninterested in their Canadian gamekeeper's enthusiasm for growth. Meanwhile, at AGTL, president Jim Mahaffy was nearing retirement and a search was on for a successor. Blair made his move to AGTL in 1969 as a vice-president, but with a firm commitment from AGTL that he would be president when the time came.

This may not seem to have been a major change for Blair in that AGTL was also, in a sense, a utility which had been set up for limited purposes. But Bob Blair felt there was a great difference in that his new shareholders were Canadian (in fact, mostly Albertan) and his new board was interested in his ambitions for growth. In a 1970 interview, Blair said:

Bob Blair became president of AGTL in 1970.

"(AGTL) is a company of substance, a company with operating experience and financial capacity. We owe to our investor-owners and to the general community to make the most of those strengths." If the company was not allowed to grow, that would make it like "a mine with one ore body which is not allowed to look for a second ore body." "Nothing goes downhill faster," says Blair, "than a pipeline with no growth left."

Expansionist noises like these were not well received in the Alberta oil patch. The companies which had resented AGTL when it was first inserted between the producers and the transmission companies back in the '50's thoroughly resented the idea of its spreading itself deeper into the private sector. But Blair was never swayed; he *was* the private sector, he argued, with shareholders who deserved "some action" as much as any shareholders anywhere.

The first tangible sign that Blair was serious came very early in his days with AGTL. Alberta's Premier at the time was Harry Strom and Premier Strom warned Blair that TCPL was planning to bring gas down from the Yukon and Northwest Territories through northern Alberta, distributing some of it along the way. As of yet, AGTL's distribution grid did not extend into northern Alberta and TCPL saw an opportunity to take the Alberta company's place in that zone. Blair went to TCPL and expressed interest in participating in the northern project. TCPL declined the offer with thanks. That, for Blair, meant "the gauntlet was down." The prolific discoveries at Prudhoe Bay, Alaska, meanwhile "raised the stakes" considerably and Blair assembled his own group to compete for gas transmission from the north.

What came out of this finally is one of the most talked about, written about sagas of Canada's last decade: the Canadian Arctic Gas consortium, the Berger Inquiry, Bob Blair's exit from the consortium to form Foothills Pipe Line; Foothills' final victory, the right to build by an alternate route, if a pipeline is ever built. That is indeed another story, for which we refer you to other books.

The other factor that would soon affect the Cochin project was the 1971 election of Peter Lougheed's Conservative Government to the Alberta Legislature. By landslide, the Lougheed Conservatives unseated the Social Credit Government that had ruled Alberta since the Aberhart summer of 1935. The new Premier of Alberta was a man whose notions and ambitions bear some comparison to those of Robert Blair. Peter Lougheed was also several generations an Albertan and he was also tired of being affiliated with

Peter Lougheed in 1971, the year his Conservatives took the Alberta election by landslide.

a branch plant that took its orders from a non-resident parent. The parent in this analogy was the federal government, and Lougheed wished to see an end to what he perceived as that government's colonial attitude toward Alberta. He was convinced that Alberta was not respected in the East and that it was regarded simply as a *resource bank* for the East to draw upon at its pleasure. He meant to change things.

One of the ways in which Premier Lougheed planned to make this change was by defying the notion that a petrochemical industry based on Alberta ethane had to be located in Eastern Canada. He wanted the jobs and wealth associated with any petrochemical industry relying on Alberta feedstock to stay right in Alberta so he went looking for a Canadian-controlled company that could accomplish such a feat. Bob Blair's revitalized AGTL eventually won that opportunity, but Blair is careful to explain that it was not handed across to him on a plate. AGTL had to prove to Lougheed that it could do the job. "We worked our way into it," says Blair.

The result was AGTL's planning for a world scale petrochemical complex in Alberta. An AGTL subsidiary, Alberta Gas Ethylene (AGE), was founded to do the job. The first stage of the project was the extraction of ethane from a gas stream leaving Alberta and an ethylene plant that could convert that ethane into a billion pounds of ethylene per year. AGTL also worked with CIL on the concept of a plant to upgrade the ethylene to polyethylene resin. CIL already had one such plant in Edmonton. Other potential customers for the ethylene were B. F. Goodrich and Dupont. All this would be done in Alberta and would therefore be free of NEB and other federal approvals and restrictions.

This was made public in 1973, the same year that Dome and Dow announced their plan to build an ethylene plant based on Empress ethane. Dow dropped out of, but SOAP in 1973 to put all its eggs in the Alberta basket. Before leaving SOAP, Dow showed the SOAP partners its Alberta ethylene study in hopes of enticing SOAP to join in that venture, but SOAP again declined. The SOAP partners had plans for butadiene and isobutylene plants at Sarnia, applications that could not be supplied in Alberta by the proposed Dow-Dome project.*

Dome and Dow may not have been entirely surprised by AGTL's announcement of a rival petrochemical scheme. The Alberta Government had recently been telling Cliff Mort that if Dow wished to export ethane from the province, the company would have to replace the lost BTUs with supplies of natural gas. Dow therefore went in search of "gas in the ground" and could not find enough for sale. When Cliff Mort went to AGTL for this purpose, he was told that, rather than supplying gas, AGTL would be more interested in taking part on the petrochemical side of the venture.

The search for gas to support the Dow-Dome ethylene project gave rise to an exploration agreement between Dow and Dome worth $90 million ($60 million from Dow; $30 million from Dome). Eventually this

---

*The remaining SOAP partners created Petrosar Ltd. in 1974.

search for gas led to Dow's owning 25% of all Dome's onshore wildcat lands. In 1979, Dow sold half of its participation in Dome to TCPL.

In 1974, the Dow-Dome and AGTL-AGE ethylene projects stood smack in one another's path. They were in competition at almost every level: for feedstocks, for government approvals, for customers. Premier Lougheed, who in 1971 had inherited a province generally acknowledged to be a petrochemicals backwater, was now having to grapple with a slight overfulfillment of his plans for change. The question was, did Alberta have room for two world scale ethylene plants? And the almost certain answer was no.

A good student of Canadian energy history should have been able to predict what was about to happen. The rule in Canada seems to be that when two capable business entities are vying for the same goal, they amalgamate and conquer. It had been true when C. D. Howe forced the marriage between Western Pipelines and TCPL; it had been true when the Alberta government suggested the joining of forces between Westcoast Transmission and Pacific Gas and Electric that became Alberta Natural Gas; it had been true of the oil and gas fields in Canada that had been unitized for the conservation and processing of natural gas. It was true again in 1974 when Alberta Gas Ethylene, Dome and Dow decided to seek a middle ground on which to amalgamate their projects.

The willingness to amalgamate stemmed in part from a problem AGTL and AGE were having lining up customers for the ethylene from their proposed plant. Dow and Dome were more solid in this regard because Dow was itself such a major market. That accounts for AGTL's interest in merger and Dow and Dome acquired an equally good reason when the NEB hearing that had granted them export approval for ethylene was challenged by AGTL and certain provincial governments in the Federal Court. The Court ruled that the hearings had been improper. At this point, Cliff Mort admits Dow and Dome were ready to give up. In that atmosphere, Jack Gallagher suggested that Don Wolcott visit AGTL and AGE in search of a project-saving compromise.

The amalgamated project resulting from this mission of conciliation had quite a new look. Dome's and Dow's ethane gathering system would be rerouted to supply new ethylene plants at Joffre, near Red Deer. Most of the Joffre ethylene would be upgraded within Alberta, but some would also be pipelined to Dow Chemical's Sarnia facilities. The Dow Chemical Co. in the U.S. also backstopped the project by agreeing to take Alberta ethylene at Midland, Michigan, though very little ethylene actually went to that destination. Because Dow represented such a considerable portion of the market, that company won the right to design the ethylene plants and to supervise their construction, start-up and the training of their staff.

Originally, Dupont and CIL were also to take some of the ethylene from Joffre, but they were reluctant to commit to the economics of the project. Finally, in June of 1975, Bill Richards for Dome and Cliff Mort for Dow met with the Alberta Government and said flatly that they could go no further without Alberta approval. Dome was prepared to sell its pipe and abandon its hard-won NEB approval for the Cochin line. What saved the project was that Dow offered to take all the ethylene from the first Joffre plant subject to certain conditions. That elicited the signing of a 1975 document by the Alberta Government approving the project for the first time.

The last hurdle was negotiating with the straddle plant owners to install turbo-expanders in order to supply the project with ethane. This was finally achieved and Pacific Empress, ANG Cochrane, and the Dome-Northwestern Utilities Edmonton gas plant all joined Dome Empress as ethane plants. The Dome-NUL Edmonton facility was tripled in size achieving an ethane recovery rate of 90%.

In its final form, after any number of drawing-board changes in size and passenger list, the Cochin Pipeline was a 1875 mile, 12", high vapour pressure line from Fort Saskatchewan (near Edmonton) to Sarnia, Ontario, passing through Detroit to Green Springs, Ohio. What the right-of-way purchase situation must have been like is hinted at by a Don Wolcott anecdote about Cochin. He was in the U.S. to have a look at the line and his guide was leading him on what seemed to be a wild goose chase through a tough, densely populated part of Detroit City. Getting a bit impatient, Wolcott finally asked "where in hell" the pipeline was. "You're standing on it," was the reply.

The technology of the pipeline was strictly frontier. The passengers for this single, "string-bean" pipeline were ethane, propane and ethylene and no one had ever tried to do that before. In fact, as John Beddome says, it may never be done again; not, he adds, because others could not do it but because the unique set of circumstances that led Dome to try it may never be duplicated. Engineers like Dr. Andy Younger, Bernie Hanna and Earl Forgues grappled with the theoretical basis of the line with help from Dr. Khalid Aziz of the University of Calgary. The ethylene which travels as a super-critical fluid, neither liquid nor gas, must always be cradled between batches of ethane; the ethane between batches of propane. Dr. Aziz assured the project team that it could work as long as the batches were large (300,000-500,000 barrels). That way contamination at the interfaces could be kept to a small percentage.

Operation of the Cochin Pipeline, done according to these theoretical parameters and constraints, worked nicely. The first 4000 barrels of direct interface between ethane and ethylene were diverted to underground storage at Windsor; the next 50,000 barrels were labelled grade two ethylene. The rest of the batch was pure. The line has a high degree of automation and is controlled completely from Dome's head offices in Toronto Dominion Square, Calgary.

The 1875 mile Cochin pipeline is controlled from this room in a Calgary office tower.

By the time Cochin Pipeline went into operation in the fall of 1979, one of its initial architects, Don Wolcott, was no longer an employee of Dome. Wolcott left Dome in 1976 in search of new frontiers. Not surprisingly, a number of companies went after him. He finally decided to go to work for one of his old Dome compatriots Maurice Strong, who was currently president of Petro-Canada, the new national oil company. When Don Wolcott left Dome, 80% of that company's very large revenues came from the marketing schemes and transportation systems he had instituted.

One of the general principles that the gas processing industry lives by, one which the Alberta Conservation Board has always based its planning on, is that the processing industry only extracts that which it has an incentive to extract. One of the keys to Don Wolcott's uniqueness in that industry is that he has tended to move first and then justify those moves through salesmanship. Had he not gone for ethane extraction and started the ball rolling on the Cochin Pipeline project, ethane extraction in Canada would almost certainly have been delayed. John Beddome believes that the ethylene industry in Alberta would have been delayed so long, had Dome not made its move into ethane when it did, that the recession of the '80's would have come first. If there had been no ethylene projects underway in 1982, ethylene in Alberta could have gone on the shelf forever.

Alberta's first ethane extraction and ethylene plants started a vigorous trend. Alberta Gas Ethylene built not one but two ethylene plants, the second coming on stream in 1984. The second plant was a technological improvement on the first and, with ethylene demand falling behind the production capacity of both plants, the second plant is supplying all the present requirements while the #1 plant remains on standby. The world recession also caught up with plans for a third ethylene plant and this will remain on the drawing board until conditions improve. No one will say that the timing of these ventures was fortuitous, but the ethylene plants *do* exist, and they *have* spawned a considerable number of new and expanded petrochemical ventures.

Dow Chemical of Canada led the parade of plant expansions in Alberta with the addition of ethylene oxide facilities at its Fort Saskatchewan plant. This had direct application back to the gas processing industry in that the ethylene oxide was used in turn to make glycols and amines used in processing plants. Dow also expanded into the manufacture of ethylene dichloride and vinyl chloride. This latter product was pipelined to another

Alberta Gas Ethylene #1 and #2 at Joffre, the centre from which the new, ethylene-based Alberta petrochemical industry will spread.

expanded plant, the Diamond Shamrock Alberta Gas Ltd. facility at Fort Saskatchewan. The vinyl chloride is used to make polyvinyl chloride.

Completely new plants have been spurred to life as well by Alberta ethylene. Shell Chemicals now makes ethyl benzene and styrene at Scotford near Fort Saskatchewan. Union Carbide manufactures glycol at Prentiss, Alberta. Novacor Chemicals Ltd., a NOVA* subsidiary, built a linear, low-density polyethylene plant at Joffre. Dow Chemical is also constructing a polyethylene plant at Fort Saskatchewan.

This amazing petrochemical expansion can all be traced by a circumlocutious path to the entrepreneurial ambitions of Dome Petroleum and Dow Chemical, to the desire of Bob Blair to turn AGTL (NOVA) into a multi-faceted and growing company, and to the determination of Peter Lougheed to see Alberta progress beyond the export of raw materials.

INSTRUMENTATION, CONTROL AND THE MAGIC OF TELEMETRY

On September 26, 1984, C. R. "Nip" Guest spoke to the Calgary section of the Instrument Society of America on the origins of that Society in Canada and the development of instrumentation and control in Western Canada. The talk soon turned to the subject of control and communication in the gas processing industry:

In my opinion, the reason for the slow growth of instrumentation as a discipline in southern Alberta was because the main instrument users here were gas plants and the gas production industry. Gas was really the only game in town, and gas, in turn, was part of the production side of the oil companies, where "real men" drilled for oil and gas and gas plants were just over-sized separators fit only for guys who ate quiche. However, the drilling and oil business had its ups and downs while gas production seemed on a growth curve that would never bend. Not only that, gas became a significant money earner.

As the gas processing industry became respectable, the purveyors of instruments for that industry flourished as well, as did the role of instrument man within the plants. One aspect of

*In September of 1980, AGTL's name was changed to NOVA, AN ALBERTA CORPORATION.

Nip Guest of Sparton Controls.

instrumentation that did nothing to enhance the cause of instrumentation in general, however, was the move into telemetry. When
interviewed for this book, Martin Bretz made special mention of
the telemetry system that connected the B.A. Pincher Creek plant
to its field way back in the 1950's. "Of course it didn't work," he
added. As Nip Guest informed the I.S.A., most of the early
telemetry systems did not:

*Telemetry, a fad of the '50's, found its way to the oil and gas
production fields. This new electronic marvel ran amuck as
production managers had visions of push-button field control
from a central location in the field, the plant or heavens
knows, even from head office in Calgary. No more driving
over rough, dusty roads in the summer and fighting snow
drifts in the winter to get to the wells. Costs would go down
and profits up. Electronics would do it all. Alas, the vision
exceeded technology and many projects went too far, too fast.
Electronics got a black eye, with production departments
and went into limbo. I remember Wally Scrimes, Imperial
Oil's telemetry guru, lamenting at an I.S.A. meeting that
most of the information they tried to send around the country
at the speed of light could be just as usefully transmitted by a
postcard. For a while there, it seemed that every time I made
a call at a gas plant, the instrument crew were out fixing the*

*telemetry system. To ask "How is your telemetry system
working?" became the worst possible way to open a sales call.*

For reasons like these, high speed electronics had to be proven
in a variety of other applications — pipelines, computers, calcula-
tors — before it was wholeheartedly accepted into the bosom of the
gas processing industry. But accept the electronic revolution the
industry eventually did; to such a degree in fact that control rooms
became what Guest calls "a sort of oasis in the midst of hazardous
surroundings; a clean, bright place to meet for coffee, a smoke and
fine tune the process." Operators became more and more able
through digital control devices to manipulate the minute details of
process and thereby maximize efficiency. Nip Guest explains that
instrumentation thus made the move from a convenience to an
economic necessity. Now, "operating efficiency is the principal
cost justification, followed by safety and reliability of operation."

GULF HANLAN-ROBB

In 1980, Gulf Canada began construction of its 300 million
cubic foot per day plant near Robb, Alberta. Partec Lavalin was the
contractor and the plant went on stream in March, 1983, just in
time to take part fully in the gas glut. At the time of writing, the
plant was running on about one-quarter of its maximum
throughput. Because of the gas glut Hanlan-Robb was born into,
it was the last large gas processing plant built in Canada — not the
last ever, we hope, but the last for a considerable length of time
almost certainly.

The first wells drilled in the area were completed in 1956.
The gas discovered in the area's Mountain Park pool was high in
CO_2 relative to H_2S which presented a problem for the sulphur
producing technology of the day. Consequently, the gas was left
shut in. Exploration continued and more gas was found straddling
the Nordegg-Edson forestry road. While stepping out from the
Erith field south of Edson, a new field called Hanlan was found and
this in conjunction with all the other finds was estimated to

contain enough gas to support a processing venture. The nineteen partners agreed on a plant site close to the railroad, also reasonably close to the village of Robb, on a hilltop which had already been cleared by a lumber company.

Around this time, yet another reservoir was discovered, a sour reservoir called Medicine Lodge. Graeme Tuttle, who was in on the design of the plant for Gulf, explains that the partners named the Hanlan-Robb plant for the pools at each end of the chain of gas accumulations. Had Medicine Lodge been found before the naming, the plant almost certainly would have been known to the world as Hanlan-Medicine Lodge.

It is interesting to look at the Hanlan-Robb plant after all that has been written in this book just to see where all the progress and innovation arrived at in the end. All the years of struggle with gathering lines to keep the flow into the plant unencumbered contributed to a system at Hanlan-Robb that is suitably complicated. The gas from each of the three areas gathered is so different that three totally different gathering systems are employed. Hanlan gas is sour and wet, so it is heated into a satellite where it is dehydrated and stripped of liquids before being sent to the main plant. Shaw and Mountain Park gas is heated into a compressor station then sent to the plant in a three-phase flow. Medicine Lodge gas, being sour and dry, is line-heated all the way from the wells into the plant. The lines are juggled to keep the H_2S level above the CO_2 level when the three streams combine. This is done to maintain a satisfactory sour gas feed stream to the sulphur plant.

But even a gathering scheme as gas sensitive as this one got into trouble when the old problem of imperfect gas analysis raised its hoary head. Hanlan gas was analyzed as having no liquefiable hydrocarbons which explains the choice of a dehydrated, single-phase flow into the plant. But the analysis missed the colourless hydrocarbon benzene and the operators have had to contend with a pressure drop in the Hanlan gathering line caused by benzene's condensation.

The Hanlan-Robb plant sweetens with DEA, and meets the water and hydrocarbon dew point specifications by refrigeration. Ammonia was chosen for the refrigerant, rather than propane, because the raw gas for the plant is so lacking in liquids. The plant

Gulf Hanlan-Robb.

would not make enough propane to cover its losses if it were propane chilled. Hanlan-Robb makes 200 barrels of condensate per day compared to, for example, the 7000 barrels a day that pour from Gulf's 1970 Strachan plant.

Hanlan-Robb also has the capacity to produce 1100 long tons of sulphur per day. It meets its sulphur recovery standard by supplementing the modified-Claus process with a Sulfreen tail gas cleanup unit. After its experience at Strachan, Gulf is expert in Polish prilling and proved it by installing a Polish prilling tower at Hanlan-Robb that was turning out specification prills thirty minutes after start-up.

Last of all, Hanlan-Robb is highly computerized. It has 212 control loops regulating plant processes, a system that provides a bewildering array of programming options to its staff. For those of us who are being dragged into the computer age with claws firmly gripped in the keys of a manual typewriter, it is heartening to hear from Graeme Tuttle that the space age system at Hanlan-Robb had a problem at the outset. It seems that the field computer and the plant computer could not speak to one another and it was necessary to resort to that antiquated intermediary, the human being, for translation. John Law and R. D. Siedlitz of Gulf have also pointed out that computer hardware deteriorates rapidly in the presence of low concentrations of H_2S and SO_2. Another victory for the Luddites!

1974-84: THE POLITICAL DECADE

In the eight or so years it took to get the Cochin Pipeline approved and built, it can be said that the complexion of the gas industry changed entirely. The oil price manipulations of the OPEC cartel produced a worldwide sense of energy shortage, of imminent crisis, no less in Canada than anywhere else. In 1975, there was talk of immediate shortages of gas, and speculation that the pipeline companies might not be able to fulfill their gas contracts. Even if they could meet Canada's immediate needs, there were almost certain shortages to be faced in the 1980's unless we could get at gas from the north. Estimates of northern Canadian gas reserves fluctuated wildly and companies like Alberta and Southern were aggressively buying trillions of cubic feet of Mackenzie Delta gas that had not been found yet (which may never be found). What's more, the NEB was reprimanding A & S for tying up so much of this imagined gas.

In a world clamouring for energy supplies, energy producing centres become powerful; they also become targets for anger, jealousy and criticism. After 1973, there was a definite shift in Canadian economic power from East to West. Central Canada resented it and the West probably gloated too much over it. One result was a steady spiraling of animosity between the centre of Canada and its parts, particularly between Ottawa and Alberta. It was politically popular in Alberta to make no accommodation with the feds. It was politically popular in the rest of the country to hardline the *greedy* Province of Alberta. In a democratic society, that is a formula for a fight with no end.

Probably the most interesting question is how Canada's energy complacency turned into fear of energy shortage in the narrow space of a few months. The public was inclined to blame the oil companies; surely someone had lied in order to get the right to export millions of barrels of oil and billions of cubic feet of gas from an energy short country. Given the immense regulatory presence in Canada, this was obviously ridiculous. Certainly oil and gas companies will always estimate reserves as high as they possibly can, but the Alberta Conservation Board and the NEB are in the business of showing such estimates to be true or false, of comparing domestic supply with future domestic demand.

The simpler truth was that bodies like the Conservation Board in Alberta had been warning for some time that Canada had reached the peak of its energy mountain and, barring some magnificent Arctic or offshore discoveries, was swiftly skidding down the other side.

But, whatever the causes of the problem, and whatever amplifications it underwent in the press, energy shortage was seen as one of Canada's most urgent dilemmas by 1975. Jolted into action by public anxiety, both the federal and provincial levels of government began rapidly moving in on the oil and gas industry. Every day for years the papers were full of battle reports from Ottawa and Alberta, describing the latest move in the struggle over who had the right to price and tax energy. For the industry itself, the writing at the bottom of the page was that oil and gas were in for more royalties, more taxation and more price control no matter which side won.

Effective January 1, 1975, the NEB raised the Canadian export price of gas to $1 per MCF. On August 1, 1975, the price jumped to $1.40; on November 1, 1975, to $1.60. In 1976, adjustments in the sharing of proceeds from the oil and gas industry raised the provincial share from 36.6% to 40.8%, while industry's piece shrank 6% to 48.8%. By 1977, industry's share was down to 41.3%. The counter-argument when industry complained was that the pie was getting much larger due to price increases and the profits were never higher and still going up. It was true to a point, but inevitably the volumes of export gas began to drop; first because the federal government wanted the gas to alleviate Canada's shortage, and later because the world shortages had eased and the Canadian price was becoming steadily less competitive in the U.S. The NEB criterion for export price was the substitution price of oil. However, as A & S president Harry Booth points out, gas often sold in places where the alternative wasn't oil. For a time, the higher Canadian prices could be folded into the U.S. pricing scheme, but eventually, the gas began to price itself out of the market. As Dome's Al Kiernan says, suddenly you "couldn't assume that you could sell all the gas you drilled."

As export volumes dropped, the so-called *gas bubble* began to swell. The massive plants built in the boom years had to struggle along on volumes of gas far below that for which they were designed. Exploration in the industry moved out of the foothills and onto the prairies where small, shallow, sweet gas accumulations had become economical to drill under the new pricing situation. The building of huge plants gave way to the building of what were really only compressor stations.

The other major change that government introduced into the gas industry in 1975 was Petro-Canada. Canada was one of the few energy producing countries in the world that did not have a state oil company. The Trudeau government chose the frantic days of 1975 to create one. The Petro-Canada Act was a popular move with the Canadian people and a very unpopular move with the oil and gas industry and most people in Alberta. The industry became even more hostile when Petrocan started sidling up to companies with an eye to taking them over. In 1976, Petrocan bought control of Atlantic Richfield Canada; in 1978, it set its sites on Husky Oil and would have bought it had Bob Blair at AGTL not been quicker on the draw. Then Bill Hopper, who had taken over from Maurice Strong as Petrocan president, went after Pacific Petroleums, buying control of the company from Phillips Petroleum of Bartlesville, Oklahoma, in 1978.

Hal Knapp was Atlantic Richfield Canada's production manager when that company was taken over by Petro-Canada. When he got the news, he immediately phoned over to an old friend who had been with Petro-Canada for a while to ask, "What's Petrocan all about? Will your old friends still talk to you on the street?" The friend said that he did get the cold shoulder on occasion, but that usually "they look upon you like a rich uncle."

The rich uncle's spending spree was not over with the acquisition of Pacific. In 1981, Petrocan bought out Petrofina for $1.5 billion, a price that ex-Fina president Trajan Nitescu thought so outrageous he took out a full page in the *Calgary Herald* to complain about it.

What this was all about, of course, was foreign control of the petroleum industry, an issue far from new in Canada. It had been an intermittent matter of concern for many years, particularly since a rash of foreign takeovers hit the industry in the late '50's and early '60's. Pacific Petroleums, one of the largest Canadian-owned oil and gas companies, was taken over by Phillips in the late '50's. In 1962, the largest Canadian-owned integrated oil company, Canadian Oil Companies Ltd. (and its marketing arm White Rose) were caught in a surprise takeover by Shell.

Government scrutiny of the situation showed that no industry in Canada was owned and controlled by non-residents to the extent that the petroleum industry was. Non-resident ownership in 1962 was 63% and non-resident control was 74%. Liberal finance minister Walter Gordon's budget of 1965 was the first government attempt to do something about it.

In 1967, Walter Gordon came to Calgary and faced an audience of 500. He was facing people who had watched Western Canada flourish in the post-war era largely on the basis of the foreign-owned industry he was so concerned about. He was facing people many individuals who owed their expertise and good livings to training by and careers with foreign-owned companies. In the face of this great potential for hostility, Gordon's Canadianization pitch was toned down. Canada would continue to require foreign investment for a long time, he said, and "any policies which would tend to slow down development are just too foolish to consider." At the same time something had to be done about 70% foreign control. Gordon got a good round of applause at the end, but *Oilweek* thought it was probably for the courage Gordon showed in coming to say his piece in "the capital of foreign capital", rather than for any love of what he had to say.

Not a great deal was done in those years to back up Walter Gordon's rhetoric, and it was not until the creation of Petrocan that the buying back of the industry began. It is interesting that Maurice Strong, who became the first president of Petrocan, had not been all that concerned about foreign ownership back in 1966. He believed at that time that too much emphasis was being placed on foreign investment, on the purchase of pieces of American subsidiaries. He pointed out that we could use every penny of Canada's available capital buying up just 25% of the American subsidiaries operating in Canada. A much wiser idea, he felt, would be to use that capital to develop major enterprises that were Canadian from the ground up.

But, in the late '70's, when Pierre Elliot Trudeau's government attacked the foreign ownership question, the method chosen was very definitely to buy back the petroleum industry with taxpayers' money. The instrument most often used for that buy-back was Petro-Canada and some of the takeovers were financed by a special tax at the pump.

The policy-makers of the 1960's were always careful to begin their pitch with a restatement of Canada's need for foreign investment on which to grow. Rather than snubbing foreign investment dollars, they sought to limit that investment and to channel it in such a way that it did not result in foreign control. The Liberal policy-makers of 1980 did not seem to agree. What they said with their policies was that foreign investment in the Canadian oil and gas industry must stop, and they went a long way toward achieving that goal with the National Energy Policy of 1980.

N, E and P have to be the three most hated letters in the Canadian oil and gas industry. The policy that wore those letters was the one at the heart of Alan MacEachen's fall budget of 1980. It swept a few billion off the top of oil and gas revenues; it cut industry's share of those revenues to a third; it took away industry-wide exploration incentives and replaced them with grants favouring Canadian-owned companies. The message was simple: the oil and gas industry must be Canadianized; the wealth of Canada must be spread across the country rather than just swelling purses in Alberta.

A government policy usually takes a while to make itself felt. Not so, the NEP. In the days that followed the budget, oil and gas stocks in Canada — and not just those of the foreign-owned subsidiaries — hit the skids. The crash nurtured a belief in the oil patch that the whole purpose of the exercise was to cheapen the subsidiaries so they would be easy pickings for Petrocan and the favoured Canadian companies. That may or may not have been the goal of the NEP, but it was to some extent the result. In 1981, as mentioned, Petro-Canada bought out Petrofina, and, the same year, Dome took over Hudson's Bay Oil and Gas. No one can really say, however, that either company went for a song.

The city of Calgary, administrative heart of the Canadian oil and gas business, mirrored the change in industry fortunes almost exactly. At the peak of the boom when oil and gas industry activity had been furious, the corresponding frenzy on the streets of Calgary could hardly be missed: traffic tie-ups; construction on every downtown block; cranes moving atop skeletal office towers. The whole city seemed too busy to take a breath. Then: the crash. As the Canadian rigs stopped drilling, the Calgary pile drivers stopped driving. As processing plant construction petered out, Calgary office tower construction ceased. The lack of gas passing through the mammoth gas plants of Alberta's foothills had its mirror image in the empty halls and offices of many Calgary office buildings completed just before boom turned to bust. The frantic activity of '70's Calgary was replaced in the '80's by a kind of worried somnolence. The competitive hiring had turned to systematic laying off, and the best people could do was adopt a kind of devil-may-care attitude: "Let's have fun for tomorrow we may get a pink slip."

Others were not so acceptant. To move in on Alberta's energy revenues to the extent it had, the federal Liberals had taken a few liberties with Alberta's control of its natural resources. Given that Premier Brownlee had solicited the King's signature on a document guaranteeing Alberta control of those resources back in 1930, many, including Alberta's Premier, believed the Province to be the victim of a resource grab that went against the rules of Confederation. Former Premier Ernest Manning, now a federal Senator, tried to warn Ottawa that Albertans were joining separatist parties "not in their hundreds, but in their thousands." While political historians mumbled darkly about the strong tradition of radicalism on the prairie, Prime Minister Trudeau poured measured quantities of salt into the wound with statements like: "I saved Quebec; someone else will have to save Alberta." But in the years of dull economic performance that followed, the Western mood that *Maclean's* called "mean and hawkish" in 1980 seemed to dull as well. Western separatist sentiment slipped out of sight again, back to that place where it can always be found if you care to look.

This discussion may seem to have wandered a long way from the subject of gas processing, but so pervasive was the effect of government on the industry in the last decade that it is nearly impossible to talk about gas *without* extensive reference to politics. It is a telling thing that most of the interviews done for this book stopped voluntarily somewhere in the early '70's, usually with a closing statement like: "That's when the government really got involved in our business." Another informant said of his thirty year career in gas processing: "It was a lot of fun — until the NEP."

At the time this book was written, the industry it celebrates was still doing battle with the *gas bubble*. That bubble was so large and apparently stable, it was beginning to seem poorly named. Perhaps a better name would be *gas knot*, stirring up visions of some permanent deformity like a knot in an old tree, or a steel granny tied tightly in the middle of a pipeline.

But then, even as the manuscript pages piled up, a change in regulation was announced allowing flexibility in the export price of gas; the federal government changed in landslide fashion and the words "foreign investment" were again being spoken, even in Ottawa. One by one, the heads of the incurable optimists began to emerge from their bunkers. When a couple of major export gas sales were executed in the fall of 1984, a bit of genuine excitement began to stir. Perhaps, just perhaps, the dark days of NEP were coming to an end.

Prairie sky above Amoco East Crossfield — sulphur in the block is sulphur kept out of the atmosphere

SAFETY AND THE ENVIRONMENT: STINK GAS, WHITE RATS AND BIRDHOUSES

11

Those working in the gas processing industry do not shrink from discussions of either safety or the environment. They are proud of their record in both. They claim that theirs is a safer than average industry and the contention is backed up by such keepers of statistics as the Workers' Compensation Board. They claim that their industry has been protective of air and landscape and again the numbers lend support. The Canadian industry has become internationalized. Its best people are vending their expertise world-wide. As they travel and breath the foreign air, as they watch the towering flares that scorch deserts in the Middle East, they come to have a higher regard for our environmental and conservation efforts. One well-travelled chemical supplier claims that Alberta, the centre of the gas processing industry in Canada, "has to have the cleanest air of any industrialized part of the continent."

Environmental and safety records are a bit like war records; they mean little in the absence of risk. You don't win medals in the officers' mess, and you don't win accolades for safety and environmental awareness if your industry is non-threatening and non-polluting to begin with. Canadian processing passes its test of valour in that it *could* be both tremendously dangerous and terribly polluting, but is not. Hydrogen sulphide, a significant factor in much Canadian gas, kills more efficiently than almost any other compound, much more quickly than carbon monoxide; and yet, the men and women who work every day in plants processing millions of cubic feet of high H_2S gas are seldom injured, rarely killed. Hydrogen sulphide emitted to the atmosphere could also gather in concentrations dangerous to the community, yet no member of the public has ever been seriously injured or killed by hydrogen sulphide from a Canadian processing plant.

Other sulphur compounds such as sulphur dioxide are more irritating than lethal, but in large quantities may have serious effects on soil. The *acid rain* that is killing lakes on the Canadian Shield and which threatens extensive damage to Eastern Canada and the Eastern U.S. is a result of sulphur compounds emitted by industry. Again, the sour gas processing industry in Western Canada has the potential to add to that problem, but thanks to strict government regulation and skilful compliance by industry, has not. Most of the pollutants are recovered at the source.

THE BAD GOOD OLD DAYS

Not surprisingly, the safety and pollution record of the gas processing industry gets steadily worse as you work backward through its history. In terms of pollution especially, the public perception of the problem several decades ago was almost opposite what it is today. One could say that the people of Turner Valley did not cry over spilled oil. The rotten-egg stench from the 3% H_2S gas was a fact of daily life in the Valley and was probably regarded as an inevitable consequence of industry; the price you paid for having a job.

Blowing a drip on the gas line between the Madison scrubbing plant and Canadian Western's metering station; 1945.

A similar attitude prevailed with regard to safety. The work was dangerous; that's why it paid well. Safety measures were looked upon as a bit sissy. This was most evident on the drilling floor. Old-timers who roughnecked in the early days usually have a repertoire of gruesome tales to tell. Frederick Wright was a young roughneck in Turner Valley and, in a Glenbow Archives recording of his memories, he told of surviving two drill rig explosions: one when a flare line backfired and tore a control head apart; the other when a spark ignited escaping gas. Both times, he was blown off the floor.

Wright told of reckless Oklahoma crews who flaunted their experience when they got to the Valley, but were not prepared for the reservoir rock or the high pressures in the Turner Valley gas cap. Their holes went crooked and one crew reefed so hard on a stuck bit that the cable snapped, the travelling block dropped and crushed a man through the floor.

On another occasion, at the Royalite #23 well, 125 quarts of nitro-glycerine were waiting in the doghouse to be poured down the well come morning. The nitro "got warm" in the night and blew, lifting the entire rig into the air and blasting the three ton kelly bar out of sight into the ground a hundred yards away. In the close-at-hand village of Turner Valley, not a window or plate was left unbroken. Fred Wright was asleep in town when the nitro went up and:

> It blew me right out of bed. I came right up on my feet, bouncing. I thought somebody hit me or something. I was ready to clean up on anybody that got in my road. If you're sound asleep in bed, and you're blown out of bed like that, it's quite a jar to your whole system.

In the gas processing industry, not as many of the anecdotes end with a tragedy. The plants were more stable places of employment and less hurried than the drilling rigs; the men attracted to plant work were probably a little quieter, a little less inclined to plunge into danger with a swashbuckling air. Evidence for this is the fact that both the B.A. Long-view plant and the Turner Valley Royalite plant had quite good safety records and safety programs during the 1940's. At B.A. Longview, an employees' association organized safety meetings once a month for discussion of dangers in the plant. One recurring topic was *gas eyes*, the eye irritation that develops from working long hours in low concentrations of H_2S. Bob Graves, plant superintendent at B.A. Longview, recalls using goggles with a bit of water in them to try and prevent the soreness. Other things talked about in these meetings were unprotected gauge glasses on sour gas vessels and the need for non-sparking tools for work in explosive atmospheres.

At the *north end*, in Royalite's plant, the operating staff held similar safety meetings. Imperial had safety programs in action at its refineries and the gas plant men adapted them to suit.

When asked if the companies were supportive of their safety efforts, the Turner Valley old-timers will usually say yes. In 1948, B.A. Longview celebrated a full year without a lost time accident and company management's way of showing appreciation was to give each man an extra day's pay. But still, safety cannot be said to have been company policy. The men were responsible for their own safety, their own safety meetings, their own safety programs; with the company kicking in some cash when needed to make a change. Safety meetings had to be at lunch hour or after shift; the company wasn't paying for them.

Although credit should be given to these early superintendents,

The crew at B.A. Longview, celebrating a full year without a lost time accident in 1948.

foremen and operators for having the wisdom to work toward making their plants safe, it must also be recognized that knowledge of the hazards was lacking in this era. Tommy Grisdale says that he was "out" from H_2S lots of times in his thirty-seven year career at Turner Valley Royalite, and that he and the other men didn't make too big a deal about it. The reason for this may have been the dangerous illusion mentioned by other informants that repeated exposure to H_2S would build up a resistance to the gas; that an experienced hand could not be knocked out as easily. Modern studies indicate the opposite; that the more you are exposed, the more sensitive to hydrogen sulphide you become.

Even if an operator was wary of H_2S, he might still run into trouble because of the poor safety equipment available at the time. The plant operator's technical defence against H_2S was the *gauger's mask*, a cannister-type mask with an activated carbon filter to absorb the H_2S. It was similar to those provided to the army during World War I against gas attack.

There were definite limits to how long such a mask was useful (in war or industry). When the carbon became saturated with hydrogen sulphide, the safeguard ceased, leaving the operator naked to the danger. Fifteen to twenty minutes in a 2% H_2S atmosphere were the gauger's mask's limits of effectiveness.

As for pollution beyond the gas plants, the rotten-egg smell of hydrogen sulphide was always present in Turner Valley. When the wind went to the southwest, Calgary would have a turn as well. Most of that stench originated from two stacks atop the Turner Valley Royalite scrubbing plant. A Seaboard process unit was installed in 1925 to remove H_2S

from gas destined for the mains of Canadian Western Natural Gas. A soda ash solution absorbed the H_2S and then gave it up again to a countercurrent of low pressure air. Two sixty horsepower blowers then mixed the acid gas with air and drove it up two ninety-eight foot stacks to atmosphere. Being heavier than air, the H_2S did not stay up there for long; it was soon back down where local and regional nostrils and eyes could attest to its presence.

One of the worst accidents recollected by early Turner Valley plant operators occurred when those electric blowers stopped. The building at the foot of the stack contained the switch for the blowers. On one occasion when the blowers went down, an operator entered the building to restart them and was knocked down by the gas settling down the stack into the enclosure. A second operator went in to save the first and he too was knocked out. Both men died.

It is possible that these men thought they were safe because they could not smell the rotten-egg odour. One of the things that makes H_2S so dangerous is that, even at low concentrations, it can paralyze the sense of smell.

Imperial veteran Bill Sage remembers the incident well. He says that it took those two deaths to make them move the switches outside where they should have been in the first place. Unfortunately, new safety designs and procedures often came as a result of tragic accidents.

SAFETY IN THE 1950's

As the Canadian gas processing industry moved out of Turner Valley in the 1950's, safety within the plants began to acquire a higher profile. The safety meeting went from being extra-curricular and unpaid to being a paid portion of a normal work month. The employer attitude toward safety was clearly changing.

Employees whose main job was safety also made their emergence during the decade. Imperial, the largest operator in Western Canada, had a considerable safety staff. Jim Pace began as an Imperial safety man in 1951 and Pace says that Archie Langelle was at work in safety before him. In safety for Imperial at the same time as Pace were Bill Moore, Dave Cuthbert, Bruce Beattie and Warren Shaw.

Pace had responsibility for safety at gas plants between 1951-59 and he travelled from plant to plant instructing and participating in safety meetings. He taught fire fighting, breathing apparatus training and the myriad other safety skills needed when working with poisonous, explosive, high pressure gases and large, powerful machinery.

Shell also hired safety specialists for its oilfield and gas plant operations in the 1950's. George Austin started in safety for Shell in 1951 after being the City of Calgary's safety man. Working for Austin during the '50's were Ralph Archibald, Mike Falby, Leo Nugent and Al Tone.

Although he started out in the industry as a roughneck, one could say that Ralph Archibald was born into the safety trade. He grew up in Turner Valley where his father was a welder and, during the Hungry Thirties, the Archibalds burned sour gas, *stink gas*, in their garbage can *and* their kitchen stove. If the flame went out, you ran outside immediately. Ralph's brother, Lew, used to claim the gas came into their house at such a pressure that the stove lids would flip in the air when their mother turned it on. It is fitting that Ralph Archibald would wind up spending much of his working life telling people about hydrogen sulphide and demonstrating ways to avoid its toxic effects.

Ralph Archibald (2nd from right) in his days as a roughneck. The shift truck is on its way to Imperial Leduc #2 (1947).

On March 27, 1958, Archibald gave a talk on hydrogen sulphide to the Calgary Branch of the Canadian Oilfield Technical Society and demonstrated a variety of safety devices. The equipment array included the old carbon-filter gauger's mask, but "Arch" was also able to show the audience several more sophisticated means of protecting themselves from hydrogen sulphide. The Chemox mask was another cannister-type mask, but it released oxygen rather than just filtering the air. The Scott Air Pack had a forty cubic foot, refillable air or oxygen bottle to be worn on the back, feeding a mask that completely covered the face (thus protecting the eyes as well as the lungs). A variation on this was a mask connected by a long hose to a large oxygen container. The ultimate in mobility was the *short snorter*, an air bottle worn on the belt, good for eighteen minutes use.

Archibald also demonstrated H_2S detectors, tubes containing strips of treated material that would darken or blacken depending on the concentration of H_2S encountered; and procedures, techniques and equipment for resuscitating people who had been knocked out.

All of this represented one swiftly developing side of the struggle for safety in the petroleum industry; for gas plants, the other side was to design a plant that minimized the potential for accidents. In the early years in Canada, design was more of an aggravation to safety problems because the designers were not taking adequate heed of the climate and the toxic nature of much Canadian gas. It has been mentioned that the original Jumping Pound plant was an open, California-style design, set down in the frequently frigid foothills of Alberta. When this open plant proved inoperable in the Alberta climate, housing was built over top. This created a new problem in that all the leaks and intentional vents on sour gas equipment were now trapped. Designs that were acceptable in the open air could be lethal inside buildings.

The next generation of plants, learning from Jumping Pound's early climate problems, were also largely enclosed. Terry Smith went from being superintendent at Jumping Pound to occupying the same position for Pacific at Taylor, another enclosed plant. In a talk he gave in Calgary in 1956, Smith made special mention of the fact that air in the enclosed plant, in addition to having to be heated, would have to be replaced at least every five minutes to avoid the sour gas hazard. By the early 1960's, plant designers had found ways of building plants that were more open and thus safer, which at the same time could operate at Canada's extremes of temperature.

The first stage of the B.A. Pincher Creek plant, completed at the end of 1956, was another plant which experienced problems because of the sour gas and the local weather. As at Jumping Pound, low-hazard locations were made high-hazard by enclosure, and by not providing sufficient air changes in the working area. Choosing to put a filter on the H_2S-rich side rather than the H_2S-lean side of the amine system proved fatal for one Pincher Creek operator. The man was killed by hydrogen sulphide while changing the filter. Again, it took a tragedy to alert the industry to danger: from that day forward, all plants put their amine filters on the lean side of the sweetening system, or took special precautions during filter changes.

But the greatest safety problem besetting Pincher Creek was the rapid failure of its equipment in the presence of high pressure, highly sour gas. Operator Murray Wright was fortunate not to be gassed the night a B.A. Pincher Creek valve on a 1500 pound sour line came off in his hand. It was one in a series of dangerous incidents from the same cause. Material failures had created the same kinds of hazards at other plants, but the greater pressure combined with the high H_2S content at Pincher Creek took a bad problem and made it intolerable.

A similar crisis beset Shell Waterton when it started up a few years later. A metal failure in a valve that had not been supplied to the ordered specification resulted in a dangerous spill of liquid H_2S. Valiant operators put on their masks and shut the area in. The smallest gap between mask and face would have meant a certain gassing; the tiniest spark from tool or boot would have sent the building into orbit.

The Canadian sub-committee T1B of the National Association of Corrosion Engineers did as much as anyone to ensure that operators would not have to be so heroic in future. When the committee succeeded in standardizing the specifications for equipment in sour service, and in finding suppliers willing to build to that specification, a very dangerous aspect of the industry was brought under control.

During the years that it took to standardize sour service materials and to learn to design safety into the new kinds of plants demanded for Canadian climate and gas, plants continued to be built and operated. The dangers had to be controlled through operating procedures and through the proper use of safety equipment. Martin Bretz, the first superintendent at Pincher Creek, responded to the dangers in his plant by strictly enforcing a system of safety practices he had learned in sulphur plants in the United States. There was little sour gas being processed in the U.S. then, and it was all at lower pressures and concentrations than that at Pincher Creek, but Bretz used his considerable experience to make a fast adaptation.

John Law, now supervisor of joint interest plants for Gulf, worked at Pincher Creek in its early years, and he says that you soon realized safety was an important matter when you entered Martin Bretz' plant. Bretz insisted that safety procedures be followed and was quite capable of chewing out anyone who did not comply. He would not abide "horsing around". Another engineer at B.A. Pincher Creek at that time, Elmer Berlie, credits Bretz with a great ability to perceive hazard. The safety situation at Pincher Creek was not good, Berlie admits, but "it would have been a helluva lot worse without Martin Bretz." Bretz trained so many people who went on to be leaders in Canada's gas processing industry, it can truthfully be said that he affected the safety values of the entire industry.

Texas Gulf's 1959 plant at Okotoks was a direct inheritor of those Martin Bretz safety values. The new plant was to process a stream of gas that contained 35% H_2S, the highest in Canada to date. Although safety men will tell you that 1% can kill as well as 35%, the high concentration of the deadly Okotoks gas made the owners and operator extra cautious in their approach. To start with, some very able people were brought in to supervise. James Estep, manager of the gas division, had extensive experience at the company's Worland, Wyoming plant, the largest sulphur plant in the world when it was built in 1949. He and Fred Ronicker, the plant manager at Okotoks, had the reputation of having an enlightened management attitude towards safety.

Texas Gulf also lured three experienced sour gas men away from B.A. Pincher Creek for its Okotoks operation. Elmer Berlie was named assistant plant manager (assistant to Ronicker), and Les Whitley and Murray Wright were brought over as shift foremen.

When talking to Wright, there is no mistaking a certain bitterness in

Texas Gulf Okotoks showing the Canadian flag.

him on the subject of safety. He remembers all too clearly the fatalities he witnessed in his career, the stupid deaths that could have been avoided. In his own youth, he took too many chances. Like so many survivors, he can look back at a time when he would have probably died except for the random fact that he fell out of a building after being gassed instead of back into it. That kind of experience and anger makes a good safety man.

At Pincher Creek, Elmer Berlie had been working with Bruce Holbrook, B.A.'s director of safety, his assistant Reg Havard and Harvey

Elmer Berlie testing a safety mask at Okotoks.

Whitworth of Canwest Safety Services Supplies Ltd. on a comprehensive breathing air system. The idea was Whitworth's and it consisted of a lightweight breathing apparatus that could be attached by umbilical hose to a purified airline system running throughout the plant. The breathing apparatus itself was fitted with quick-connect fittings that would allow it to be hooked to a forty cubic foot air tank or a small oxygen bottle worn on the belt. The latter was for escape purposes only, should the plant airline or the umbilical hose be somehow blocked or severed. Glen Smilg of Globe Safety Products in Dayton, Ohio, developed and assembled the apparatus from Whitworth's idea.

Elmer Berlie put in an application for expenditure to install Whitworth's integrated safety system at B.A. Pincher Creek, but at the time of his move to Okotoks, the AFE had not been approved. Berlie's explanation for this reluctance is that the proposed system did not meet U.S. Bureau of Mines standards. The U.S. Bureau of Mines standard was the bible on these matters and management took much convincing that the Canadian sour gas situation was sufficiently different to merit deviation from that standard.

Texas Gulf, with its 35% H_2S gas stream, was more willing to act. Harvey Whitworth says that it took five minutes for Jim Estep to buy the system. He is fairly sure about that timing because that was how long Estep gave him to demonstrate it. When Whitworth was finished, Estep called it the most comprehensive system he had ever seen. Estep bought it; George Milne approved it on behalf of the Workers' Compensation Board; and Elmer Berlie and Harvey Whitworth worked together on getting it into the plant. Later, B.A. also approved the Berlie AFE for Pincher Creek and Canwest had another breathing air system contract.

Although Okotoks did not have anyone who was dedicated solely to safety, the plant did make use of a shift foreman, the *swing man*, as a part-time plant safety man. The swing foreman always had a couple of days a week that were unassigned; at Okotoks, this foreman was given the responsibility of checking and maintaining all safety equipment during this unassigned period. Bill Montgomery, the original safety man at Okotoks, retired on June 30, 1984.

Nothing speaks more loudly about the safety devices and programs at Okotoks than the plant's safety record. One of the original shift foremen at the plant, Don Davies, can remember only one man ever being overcome by H_2S at Okotoks. First aid was another feature pushed by plant management and Davies remembers that the men at Okotoks were learning Cardio-Pulmonary Resuscitation and mouth-to-mouth over twenty years ago. At one time everyone in the plant had a St. John Ambulance first-aid certifi-

The safety-minded team at Texas Gulf Okotoks included plant manager Fred Ronicker.

cate. Okotoks was also the first plant to adopt an emergency contingency plan for its gathering system and plant vicinities.

A first-class steam certificate brought Karl Balzun to Okotoks and he is another graduate of that plant who speaks highly of its safety program. Trying to determine what made safety work so well at Okotoks, Balzun points to the positive attitude displayed by management. Jim Estep, Fred Ronicker and Elmer Berlie were always behind safety initiatives and, rather than imposing safety on the men, they invited them to help evolve a better system. When a good suggestion was made at a safety meeting, it was acted upon. Minutes of the safety meetings were posted on bulletin boards and a copy was sent out to the Worker's Compensation Board. The old hostility toward the *sissy* science of safety was pushed aside by a sense of pride in the good safety record the plant enjoyed in spite of the lethal gas that travelled in its veins.

THE HOME CARSTAIRS FLAGPOLE

Fred Brooks has a healthy respect for hydrogen sulphide and for safety regulations that protect men from it. In his days with Home Oil at its Carstairs plant, he says the men were regimented like soldiers. One of the safety devices was a common flagpole. It was Fred's rule that the first thing you did when you came on shift was to look at that flag and note which way the wind was blowing. Later when he supervised the start-up of the Thiopet Chemicals Ltd. plant in Fort Saskatchewan, he kept a canary in his office. It was a good idea in a plant that produced pure H_2S.

Engineer and film-maker, Fred Brooks.

TRAINING FOR SAFETY

An aspect of gas plant operation that is hazardous and cannot always be conquered by equipment, procedures and design is simple lack of training. Even in the fledgling years of the Canadian industry when few plants existed, experienced operators could not be found in sufficient number to go around. In later years, when the industry grew on the coattails of the major pipelines, the situation got much worse.

Shell's plant at Jumping Pound eventually supplied men to plants all over Western Canada, but when it started in 1951, superintendent Terry Smith was surrounded by troops most of whom had never logged a single hour in a gas plant. He had a few ex-roughnecks, some local farm boys, and in 1952, he received a group of green engineers from Canadian universities, the great white hopes in Shell's Canadianization scheme.

At Gulf's (then B.A.'s) Stettler Area Conservation Project, the situation was similar: a few veterans from the U.S., backing up a number of fresh-faced Canadian engineers and a troop of would-be operators. On December 31, 1956, when Martin Bretz arrived at B.A. Pincher Creek, the start-up day for stage one of that plant, he must have been a bit discomfited to learn the average experience of his men. No one but himself had ever been in a sulphur plant, and only Murray Wright had ever worked with H_2S. Again, it is a credit to Bretz' tenacious insistence on procedure that the plant did not suffer more casualties than it did.

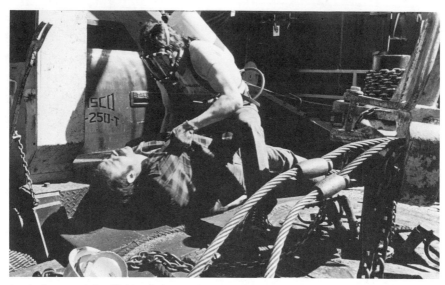

A trained operator is less likely to find himself in the situation depicted in this Esso rescue exercise.

The training problem in gas plants, though bad, was still over-shadowed by the magnitude of the problem in the field. Things were moving fast as explorers climbed over one another to delineate the new-found Devonian reefs and boys were being hired, mostly off local farms, at a rapid clip. They were also being promoted too quickly and hurt too often. It's a standard saying that farm boys make the best roughnecks because they know machinery and they are willing to work, but when Tuesday's rough-neck became Saturday's driller, the farm boys had accidents just like everyone else.

This poor safety record on the rigs in the years after Leduc led the Canadian Association of Oilwell Drilling Contractors (CAODC) to create in 1949 an autonomous, educational establishment to train personnel for the field. The school was called the Petroleum Industry Training Service (PITS). The Alberta Government's Donald Cameron (the creator of the Banff School of Fine Arts and a future senator) was quick to see both the need for and the potential of this service. Cameron brought PITS under the auspices of the University of Alberta's Department of Extension. The Workers' Compensation Board and the Canadian Petroleum Association also took an interest and PITS was eventually funded by industry with matching contributions from the Alberta government.

In the early years of PITS, the Petroleum Extension Service of the University of Texas was asked for its help and it sent John Woodruff to advise PITS. A University of Texas instructor lectured the first course PITS ever offered. By 1957, PITS was serving 1000 students and had three full-time instructors.

In the mid-50's, PITS offered a few short courses of interest to gas processors but its main thrust remained training for the field. But then, with the first major gas pipelines nearing approval and a consequent surge of plant construction expected, *Oilweek* wrote an editorial stating that it was high time PITS got moving and offered a course in gas plant operation. Walter Gabert, a native of Bruderheim, Alberta, who had recently taken over supervision of PITS, went to Dr. George Govier, a member of the PITS advisory board, with a proposal for such a course. Gabert still remembers how inexperienced he felt and how inadequately briefed as he faced the pinpoint questioning of Dr. Govier. Nonetheless, the conversation led to the Gas Operator's Correspondence Course with a Texas A and M manual serving as a course textbook.

Soon, Walter Gabert had students "pouring out his ears". He desperately needed help in marking and one of those he hit up was the indefatigable Elmer Berlie. In amongst his many other duties and initiatives, Berlie found time to "thoroughly" mark lessons for students of Gabert's correspondence course.

Gabert and Berlie, who had known each other earlier in the '50's when Gabert had been an oilfield worker and Berlie had been with the Conservation Board, joined forces again to discuss the operator's course with the Boilers Branch of the Department of Labour. The Boilers Branch was responsible for the certification of steam engineers to be hired wherever steam boilers were operated. At gas plants this occasionally created a split among personnel. In the utility building, a certain class of steam engineer was required on shift depending on the size and pressure of boilers involved; in the control room of the gas plant, another highly qualified individual was required to supervise the operations staff. These two heirarchies were physically separate and often hostile toward one another. According to Dr. Andy Younger, the operations staff and the steam engineers at Taylor were barely on speaking terms.

Toward the end of the 1950's, plant administrators like Elmer Berlie and Andy Younger became convinced that this system no longer made sense. In the large new plants, the most experienced, most highly qualified individuals were often the steam engineers, but the utility plant they ran tended to be one of the safer areas in the plant. Meanwhile, uncertified operators were often at work on much more powerful compressors and steam turbines, dealing with higher pressures and temperatures elsewhere in the plant. What Berlie and Walter Gabert tried to convince the Boilers Branch of was that steam engineers should become gas plant operators and some gas plant operators should become steam engineers; that such an arrangement would be more practical and more satisfying for the individuals involved.

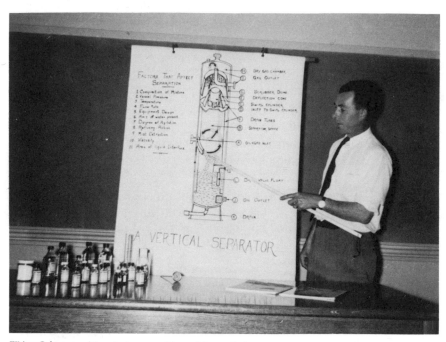

Walter Gabert, teaching the inner workings of the vertical separator.

This and other representations from industry to the government eventually resulted in a system by which the plants could qualify their own certified engineers based on what Elmer Berlie called "a careful evaluation of their responsibilities and the experience of each man in various process units." In other words, the men got credit for the time they had worked on plant equipment toward their steam certification.

The Boilers Branch agreed and over a three year period Berlie's Okotoks plant was able to fill eight vacancies for certified stationary engineers by promoting personnel from within. In all, Texas-Gulf Okotoks had qualified one first-class, three second-class, thirteen third-class, and eleven fourth-class steam engineers over that three year period.

In a paper delivered to the Annual Convention of the Institute of Power Engineers, Elmer Berlie sang the praises of the program. At Okotoks, they were now hiring young men with a minimum of grade eleven and letting them know from the start that their promotion would depend on their studying to obtain steam engineering certificates. In this kind of system, said Berlie, employees have an incentive to improve their understanding of the work they do. It was a fair program through which everyone could improve himself according to his ability. As one informant put it, if you wanted off shift work, the best way was to study for a higher certificate.

The advantage not listed, but implied, was that plants would also become safer places as more and more of the employees came to understand their work and the procedures governing their work. It also did away with the old one-upmanship between control rooms which could not have been a great contributor to plant safety in the past. The marriage between plant operation and steam engineering certification has become the norm in the Canadian processing industry.

The day when experienced operators could not be found on this side of the 49th parallel is long behind us. Canada is fast becoming a net exporter of plant operations expertise.

TRY NOT TO KILL ANY WHITE RATS

Safety men and those in charge of training personnel for the sour gas industry needed a good way to shock people into believing in the lethal powers of hydrogen sulphide. In the mid-50's, a means was found in the so-called *white rat demonstration*. The idea for it is believed to have come to Canada from Texas, probably brought by Shell's George Austin who had seen it done by the U.S. Bureau of Mines demonstration team, Kintz and Brown. In any case, it was pioneered by Shell in Canada, then shared with both the Petroleum Industry Training Service and the Workers' Compensation Board.

Live rats were taken from the University of Alberta and knocked out with hydrogen sulphide before a paying audience. That alone was pretty impressive, but the demonstration did not stop there. Next, the rat was resuscitated with oxygen. Walter Gabert of PITS says that they used to arrive in a town and slap up posters wherever they could. They charged $5 a head and never had any trouble packing a hall. Two days after joining PITS, Gabert had to fill in for someone on a white rat demonstration in Fort St. John. He had never done one before and had only seen it done twice. Gabert gave the rat "such a snootful" it died — or so he thought until he arrived in Edmonton and found that the deceased had been miraculously revived, literally jiggled back to life by the long journey on the rough road. Another white rat, given away to a Rimbey resident as a pet by a travelling safety man, got away and triggered a provincial rat scare.

In the end, the person to give the most white rat demonstrations in Canada was probably the late George Milne. As the Workers' Compensation Board's oilfield safety specialist, Milne knocked out and revived rats all over the province. Many of the early safety specialists asked that George Milne be mentioned in this text. Jim Pace who worked in safety for Imperial in the old days and now works for Amoco, calls George Milne "the best safety evangelist in the industry."

THREE MINUTES TO LIVE

Ralph Archibald was chairman of the CGPA's safety committee for so long one person called the position "semi-permanent". He was also chairman of the Petrochemical Safety Council for many years and, under that hat, he began to pursue the Workers' Compensation Board for money to make a film about hydrogen sulphide. The Board was a bit slow to budge and finally Archibald took his case to Alberta Premier Peter Lougheed. He had recently met the Premier during a tour of gas plants and, in his letter, Archibald reminded Peter Lougheed of a statement he had made about cleaning up the Alberta industry. Couldn't the Province start by putting money into a good safety film about one of its biggest industrial menaces? Archibald had a letter back in seven days and, not long after, support for the project from the Workers' Compensation was forthcoming.

Ralph Archibald chaired a committee charged with making the film, and was assisted on that committee by Jim Pace, Walter Gabert, Elmer Berlie, Clayton Edgelow, and Ron Davies of the Compensation Board. (Archibald also credits Chris Christianson of Standard Safety of Edmonton with helping him.) The resulting thirty-minute, colour film, *Three Minutes to Live*, was made by the Edmonton film company Film West, with Albertan Dale Phillips producing. It was done in the early '70's and the film committee at first looked askance at the long-haired troop of film makers. They were soon to learn, though, that chaps in long hair and beards, while not tolerable for safety reasons in a gas plant, could be very handy types behind a camera. *Three Minutes to Live*, says Archibald, "was a winner from the beginning." The film premiered in 1974 and has been shown all over the world. It gave rise to a set of five more training films by Film West, all done with the assistance of the Workers' Compensation Board.

Ralph Archibald with a print of Three Minutes To Live *in hand.*

GAS PROCESSING AND THE ENVIRONMENT

Throughout the twenty-five year life of the Canadian Gas Processors Association, the story of gas processing and the environment has been a tale of ever more stringent emission regulations. The Alberta Conservation Board was once again the engine of change, setting the toughest standards for the industry that it felt were economically feasible. The Board had no formal responsibility for air pollution through much of this time, but saw it as a natural adjunct to its conservation mandate. If natural gas by-products, particularly sulphur, were conserved at the plants, they were not going into the environment as pollution.

To start with, little worrying went on about pollution, probably because the plants were small, few in number, and the gas processed was not high in H_2S. Until 1952, all the hydrogen sulphide recovered by Canadian plants was blown to atmosphere. In '52, the Shell plant at Jumping Pound and the Madison Gas Plant at Turner Valley added sulphur units to their operations. Shell Jumping Pound was the environmental Cadillac of its day having not one but two stages of catalytic conversion.

Serious concern about pollution did not begin until the first large sour gas plants were built to serve the TCPL and Westcoast pipeline systems. The first air quality monitoring program was undertaken by B.A. at its Pincher Creek plant in 1957. The monitoring system consisted of forty-four candle stations, called *bird houses* for the louvred boxes that contained the sulphation testing devices. Each bird house contained two jars with bands of filter paper tied round them. One of the bands was impregnated with lead acetate which reacted with H_2S in the air; the other with lead peroxide which reacted with SO_2. Lab tests run on the papers at month's end could determine the average quantity of these compounds they had been exposed to over the period.

The problem with this kind of system is that the danger from pollution, especially H_2S pollution, is not a month-long average phenomenon. What a person is most worried about is any short-term, high concentration. Exposure to such a concentration could kill you without being noticed on the candle station filter paper if the rest of the month was clean. At B.A.'s Nevis plant, the company introduced another pollution measuring device, the Thomas Autometer which gave nearly instantaneous readings. This piece of equipment had been developed to monitor pollution at Cominco's smelter in Trail, British Columbia. It was moved to Pincher Creek from Nevis in 1959. Again, the system was not ideal. In Elmer Berlie's "History of Environmental Control for the Petroleum Industry in Alberta", he describes the Autometer as having been "subject to interferences". Its "plumbing and size made it too cumbersome for the field." Berlie worked with Gerry Gainer of B.A.'s Calgary production lab, and with consultant Dr. Morris Katz, on these air quality monitoring programs at Pincher Creek.

The Alberta Department of Health also mobilized for air pollution monitoring at Pincher Creek. It decided that the kinds of sulphur stacks that had been used round the province to vent low volumes of hydrogen sulphide and sulphur dioxide would not be sufficient for the volume of emissions produced by the larger plants like B.A. Pincher Creek. For the

The bird house *was the first of the sulphation testing devices.*

first stage of B.A. Pincher Creek, a ninety-five foot stack had been approved, and the first incinerator for converting tail gas sulphur to sulphur dioxide had been called for. But for the second stage, which was to triple plant capacity, the Department demanded a 350 foot stack. The height was arrived at after surveying ground level concentrations in 1957. In 1959, the Department of Health sent out its first pollution monitoring trailer to Pincher Creek. It contained devices for measuring both hydrogen sulphide and sulphur dioxide.

One might ask, why all the sudden fuss about pollution at Pincher Creek? The reasons were, first, that the plant was so sour, so high pressure, so large, and in such a relatively well populated area (relative to, say, Whitecourt) that it represented a greater potential hazard than plants which had preceded it. Second, the local populace was beginning to complain. In the first months of operation at Pincher Creek, Stage One, with metallurgical failure and plant upset the rule, complaints from local farmers began to roll in. The lead-based paint on their buildings was turning rainbow colour; their barbed wire was corroding; and when 180 million cubic feet of gas and products went up the emergency flare stack, especially in winter with snow on the ground and a low cloud ceiling overhead, the roar and the blanket of illumination for miles around gave rise to simple, honest-to-goodness fear. Martin Bretz had a policy that all pollution complaints must be answered within a half-hour but, nonetheless, people were growing angry with their new industrial neighbour. Unfortunately, the two sides in this dispute began to polarize, with government busily running tests in the middle.

The testing done by B.A. and by government seemed generally to confirm the operator's contention that pollution was within accepted limits, but the local farmers were suspicious. The company itself was not entirely confident in the accuracy and sensitivity of the devices being used to monitor the air. When the Shell Waterton plant was built in the same area, straight west of B.A. Pincher Creek at the foot of the mountains, farmer complaint translated into an air pollution law suit launched by several farming families against both Shell and B.A. Eventually, the families settled out of court for a total of $750,000.

To understand why this organized protest occurred at this time and place, and not in, say, Turner Valley which everyone *agreed* was polluted, it is probably necessary to study the differences between Pincher Creek and Turner Valley, and between the pre-war decades and 1960. Turner Valley had been like a big, shifting company town. Those who made their dollar off the oil and gas industry outnumbered those who lived by other means. That produced a natural sympathy for the industry, or at least a desire not to antagonize the industry with complaints. Among the farmers south of Pincher Creek, that sympathy or deference did not exist. The farmers saw themselves as having little to gain from the presence of the industry, and perhaps something to lose. There had been no big industry in this part of the country before and people did not like the idea of companies moving in and changing the established pattern of life in any way. Some might argue that royalties and taxes going from the industry into government coffers returned to the farmers in the form of fuel subsidies, farm price support or low interest loans, but even if that were true, it was too circuitous a route to be strongly in the minds of those living downwind of the plants.

Timing was the other factor. As mentioned earlier, the heyday of Turner Valley was not a time when the public concerned itself overly about pollution. That awareness became popular in the 1960's. Concern for what industrial effluents *might* be doing to us grew rapidly in the '60's and '70's, and sour gas processing was one of the most visible industries swept by that tide.

In 1960, with the export contracts to TCPL and A & S promising to bring several large sour gas plants into production, the Alberta Department of Health created an Air Pollution Branch. Serge Dobko was hired by the Department, the first engineer hired to work specifically on air quality control. In 1961, new regulations for the control of air pollution were passed in Alberta, effective immediately for new plants and within five years for existing plants. (The period of compliance was eventually extended two years.)

In an address to the CNGPA in 1961, Jack Stabback of the Conservation Board outlined what was expected of gas processors. The Board's ongoing contention was that plants must recover as high a percentage of sulphur as was economically feasible, and that all sulphur not recovered must be incinerated to sulphur dioxide before being discharged up a stack. They must construct their stacks in such a way that ground level concentration did not exceed 0.2 to 0.3 parts per million sulphur dioxide over a thirty minute period. Sampling ports must be provided in the stacks for testing of effluent temperature and composition. Air monitoring programs must be instituted satisfactory to the Department of Health. These regulations set in motion a series of improvements in the sulphur recovery process and in plant operation which are discussed in detail in Chapter Nine.

Meeting the new regulations was seldom a simple matter. One of the more difficult problems involved the installation of stack sampling ports. Elmer Berlie writes:

> Most of (the stacks) were not equipped with ports for conducting the stack survey, or with walkarounds from which to do the work. Some stacks didn't even have ladders. One 350 foot stack had rungs every ten feet, the idea being that you leap-frogged two, ten foot ladders as you climbed, and there was no safety cage!

It was while drilling these sampling ports that many operators found that their stacks were seriously corroded, a fact which led to a number of stacks having to be chopped down and replaced. Another interesting aspect of the stack surveys mentioned by Elmer Berlie is that companies could not as a rule convince their employees to climb the monstrous sulphur stacks. (Given the height and the strength of winds in southern Alberta that probably attests to their general intelligence.) Western Research and Development, Joe Lukacs' company, was the first firm to do environmental control consulting in Canada, but Elmer Berlie notes that the company really got its start in 1966 because it had "personnel who were technically qualified and willing to climb stacks." Lukacs' company eventually developed a continuous stack monitoring program that made the job less death-defying. The first field tests on continuous monitoring of emissions from sulphur stacks were conducted at HBOG's Edson and Kaybob plants and at Shell Waterton in 1969-70.

Air pollution is of course not the only kind, and the Department of Health recognized that fact by creating another branch devoted to water pollution in 1967. A series of settling ponds became a feature of all plants and a popular way of proving successful cleanup was to put brook trout in the last pond. When Martin Bretz came to B.A. Pincher Creek in late 1956, he was surprised to find that there had been no provision for water effluent control. He went quickly to work building dykes and ponds. He had so much confidence in his work that he used to drink out of "that last pond below Cyril Bonertz' house." One of his employees from those days confirms this and adds that, after Bretz had taken his daily mouthful, he would invariable exclaim, "Gosh, that's good water!"

THERE'S A STINK IN MY OVEN

Martin Bretz made it a rule at B.A. Pincher Creek that all pollution complaints be answered within a half hour. He answered many of those calls himself, but Bretz never enjoyed doing it — except once. One afternoon, he received a call from Glen McLaughlin, an elderly farmer whose farmhouse was a mile due

Glen McLaughlin.

Martin Bretz.

east of the plant. "I've got a stink in my oven," McLaughlin said, "and it's because of your plant." Never long on patience, Martin Bretz said that was ridiculous and impossible. Did the rest of his house stink? "Nope," said Glen. "Just the oven."

Getting in a fouler mood by the second, Bretz jumped in a vehicle and drove. When he arrived at McLaughlin's, Glen led him into the kitchen and opened the oven door. The smell of fresh baked bread wafted sweetly out. "There," said Glen. "That's the stink in my oven. Now sit down and eat, I want to talk to you."

What it was all about was that Glen had found out that Martin Bretz was from Wyoming, from a town not far from Glen's own home. Glen just wanted to reminisce. For the next couple of hours, Bretz and McLaughlin ate fresh bread, hand-churned butter and home-made preserves, and traded stories of home. "That was the only pollution call I ever enjoyed," says Bretz.

A PERCEPTION OF ENVIRONMENTAL FAILURE

In its last days, Alberta's Social Credit Government created a Department of the Environment, operating under the authority of two new Acts, the Clean Air Act and the Clean Water Act. Then, in the fall of 1971, the Conservatives under Peter Lougheed swept to power and Bill Yurko was appointed to the environment portfolio. The first speeches by Premier Lougheed and Minister Yurko left little doubt that, as they put it, "a new era of environmental awareness" was at hand. Bill Yurko told the CNGPA that Alberta's government would no longer "play what had traditionally been a passive role" in environmental matters. That must have sent shivers down the spines of many who felt Alberta regulations were already too strict.

At Bill Yurko's request, the Conservation Board carried out a series of public hearings into the effects of gas plant operations; a report was filed in October, 1972. The report found that, in the year ending June 30, 1982, Alberta's sixty-four sour gas plants had together emitted an average of 1300 long tons of sulphur dioxide per day, at an average recovery efficiency of 95.3%. Environmental problems noted included the venting of H_2S, the *dusting* problem from sulphur handling, waste process water, waste chemicals and smoke. Seven hundred and seventy bird houses were in operation in the province measuring total sulphation, and three hundred and ten monitors were measuring dustfall. In summation on gas processing plants, the report said that the pollution control realized by the industy under the watchful eye of the Conservation Board was generally good. But, by the time the report was filed, an Information Letter from the Board had circulated indicating that, while good, the sulphur recovery efficiency of Alberta plants would have to get better. The letter detailed a new regime of efficiency standards in the high nineties, effective for all plants by January 1, 1975.

As related in Chapter Nine, the industry howled in protest, then set about meeting the new standards by improving the efficiency of their sulphur plants, by adding more stages of catalytic conversion, and by adding tail gas cleanup systems. In the years following 1971, the industry seemed to realize that the determination of government to improve environmental conditions was in tune with the desires of society — or, if there was any discord, that the society would have the government apply even tighter constraints. Accepting its fate, the oil and gas industry began working with government on ways to economically accomplish the new governmental goals. Examples of this cooperation are the creation of APIGEC (the Alberta Petroleum Industry/Government Environmental

Committee) and the multi-company Whitecourt Environmental Study Group.

Rather than continue to detail blow-by-blow the fine-tuning of environmental legislation in the 1970's, it might be more interesting to chart the changes in a single sour gas plant in the last two decades. Shell Waterton makes a good subject for such a look because it was a focus for community concern about pollution and because it went beyond regulations in an attempt to reduce its emissions and to prove that it had successfully done so.

Shell Waterton opened in 1962, not long after the Alberta Air Pollution Branch had set out new regulations. It was built as a three-stage Claus plant with a 375 foot stack and a 95% sulphur recovery efficiency. Its output was to be 1200 long tons of elemental sulphur a day. In 1967, that output was boosted to 1800 long tons a day, and LPG facilities were installed. Sulphur recovery jumped a percentage point to 96%. Then, in 1970-71, a completely new plant was built on the same site. This plant went to four stages of catalytic conversion in the sulphur plant and produced 1200 long tons of sulphur a day, bringing the grand total to 3000. The old 375 foot stack was replaced by one 500 feet high. (Recovery of sulphur stayed at 96%.)

No sooner was the second Shell Waterton plant built than Alberta's next set of recovery standards was announced. The new plant and the old one were suddenly not efficient enough. The goal the Conservation Board set for Shell was 98.7% sulphur recovery and, to meet it, Shell Waterton added a SCOT tail gas cleanup system in 1975. The Shell Offgas Treating system was so efficient it allowed the plant to reach 99% recovery, with a theoretical efficiency as high as 99.9%. The bill was $15 million.

Shell Waterton was one of the first plants to have a continuous stack monitor installed. It assisted Western Research and Development in coming up with the system. It also installed a sophisticated monitoring system beyond the plant. Five mobile trailers continuously checked ground level concentration of sulphur compounds and telemetered those readings to the control room. (Petrogas Calgary at Balzac was actually the first Canadian plant to install such a system.) The readings from the Waterton mobile trailers were fed to a computer which varied the throughput of the plant accordingly. Any excess of pollutants was checked immediately at the source. Besides the trailers, the Waterton monitoring system included forty-two regularly inspected bird houses. Studies were also done on the way the wave pattern of the strong Chinook westerlies drove the stack plume to ground.

In 1974, Shell Waterton added charcoal adsorption, bacterial treat-

One of five mobile pollution monitoring trailers at Shell Waterton.

ment and sludge incineration to its water treating facilities at a cost of $2 million. All water was treated before discharge to the Drywood River.

In response to the usual dusting problem downwind of the sulphur block, Shell Waterton switched to slating of the sulphur in 1974, and later to the formation of Polish Prills.

Shell Waterton seemed determined to be a model plant. While it undertook all these environmental initiatives, it was also setting an enviable safety record. During the '70's it won a Petrochemical Safety Council plaque and the CGPA's large plant safety award; it also became the first

The crew at Shell Waterton celebrate one million man-hours without a lost time accident in 1977.

petrochemical plant in Canada in almost ten years to work one million man-hours without a lost time accident. It did so over a two and one-half year period ending in 1977.

In 1978, the results of another Shell Waterton program were in. For five years, the plant had gone into the farming and ranching business downwind of itself. Over that period, it had raised thirty-five hogs and 398 of their offspring, 900 chickens and 290 mice. It had also raised a number of crops. No tissue damage from sulphur dioxide could be found in the livestock nor any deleterious effects on the stock's rate of gain. Some minor reductions in yield had been noted in the alfalfa crop.

During this period, what distressed those at Shell Waterton, and everyone else in the industry trying to effect environmental controls, was how unimpressed the general public seemed to be with the work they were doing and the results they were achieving. In 1974, an Environmental Management symposium at the University of Calgary heard a paper by Lee Hurd of the Canadian Gas Arctic Study Group (read by Donald Dabbs). Hurd's paper probably spoke the feelings of many in this industry when he said:

> The industry recognizes that better environmental protection is desirable, in some cases, necessary. The industry is willing to help provide that protection but the industry wants the price tag displayed.

He went on to express other common industry feelings, mainly that the public did not realize how well its interests were *already* being protected. Because pollution in the oil and gas industry had been well controlled for so long, people were not conscious of the degree to which environmental pollution had been cleaned up. Interestingly, an almost identical point of view was expressed by Alberta's Energy Resources Conservation Board chairman, Vern Millard, in a paper he presented to the Canadian Society of Chemical Engineers in Calgary in 1983. The purpose of Millard's paper was to prove that the sour gas industry in Alberta *was* controlled, in view of the fact that "there appears to be a popular perception that the province does not have a sound system."

Millard listed the weapons in Alberta's arsenal of environmental defence: the air and water emission standards, the reporting systems, the surveillance and inspection systems, the safety programs, the research, the public hearing process. He noted that, in 1972, when the National Ambient Air Quality Standards for SO_2 were published, Alberta Environment had selected the most rigorous of the three standards described: the Maximum Desirable Limit of 0.17 parts per million over one hour. Environment Canada had recently reapproved these standards.

The system was working so well that the approved rate of sulphur dioxide emissions for 1981 (800 tonnes/day) had not only been met by the plants but had been improved upon by a margin of 55%. The actual emissions were 350 tonnes per day. (It will be remembered that the *actual* emissions for the year ending June 30, 1972, were 1300 long tons/day).

In conclusion, Millard could only wonder that the government perception of success in the environment could exist side-by-side with the public's apparent perception of failure. Millard's predecessor, Dr. George Govier, had scolded the industry in 1971 for a failure in public relations that was lessening the impact of their technological success. It would seem that in 1983 the government was having to shoulder some of the blame for the fact that the public still did not know what industry and government together had accomplished. In 1983, Albertans were breathing cleaner air than over 80% of the Canadian population. Canada as a whole was doing well relative to the industrialized world. The problem remains to convince the public that it is true and that it will continue to be true.

THE ASSOCIATIONS: A SILVER ANNIVERSARY RETROSPECTIVE

12

For twenty-five years, the Canadian Gas Processors Association and the Canadian Gas Processors Suppliers' Association have enjoyed a harmonious relationship rare in organizations, no matter how closely affiliated. The reason is probably that the two were *designed to get along*, one being the perfect complement and puzzle-fit of the other. While the processors lined up technical papers to inform the membership, the suppliers laid on the liquid refreshment, golf tournaments and dinner dances that put everyone in a sociable mood. The perfect symbiosis, in other words. As for why the Suppliers were so willing to serve up drinks to the Processors, a sound business motive stood at the bottom of it: it is easier to sell products to people you know, and people tend to be more sociable away from the office with a drink or two under their belts. The Suppliers' Association has also been an important source of the technical papers delivered at Association meetings.

During their lives, the two Associations have developed a character that is a reliable reflection of the industry they represent. For example, the Associations have always had a strong work ethic. The members came together first and foremost to learn through study, to solve problems, to compare notes. But when the hard work was done, the hard play began: the golfing, the drinking, the dancing, the telling of tall tales — all conducted with a determined enthusiasm, even a slight wild streak as in the days of the *party train* from Calgary to Edmonton. (The good times aboard this train were so exuberant that the CPR was finally obliged to cancel the offer of a special car.)

This balance between long stretches of hard work and short bursts of intense fun mimics in a way the work and play habits that have always been part of the processing business in Canada. Old-timers love to tell of the long stretches of work they put in, of how the watches were put away until the job was done; and then, of how they would repair to the nearest tavern for some equally serious relaxation. This is not to say that the form of release was always found in a tavern. After his umpteenth sixteen hour day in a row at B.A. Pincher Creek, Martin Bretz liked to slip over the hill to his favourite fishing hole; and at B.A. Nevis, Gordon Barnes' tonic for a long day of harrassing problems was to hop in his airplane and fly up as high as he

Sam Mozell of Barber Engineering and Controls Ltd.,
perennial organizer of the supply men's and processors'
annual golf tournament.

dared. Looking down at the tiny clump of silver that was his plant, Barnes would tell himself, "I'm not going to let myself be driven nuts by that little thing."

The CGPA and CGPSA also have in common with their industry a very particular sense of being Canadian. When the idea of Canadian associations first went on the drawing board, it was as Canadian regional branches of the Natural Gasoline Association of America and the Natural Gasoline Supply Men's Association of America. But, in the end, the charter members voted for associations that were purely Canadian and not affiliated with anyone but each other. No hostility was ever expressed toward the NGAA and NGSMA, in fact, from the very first year, members were attending one another's meetings and planning joint activities. The Canadian outfits had politely refused affiliation, that was all, in order to enjoy independence.

Many will have difficulty seeing how this independence reflects the Canadian gas processing industry. The tendency in Canada is to view that industry as foreign-owned, foreign-controlled and, therefore, somehow hostile to the interests of Canada. Within the industry, the feeling is quite different. The Canadian industry, like the Canadian Processors and Suppliers' Associations, *is* deeply influenced by its American counterpart, for several excellent reasons. One reason is that many Canadian processing companies are branch plants of foreign-owned parents (mainly American parents). Another reason is the acknowledgement within Canada that much of what we do in processing was done first south of the border. For many leaders in the Canadian industry, recognition of this came in the early years when they were taking training courses in the U.S., or when they were learning their profession or trade under an experienced American mentor.

Those who grew up with the Canadian processing industry are also aware that much of what we do, particularly in sour gas processing, has been developed right here; that it had to be pioneered here because no handy foreign precedents existed to be drawn upon. Canadian processors and supply men are proud of these Canadian accomplishments. The fact that most of the money paying for the innovations was foreign and that assistance periodically came from foreign engineers or foreign laboratories does not diminish that pride. The fact remains that Canada is dominant in sour gas processing and that Canadians are presently doing an excellent job in processing, both at home and abroad.

Finally, the CGPA and CGPSA share with their industry a tendency to communicate freely across company boundaries, with no great reserve or fear of handing away a lucrative advantage. Veteran oil and gas analyst Les Rowland of *Oilweek* has frequently been amazed at Association functions by the "remarkably non-competitive exchange of information." Speakers have always been surprisingly willing, he says, to lay bare the minute details of processes both patented and unpatented. Out in the field and in Canadian plants, something similar has been going on for decades. Since at least the 1950's, operators and supervisors in this country have been *leaning over the back fence*, letting one another in on better ways of slowing down corrosion or better plans for stopping the foaming problems in an amine tower.

In this regard, the Processors Association may have done more than reflect the Canadian industry; it may have actually helped the industry to become more cooperative. When the processors began their organization they made a deliberate decision not to follow the American precedent of company membership. Instead of a system where companies belonged and nominated employees to represent them, the Canadian processors opted for individual membership. In Canada, any number of people could join from one company, all enjoying voting status if they qualified as bona fide processors. The system of organization reflected (and then institutionalized) what had always been a grass-roots tendency in the Canadian gas patch.

The willingness to cooperate and communicate is another fact that will probably ring untrue to some looking in on the industry from outside. The vision of *dog-eat-dog* capitalists, greedily hoarding their secrets, is a strong one in public folklore. Within the industry, the folklore of "let's get the damn job done" is considerably stronger. Getting the job done is such a powerful motive for processors in both Canada and the U.S. that the pool of information used toward that end is most often shared. One informant said of his experiences in the late '50's: "When I had a problem at my plant, I could phone anywhere in the world and get help with it." Says another: "I'd phone people who had never heard my name, and I'd get the information I needed right now if they had it." It was this spirit of free informational exchange that stimulated the CGPA and CGPSA into existence in 1959, and which remains their life force today.

THE ASSOCIATIONS' STORY OF GENESIS

The year was 1959. The surge of gas plant construction in Western Canada stimulated by the completion of the Westcoast and TCPL pipelines was drawing to a close, but if the governments got busy and authorized gas export through TCPL and the new Alberta and Southern line to California, another even larger construction boom would certainly begin. Growth in the industry was bringing an influx of people to Alberta and northeastern B.C., and many towns and cities in these locales were feverishly trying to keep up, in housing and amusements, with the free-spending wave.

In the gas processing industry, the rapid increase in the number of plants and in total plant capacity was paralleled by the intensification of several chronic problems. For one thing, companies processing high pressure sour gas in Canada were quickly finding out that such gas could not be handled simply by running it through standard design process plants. The problems of sudden metal failure, weight loss corrosion, solution degradation, water carryover and so on were being grappled with company-by-company, plant-by-plant, with grudging results. A feeling was growing that a better, faster way had to be found to study and solve such dangerous and expensive difficulties.

Another dilemma involved training. Experienced operators were not to be had this side of the border, save for the few who had been trained in Turner Valley and in the early conservation plants. These early plants were still in operation and the companies were hanging onto their experienced hands as tightly as possible. Some American operators came north, and experienced men were found in related industries (petrochemical, refining, power generation), but most of the manpower requirements had to be met through training. This training was usually done on the job, but a general feeling existed that it would never be comprehensive or effective enough until gas processing and operator's courses became available in Canada.

Growth had also created a brisker demand for plant equipment, replacement parts and engineering services. Traditionally, these needs had been met from abroad, mainly from the U.S. When the Canadian industry began to boom in the late '50's, the reliance on American suppliers continued. The problem with this arrangement had always been the delays involved when equipment and supplies had to come from far distant plants and factories, in places like Sarnia, Ontario; Montreal, Quebec; Mt. Vernon, Ohio; Olean, New York; and Tulsa, Oklahoma. What had been an annoyance in the conservation era became a downright disaster when the gas had a market. The processing companies lost profitable sales while supplies and equipment they needed to run their plants crawled back and forth across the continent.

One answer of course would have been to build the vessels, valves, etcetera right in Alberta, but, alas, the puddle was still too small to repay a manufacturer who located here. Failing that, Canadian suppliers argued that a partial answer would be to start using the local sales representatives. The Americans who so often ran Canada's early plants had a natural tendency to buy from the people they had always bought from; that is, south of the border. What the Canadian suppliers argued was that, because they knew the local conditions and climate and because they were *here* and not a thousand miles away, they could give better service than their U.S.-based counterparts. But, often, the Canadian suppliers could not convince anyone to give them a chance to prove it. Veteran supplier Jim Belding encountered another problem and that was that many of the managers of Canadian plants lacked authorization to make their own purchases. Belding found himself in the ludicrous position of having to go to a U.S. head office to sell a piece of equipment to a gas plant twenty miles from Calgary. Belding says that in those days the hardest thing for a Canadian to sell was the small equipment; if you were vending something big like a tank or vessel, your chances were better. Still, most of the business given to the Canadians was "token".

In order to stay in business, Canadian suppliers had to represent a large number of companies and a vast range of equipment. This of course increased the amount the supplier had to know in order to explain and service what he sold. If the supplier could not become expert on every item, it raised the odds of disappointing a client and further setting back the cause of Canadian supply. Nor were the commissions and working conditions anything to write home about. Says Jim Belding: "The U.S. agent who sold us the equipment would get 10%; we'd get 5% (a territorial commission); but we were the guys that got called out in the middle of the night to service the stuff."

For consulting engineers, many of the same problems applied. Jim Richardson's company, Barry and Richardson, was one of the very few engineering firms based in Canada recognized as having the expertise to take on large-scale gas processing contracts. Jim Richardson had estab-

Twenty-five years after signing the CNGPA charter, Jim Richardson served as a panelist at the third technical meeting of 1984.

lished much of that reputation working in the United States before he set up his Canadian operation. Aspiring Canadian engineers had to overcome the "prophet in his own land" syndrome. The Canadian governments had gone to great lengths to establish credible engineering faculties across the land, but there was still a reluctance to trust the graduates with the really big, high dollar jobs. You can hear an edge in the voices of most Canadian engineers when they speak of this period. Morris Pryde, who graduated in engineering from McGill in 1946, refers to it as the time "when Canadian engineers didn't know anything." Like the sales reps, the Canadian engineers felt that they could equal or improve upon the work done by their American competitors. They knew the climate; they were aware of at least some of the peculiarities of Canadian gas. The drastic inadequacies of some of the early American-designed plants proved that a need existed which engineers focussing exclusively on Canadian processing problems might fill. Like the suppliers of goods, the suppliers of services were very interested in any tool that could lever industry into giving them their chance.

To problems as various and complicated as those listed above, there could be no blanket solution. It is intriguing, however, to see how many people perceived some sort of association of processors and suppliers as a necessary step *toward* a solution. Rather than succumb to the temptation of citing the *first* to conceive the idea of an association of supply men, an association of processors, it is probably better to say that the idea occurred to several people in the year of 1959. Some would trace the Associations' genesis to Dallas, others to Jumping Pound, others to either the Ladies Dining Room at the Petroleum Club, the Barron Building or the 8th Avenue Legion, all in Calgary.

Jim Belding's story of genesis is that he and several other "gas hands" who were holding down office space in the Barron Building (also known as the Mobil Building) got tired of the heat one August afternoon and toddled across to the Legion for a few cooling glasses of draft. Over these refreshments, Ed Herrmann, maintenance supervisor for Mobil, asked Jim Belding to see if he could arrange a tour of Shell Jumping Pound for him. The idea was not forgotten and Belding eventually convinced Frank Wood, the Jumping Pound superintendent at the time, that he and Herrmann had friendly intentions and were not on a mission of industrial espionage.

Jim Belding played a key role in starting the CNGPSMA and was three times its president.

For an entire afternoon, Herrmann and Belding toured the Jumping Pound plant under the guidance of Frank Wood. They discussed myriad common problems as they went and, when it was all over, they had to concede that it had been a profitable exchange, something that should be repeated. Afterward, Ed Herrmann suggested to Jim Belding that an association should be started in Canada that would allow such conversations on a regular basis. He understood that some such thing existed in the States. "Jim took it right up," says Herrmann.

Another story of genesis — or rather part of the same one — is found in correspondence originating in the office of R. G. Murray and Associates Ltd. in that same summer of 1959. This does not move the manger far in any case because Jim Belding was sharing an office with George Murray in the Barron Building at the time. George Murray was currently promoting the Alberta Underground Storage project at Hughenden, Alberta. On July 29, 1959, Murray sent out a form letter to representatives of twenty-two companies asking them what they thought of organizing a chapter or affiliated unit of the Natural Gasoline Association of America in Calgary. The purpose of such an organization, he wrote, "is to serve as a forum for the exchange of ideas and information for gas producers and the gas processing industry with a view to improving plant operations and related activities concerning all phases of gas utilization." He felt the time was right for such a specialized organization because of the growth spurt the industry was currently enjoying in Canada. Murray had been to the NGAA's annual meeting in Dallas in April of that year, and he had "taken the liberty" of asking NGAA executive director William F. Lowe about such a branch. Lowe had since written back saying that the NGAA had already considered the move but had decided to wait until more plants were built. Besides the annual convention, the NGAA also staged regional meetings every year and they were thinking of holding one in Calgary in 1960. Lowe and Ron Cannon, NGAA secretary, would be glad to come up and talk about it any time.

"You may wonder about my interest in this matter," George Murray wrote in his letter to the twenty-two representatives. "During the period between 1946 and 1950, while in charge of plant operations for United Gas Pipe Line Co. at Carthage, Texas, I assisted in the formation of the East Texas Gasoline Men's Club. This group was the forerunner of what is now known as Regional Chapters of the NGAA. My experience in this group and association with NGAA for over twenty years may be of some assistance to you which I am very happy to offer at this time."

The general tone of replies to this letter was enthusiastic. Bryan Edwards of Pan American was particularly so. He wrote of how well operators working for companies in Canada had been received at the regional meetings of the Rocky Mountain division of the NGAA. On September 1, 1959, George Murray sent out a followup letter saying that the consensus of replies had been that a meeting should be held immediately and that it should be in the evening with dinner. He had gone ahead with arrangements and the dinner meeting was scheduled for the Ladies' Dining Room of the Petroleum Club, Calgary, at six p.m., September 8, 1959.

At this dinner meeting, chaired by George Murray, the organization and procedures as well as the by-laws and constitution of a regional chapter of the NGAA were circulated. Mr. Murray gave a brief history of the NGAA and outlined the relationship between the NGAA and the Natural Gasoline Supply Men's Association. But, when the time came to discuss the name and affiliations of what the group was about to create, agreement began to fail. Some felt a regional branch of the NGAA was exactly the type of association to create, others felt such an affiliation was unnecessary; still others spoke in favour of affiliating with other established organizations entirely, groups such as the California Natural Gas Association or the Canadian Gas Association.

In the end, Mr. Murray pointed out that the East Texas Gasoline Men's Club had existed separately from the NGAA for its first five years. This seemed to do away with the necessity for deciding the issue immediately.

A slate of temporary officers was elected at the Pete Club that night and the group got together two days later in the conference room of Goliad Oil and Gas. The debate on the issue of affiliation continued. According to Dan T. McDonald, then executive vice-president of Goliad and a member of the temporary slate, George Murray was pulling for affiliation with the NGAA while Dan T. himself led the forces in favour of an independent association that was "Canadian all the way". The fact that McDonald was a Texan did not enter into it. Dan T. McDonald was also pushing for individual membership. Membership in the NGAA was by company. Companies belonged and they appointed an employee to represent them. Dan T. preferred a system that company didn't enter into. The individual, he felt, should join for his own sake and self-improvement.

Under temporary chairman Charles Yarbrough of Mobil and temporary vice-chairman J. H. Geddes of Home Oil, committees were struck to study these questions further and to recommend a final form for the organization. George Murray chaired the constitution committee, Bryan Edwards chaired the policy and affiliation committee, Ed Jones was in charge of programs and membership, and Ed Stevens of Royalite took charge of nominating a slate of candidates for the organization's first election.

The temporary officers met again on October 9, and the committee chairmen presented their recommendations. Name: Canadian Natural Gas Processors Association (Alberta Chapter). * Affiliation: none, for the time

---

*The name of the association remained the same for most of the life of the organization, although "Alberta Chapter" tended to be dropped. In 1978, it was shortened to Canadian Gas Processors Association (CGPA). At the same time, the Supply Men amended their name to the Canadian Gas Processors Suppliers' Association (CGPSA).

being. Membership: voting memberships to be restricted to supervisory and technical employees of processing companies and non-voting memberships available to people such as consulting engineers who do not work in processing but who have an obvious interest. In other words, it was a system of individual not corporate membership.

All this was leading up to another dinner meeting at the Calgary Professional Club on the evening of October 27, 1959, to ratify the constitution and by-laws, elect officers and thereby unveil the association as a living organization. Twenty-eight people attended the meeting (working for fourteen companies). They heard the recommendations of the committees and adopted them with minor changes. The first executive of the CNGPA was elected by secret ballot:

> President: C. R. Yarbrough, Mobil
> Vice-President: D. F. McEachern, Imperial
> Secretary-Treasurer: E. H. Scott, Goliad

An early gathering of CNGPA members. Back row (l to r): Don Wolcott, Art Denny, Charles Buskel, Schaum McGehee, Will Donahue and John Dillon. Bottom row (l to r): Dan McDonald, Rollie Lazerte, Charles Drake and Bill Humphreys.

While the tellers checked the ballots to determine the board of directors, Charlie Yarbrough outlined the role he saw a supply men's group as playing. He said that such a group was presently being formed.

Elected to the first board of directors were:

> B. C. Edwards, Pan Am   R. M. Lazerte, Texaco
> D. M. Wolcott, Dome   D. T. McDonald, Goliad
> J. M. Dillon, Shell   E. F. T. Stevens, Royalite

Twenty-six signed as charter members and after the meeting was over, the first dues were collected. The purpose of the Association, as set out in the constitution, was very close in wording to that suggested by George Murray in his initial letter.

A supply men's association was indeed in the process of creation. Jim Belding had been rapidly working his way around town gathering support for it. The day after the creation of the CNGPA, a letter went out on "Canadian Natural Gasoline Processing Supply Men's Association (Proposed)" letterhead, requesting attendance at a November 5, 1959, luncheon meeting at the Calgary Professional Club for the purpose of forming the CNGPSMA. Charlie Yarbrough was to be at this founding meeting of the CNGPSMA in order to explain the CNGPA and to reiterate his request that the two organizations be affiliated. Those interested in the founding meeting were to contact either Earl Britton (Canadian Meter Co. Ltd.), Jim Carveth (Stearns-Roger Engineering Ltd.), Ted Van Fossen (Cooper-Bessemer Co.) or Jim Belding (Belen-Lynn McGuffy Co. Ltd.).

From the beginning the constitution of the Supply Men's Association stressed three things: the promotion of a closer relationship between supply men and processors; the encouragement of high ethical standards among suppliers; and the provision of "proper" entertainment for the CNGPA at its various conventions. Probably because membership in the Supply Men's Association was more obviously a matter of company business, the suppliers went with company rather than individual membership. Voting members were those appointed to represent a member company; associate

Jim Carveth was an engineer for Stearns-Roger in 1961 when he served as the second ever president of the CNGPSMA.

memberships were available to everyone else in the supply industry who cared to join, but associates were not allowed to vote.

On December 10, 1959, at the first ever regular meeting of the CNGPA, a dinner meeting at the Petroleum Club, Earl Britton made an address on behalf of the CNGPSMA to say that his organization was now a reality and that it had voted unanimously to affiliate with the CNGPA. He was the first elected secretary, serving under first president Jim Belding. Jim Carveth was first vice-president, Ted Van Fossen, second; Jack Hulbert had been elected treasurer.

THE FIRST YEAR

In the first month of 1960, the CNGPA held an executive meeting and had the unpleasant task of accepting two letters of resignation from their newly elected board. President Yarbrough and Director Edwards had both been transferred by their parent companies back to the United States; Bryan Edwards to be Pan Am's Assistant Manager of Gas Sales in Tulsa, and Charlie Yarbrough to be Natural Gas Manager for Canada and the U.S. in Mobil's New York office. Don McEachern automatically became the new president and Ed Stevens' nominating committee put Rollie Lazerte of Texaco forward as the new vice-president. Frank Kennedy and Art Denny were nominated as directors. At that meeting, Rollie Lazerte moved that the Supply Men's Association be officially accepted as an affiliated organization:

All these developments were announced to the membership in the first ever CNGPA Newsletter which went out in February of 1960. It also contained a triumphant proclamation of the birth of the organization

> The formation of the CNGPA emphasized the obvious coming of age of the natural gas industry in Canada. We who specialize in the production and processing of this vital resource have considered this forward step to be necessary, but most of us have been waiting for it to "happen". It has "happened" thanks to a few energetic individuals now known as charter members.

The main purpose of the newsletter, however, was to announce the first quarterly technical meeting to be held at the Palliser Hotel in Calgary on February 25. These technical meetings were to be the principal device for achieving the objectives of both the CNGPA and the CNGPSMA. At each one, several technical papers would be delivered which would serve to educate the members in the latest developments in their industry. Around the business, social events would be fitted, put on by the Supply Men, where processors and supply men could meet.

One of the most onerous tasks on the CGPA executive has always been the chairmanship of the program committee. This committee is charged with lining up the papers to be delivered at the technical meetings. To ensure a full slate, the papers must be confirmed well in advance. Despite frequent changes in industry technology, they must also be up to the minute. In other words, the program committee has always needed a liberal dose of clairvoyance.

The first to sit before this crystal ball was Dan T. McDonald, and he did it well. At the first technical meeting, Imperial's Doug Hay (a future CNGPA president) delivered a paper on gas chromatography, a rather new and important development for gas analysis which would help greatly in the precise design of plants. H. Preston Pew of Goliad gave a paper on preventive maintenance, and Angus Leitch of Barry and Richardson spoke on the hot potassium carbonate process, the latest innovation in sour gas sweetening.

The concern for plant safety which was to characterize the Association through all its years was evident from the first: the fourth paper of the day was on "the cost of accidents", delivered by W. H. Bradley of Calgary Power. A film was also presented on artificial respiration.

Another tax on Dan T. McDonald's clairvoyance that first year was the small matter of predicting how many people would attend the first technical meeting of the CNGPA/CNGPSMA. McDonald remembers having to go see Harold, the maitre d' at the Palliser, to firm up arrangements for rooms and meals the day before the meeting. Up to then, all the numbers had been tentative. As McDonald crossed 9th Avenue, the snow was blowing in "horizontally" and "the thermo was dropping fast"; it was not ideal convention weather. Harold looked Dan T. in the eye and said, "Are you still guaranteeing 100 people?" Dan T. looked him right back and said.: "Yes — as a minimum."

The next day, McDonald stood at the door and counted the heads as they passed. As number one hundred and one passed through the chute, he went to Harold and ordered twenty-five more lunches. Says Dan T.: "From that point on, I never had any qualms about this organization going all the way." The final attendance at technical meeting number one was 150.

But the first technical meeting had a sad duty to perform as well. That was to tell the membership of the recent death of Director E. F. T. Stevens. Ed Stevens had been too ill to attend the founding meeting in October and it had been agreed then that the charter be taken to him so he could sign as a charter member. At the first technical meeting, it was decided that his name would be left on the list of directors until the end of the year to honour his memory.

On June 9, 1960, the second quarterly technical meeting was held, again at the Palliser. At this meeting, no fewer than eight addresses were given. Dan T. McDonald had perhaps prevailed on his cousin Morris Palmer to send someone to describe the Devon-Palmer field operation at Okotoks. Glenn Brant of that company started the day with such an address, followed by Elmer Berlie's paper on the associated Texas Gulf Okotoks gas plant. All the morning papers were nicely dove-tailed. A key problem of sour gas plants in Alberta was turning out to be the trace compound carbonyl sulphide and following Berlie's paper was one on that subject by Charlie Hall of Dow Chemical, Sarnia. Berlie's address mentioned the new air-breathing system introduced at the Okotoks plant and the final paper of the morning was on H_2S safety by Reg Havard of B.A.. Havard, Berlie, Bruce Holbrook and Harvey Whitworth had worked together on the design of the air-breathing system at B.A. Pincher Creek before it was finally installed for the first time at Okotoks.

At lunch, the Associations heard from Ron Cannon, secretary of the NGAA in Tulsa. An amusing and engaging speaker, Cannon was often to

Ron Cannon of the NGAA was willing to come up to Canada any time to discuss the possibility of a Canadian regional branch of the American organization. When the CNGPA was formed, he did come up often to attend and speak at Association functions.

make the trip north to address his Canadian cousins and to keep a finger on the CNGPA/CNGPSMA pulse.

It is not the intention of this chapter to enumerate every paper ever given at the CNGPA technical meetings. (That number would slightly exceed four hundred.) The first few have been listed to give a sense of the direction technical meetings take and of the kinds of subjects covered. The programs have been so thorough over the years, and so up-to-date, that a list of the papers given in the order they were given reads like a comprehensive outline of the entire industry over its last twenty-five years. When a supplier came out with a new patent or process, he would often be given airtime at a CNGPA technical meeting. If the presentation was convincing, the local distributor would likely have a hot selling product; if the presentation failed or did not stand up to the cross-examination of the room full of processors, the effect on sales could be devastating.

When a new and innovative plant was built, or an old one revised and made more efficient, the company was often invited to tell the Associations how it was being done. In 1966, Dr. Andy Younger and Martin Kyllo of HBOG detailed the design and operation of their new Edson plant. In 1969, shortly before his death, Dr. Alexander Petrunic gave his paper on improvements in the sulphur plant and other parts of Fina's Wildcat Hills operation.

The luncheon spot was often reserved for political speakers or representatives of other organizations which had a relationship with the processing industry. When a government department set out new rules affecting gas processors, a high-ranking spokesperson would often be called upon to explain things at the next CNGPA luncheon. In 1961, Jack Stabback of the Oil and Gas Conservation Board detailed the Board's new air pollution regulations. A decade or so later, it was Board Chairman Dr. George Govier's turn to explain the tough new sulphur emission guidelines brought in under the Lougheed Conservatives.

In September, 1960, the CNGPA staged its third quarterly technical meeting at the Palliser, with the special twist that it was also a joint meeting with the Rocky Mountain region of the NGAA. A special program committee was put together for this joint effort, with Ray Birmingham of the Pure Oil Co., Worland, Wyoming, and John Shannon of Mobil, Denver, joining Dan T. McDonald's team of John Dillon from Shell and Ian Drum from Home Oil. The technical papers were divided among Canadian and American speakers and the luncheon address was given by that dual citizen of the Canadian and American oil and gas patch, Nathan Eldon Tanner. Thirty-two NGAA members joined the seventy-five CNGPA and sixty-nine CNGPSMA members at the meeting.

The CNGPSMA did its bit for international relations by staging a *Cooling Tower* (recognizable ancestor of today's *Pump Primer*), and a *Western Bar-B-Q* at the Lone Pine Supper Club. This was the first Association function staged at the Lone Pine, but far from the last. The

Club was on the hill west of town, beyond the end of Seventeenth Avenue, and it was evidently a popular choice for the Western Bar-B-Q; in his next newsletter, Ed Jones proclaimed that "practically the whole industry" had attended.

In that first year of existence, the CNGPA also founded a project committee and put it under the chairmanship of Elmer Berlie. The purpose of this committee came very close to that of the entire Association: it was to survey the Canadian industry, identify its needs and come up with projects which would provide some answers. In May of 1960, Berlie reported to the executive that his committee had come up with six possible projects. In the discussion that followed, it was decided that, of the six, a compilation of published and unpublished sour gas technical data was probably the most needed and best suited to the resources of the Association. A subcommittee was to be created to do the job and, toward that end, President McEachern wrote to several companies asking for the services of some of the top men in the Canadian industry: Shell's Dr. Martin Winning, Imperial's Jim Young, B.A.'s Gerry Gainer, Fina's Bernie Coady and Millard Cook from Pan Am.

By the following September, Dr. Winning was able to present a sample of the sour gas bibliography and, at the 1961 Annual Meeting in December, they were offered for sale. It marked the completion of the CNGPA's first project.

The CNGPSMA had been even more precocious, finishing its first project by May of 1960. It was a directory of equipment, services and materials available to the Canadian gas industry from within Canada, an important shot in the ongoing war to improve the Canadian supply man's share of the business being done in this country.

A third project was undertaken in 1960 under the auspices of both Associations and that was the compilation of Canadian engineering data for inclusion in the 1961 edition of the NGPSMA's engineering data book. The subcommittee charged with this project was chaired by Aki Masuda.

At the CNGPA's 1960 Annual Meeting, held in December, membership chairman Don Wolcott was able to report the fledgling organization well out of the nest with 81 members and 24 associates. Total receipts of the organization (in excess of disbursements) stood at a whopping $505.84.

TO EDMONTON BY TRAIN

That the Canadian gas processing industry would be significant enough to warrant a processors and suppliers association was guaranteed in 1960 by the Canadian and U.S. approvals for gas export to the United States from Alberta. That ensured another burst of growth for gas plant construction in Canada and established the Associations on the ground floor of a thriving industry. In a 1961 letter to members, the second Supply Men's president Jim Carveth expressed the goal of his Association with respect to this surge of growth:

> We urge that every company in the gas industry promote and encourage the use of Canadian goods and services wherever possible. By doing your share and cooperating in this worthwhile endeavour, you will assist materially in building a healthy economic climate and higher standard of living for all Canadians.

After 1960, the processors continued to confront the unsolved problems of sour gas: how to sweeten it, how to handle it safely, how to combat its corrosiveness, how to keep it from polluting the environment. Another of the problems that had first motivated the establishment of the Associations, the shortage of trained men, was attacked by Director Elmer Berlie. Berlie had been working for some time with the Petroleum Industry Training Service and its supervisor Walter Gabert. They had worked together on the gas plant operator's course at PITS and it was a natural step for Berlie as CNGPA project chairman to see what the Association could do to further improve that course. Early in 1961, it was proposed that President Rollie Lazerte send a letter to all CNGPA members asking them to reply with a list of subjects they would be willing to lecture on to the students at PITS.

Another task that Elmer Berlie was put to in 1961 was to reply to a request from the Canadian Petroleum Association for a precise definition of what a natural gas processing plant was. That may sound like a simple task, but when Elmer drafted a definition and sent it out for comment, he received eighteen significantly different replies. Eventually, Berlie was able to boil the various efforts down into a single composite:

> A natural gas processing plant is a facility composed of integrally connected and interdependent mechanical equipment designed and operated to physically or chemically separate any naturally occurring gas into its component parts, to treat for the removal and elimination of deleterious substances or to otherwise render or handle the gas or extracted substances so as to be marketable and/or transportable.

Looking back on this Elmer Berlie says, "Never has so much time been spent on so few words."

After a year of life, the two Associations still felt the need to grow, and that many in the industry were not yet being reached by their message and their membership drive. Because the Associations had been created in Calgary their membership was largely *from* Calgary. As a first step toward making the Associations more Canadian than Calgarian, it was decided to hold the September, 1961, quarterly meeting at the Mayfair Hotel in Edmonton. In the ensuing discussion, someone hatched the apparently excellent idea of chartering a special train to transport the Calgary contingent the 180 miles north to the Alberta capital. Bob Cunningham was asked to look into it.

The CPR was amenable to the idea. The railway agreed that, if enough tickets were sold, a special car would be hitched onto the regular Calgary-Edmonton Dayliner. In September, shortly after the First Annual Supply Men's Golf Tournament, a band of fifty processors and supply men boarded the Dayliner in Calgary for the three hour trip.

As institutions go, the train trip to Edmonton was not an especially long-lived one. It lasted but half a decade. But the old rolling stock gathered so much moss in those five years that the legend lived on for the next twenty. For various reasons that may become obvious, memories of these mobile galas tend to be blurred. What is retained is remembered in a lumpen way, as if all five round trips were in fact one trip — one incredibly long and eventful party.

The usual advance descriptions of the voyage sounded rather tame and proper: "A buffet dinner will be served on board." Square that with the vision of several inebriated supply men wildly hacking their way through a suitcase full of salami. This mayhem was tamed by the euphemism: "the preparation of hors d'oeuvres".* Or, what about the spectacle of an ordinarily conservative processor transformed by alcohol into a member of the *Flying Wallendas*, leaning far out the doorway of the speeding train into the falling evening, to remove the lid of a pickle jar. He didn't want to make a mess inside.

Oddly, in the early days of this bacchanal, people did not seem to mind having their names associated with it. A September 28, 1962, article entitled "Supply Men and the *Canadian Gas Journal* Present Gas Processing Train Hi-Jinks" began:

> Supply Men hastily organized a boozy bar with Exchanger Sales and Service's Howie Thom, Dow Chemical's John McMillan and Logie Dempster, Maloney Crawford's Jim Wolter, Clark Compressor's Bob Graves, B & M Dehydrator's (and ex-Stampeder) Opie Bandy as bar men. Friendly competitor Jim Armstrong served hors d'oeuvres.

The party's first year had received such good reviews that, the follow-

---

*In fact, for at least one of these voyages, hors d'oeuvres were prepared in advance by Helen Belding, "a care package for fifty men".

ing year, Mobil's Ed Herrmann, Imperial's Herb Cooper and Belmac's Ray Love all *came from* Edmonton to Calgary for the sole purpose of riding *back* to Edmonton on the special train. Imagine going to that much trouble to hear Jim Belding sing *O Dolly* for three straight hours. Another feature of the 1962 train ride was that Dan T. McDonald was carrying the newly minted first safety award, trying hard in the *mêlée* not to stick anyone in an inconvenient place with its sharp point.

The effect of the train trips was such that people ordinarily conversant with the minutest inner workings of complex processing equipment, absolute wizards with a slide rule, would climb off the train at the wrong station. With all due respect to Red Deer, there is simply no place between Calgary and Edmonton vaguely resembling Calgary or Edmonton. In honour of the colossal hangover many *began* the trip home with, the voyagers decided after a couple of years on the sensible compromise of only stocking beer for the return trip. However, when those entrusted with the purchase and delivery of this beer to the train did not show up, Jim Belding felt that he had a cause worth risking his life for. Belding stood on the tracks in front of the diesel and refused to budge. Several of his cohorts had to physically drag the supply man back on board so the train could leave. The horrible prospect of three hours without a single hair of the dog was magically averted when the prodigals met the train at the South Edmonton station, the much needed suds in hand.

The future of this grand institution began to seem doubtful when the revellers started feeling sorry for their poor, sober fellow passengers and for the good people who were obliged to stay in a parched state while making the train go. Their endeavours to spread bonhomie train-long and train-wide and, most particularly, the success these spirituous evangelists enjoyed, finally obliged CPR to say no to all requests for a special train car after 1965. Even high level pressure, exerted through friends of the CNGPA at Canadian Pacific Oil and Gas could not bring the train trip back again. The processors and supply men were dragged kicking and screaming into the age of air travel.

The idea was posed that a special plane be rented so that the traditional party could continue, but it was never done. One informant's explanation: "It's just too short a trip to get drunk on." Instead, the Calgary contingent boarded the airbus in 1966, and the CNGPSMA tried to maintain a little of the old tradition with a hospitality hour at the Edmonton Inn, just a stone's throw away from the municipal airport. "Hospitality hour" was of course code for "until the porch climber is used up."

LEADERSHIP

In his president's address delivered to the CNGPA Annual Meeting in 1962, Dan T. McDonald said, "I feel that the future captains of the gas production and processing industry are on our membership rolls right today." How accurate a statement. It has been a lasting strength of both the CGPA and the CGPSA that they have been able to elect officers who are active and powerful within the industry, "If you want something done, go to a busy man," runs the old adage, and the Associations have always adhered to it and profited by it. The presidents of the Associations are listed below:

Processors		*Suppliers*
Charlie Yarbrough	1959	Jim Belding
Don McEachern	1960	Jim Belding
Rollie Lazerte	1961	Jim Carveth
Dan McDonald	1962	Bob Newell
Art Denny	1963	Jim Belding
Elmer Berlie	1964	Harry Neuman
Kevin Milne	1965	John MacMillan
Earl Scott	1966	Bob Smith
Don Sargent	1967	Ray Junkey
Andy Younger	1968	Mac MacCrae
Clayton Edgelow	1969	Sam Mozell
Murray Ross	1970	Les Spalding
Fred Brooks	1971	Stan Rowan
Ken MacRae	1972	Doug Fairbairn
Bill Fisher	1973	Harry Neuman
Doug Hay	1974	Peter Finch
John Martin	1975	Ken Pritchard
Gordon Barnes	1976	Bill McCachen
Don Weiss	1977	Alan Armour
Earle Forgues	1978	Nes Plotke
Bob Bowser	1979	Murray Ross
Gary Bruce	1980	Doug Fraser
Al Kiernan	1981	Les Vanderlinde
Jack Willison	1982	Al Donaldson
Terry Horkoff	1983	Ray Allan
Larry Graburn	1984	Ron Kuchinka

MOTIVATION THROUGH RECOGNITION

As president of the CNGPA in its third year, Dan T. McDonald wanted to see the Association busier and bigger. His method was to encourage the creation of new committees, one of which was the safety committee. The first chairman of the safety committee was Schaumburg McGehee of California Standard and the first program he undertook was a plant safety award.

The award was to go to the plant with the highest number of accident-free days over a twelve month period. Only plants operating on a twenty-four hour a day basis would be eligible. In addition, the CNGPA would issue a certificate to every plant that operated for the entire year accident-free.

The CNGPA wanted the award to be something striking, a symbol strong enough to last. When Schaum McGehee discussed this with his wife Jane, she recommended he talk to her art instructor, the twenty-five year old Calgary artist, Katie Ohe. Ms. Ohe was given the commission and she created the 14½", burnished bronze statuette of a plant workman within a flame that has stood atop the Association's safety awards ever since.

Meanwhile, Dan T. McDonald had sent out a form letter to all eligible plants asking for their participation. All they needed to do was send the safety committee a copy of the accident information they were already compiling under obligation to the Workers' Compensation Board. George Milne, safety supervisor of the Compensation Board, asked for details of the competition as soon as he heard about it. He and Board director Ron Henderson liked the idea and backed the award always as a useful support to the Board's own programs in the gas processing sector.

A year had to pass, of course, before the first safety awards could be presented. When the 1963 executive (under president Art Denny of Pan Am) met on September 30, 1963, Schaum McGehee was able to reveal the first set of results. Eleven of the twenty-two plants participating showed perfect records over the year and the McMahon plant at Taylor was the winner by virtue of having the most accident-free man-hours of that group of eleven.

The results showed a problem with the system. It was likely that there would always be a number of accident-free plants, but the only ones in the running for the award would be the very large plants. Right then, it was moved to expand the competition to three awards: one for large plants (those working 100,000 or more man-hours in a year) one for medium-sized plants (50,000 to 100,000 man-hours per year) and one for small plants (under 50,000 man-hours per year).

The three awards were first given out at the 1964 Annual Meeting of the CNGPA. The McMahon plant again won in the large plant category (with Pan Am's Whitecourt plant finishing second). The first medium-sized plant to win an award was Home Oil Carstairs, and the first small plant to win a trophy was Shell Worsley.

Elmer Berlie, 1964 CNGPA president, presents the first ever medium-sized plant safety award to Casey Greebe, representing Home Oil Carstairs. Behind Elmer Berlie stands Jay Johnson of Socony Mobil.

In later years the awards program was expanded again, presenting plaques to plants which had been accident-free for five years, ten years and fifteen years. With good luck and continued fine operation, there may be a demand in future for twenty year and twenty-five year plaques.

A second committee struck in Dan T. McDonald's year as president was the recognition and awards committee. Unlike the plant safety award which recognized the accomplishment of a group, the recognition and awards committee would concentrate on recognizing individual accomplishments in the industry. In a March 12, 1962, letter to Kevin Milne, Harvey Menard of Canadian Industrial Gas listed six possible awards that might be established by Kevin's "new recognition committee". Four of those six became a reality: a certificate for past-presidents; a special Award of Merit "to be given to an individual who has contributed in an unusual manner, or to an unusual degree to the advancement of the natural gas processing industry in Canada"; something for the outgoing Supply Men's president that would serve to recognize the contribution of the entire Supply Men's Association; and "at least one scholarship . . . for a deserving student at the University of Alberta".

The scholarship went forward in 1963, in the form of a $200 donation to the University of Alberta to be administered as a loan fund for students in engineering and science. It was to be given for the first time by the 1964 executive, and the same donation was to be made every year until the fund was self-sustaining. (By 1967, 425 students had been assisted by no-interest loans from the fund.)

The motion creating this loan fund contribution was made at the 1963 Annual Meeting, on the same occasion that the Association gave out a Certificate of Rec $_{\text{o}}$ nition to ex-president Dan T. McDonald. Don McEachern, Martin Winning and Rollie Lazerte had received these certificates the year before. The slate of awards was not formally instituted until the fall of 1964, so McEachern, Winning, Lazerte and McDonald have the additional distinction of having been given the award before it officially existed. It was under 1964 chairman Bernie Coady that the recognition and awards committee established the individual awards by a motion at a November 16, 1964, executive meeting. The two awards created were the Certificate of Recognition, to be presented to Association members only, and the Award of Merit, which could go to any individual who had contributed to the industry in an extraordinary manner.

George Govier of the Alberta Conservation Board was given the first official CNGPA Award of Merit in 1964.

The first Award of Merit was presented at the 1964 Annual Meeting to Dr. George Govier, for his many years of exceptional service to the industry as Board Member and finally Chairman of the Oil and Gas Conservation Board of Alberta. The first official Certificates of Recognition were given out the same night to Art Denny and Will Donahue. It became a tradition thereafter to present the Certificate of Recognition to the previous year's CNGPA president, and occasionally to another member who had served the Association well. One such recipient was Bill Sage who received the certificate in 1966 (along with past-president Kevin Milne). In part, Bill Sage's award was to recognize his annual efforts in putting on the Edmonton quarterly meeting. A tradition also developed of showing appreciation for the CNGPSMA by giving each of its out-going presidents a bottle of champagne.

One of the first things Kevin Milne did as CNGPA president was to move that the recognition and awards committee look into the establishment of an annual award for best technical paper. Jay Johnson was chairing that committee in 1965 when the idea was developed to the point where it could be voted into existence at the Annual Meeting. It was left to 1966 chairman Ed Plum to create the evaluation form and procedures on which the award would be based.

Kevin Milne hard at work; the 1965 CNGPA president and the man behind the awards for best technical papers of the year.

The result was two awards, one for the best paper by a member and one for best paper by a non-member. They were first presented at the first quarterly meeting of 1967 to Dr. Andy Younger and Martin Kyllo (members) for their paper on HBOG's Edson plant, and to Steve Worley of Black, Sivalls and Bryson (non-member) for his paper on glycol dehydration. (In 1972, the best member paper was renamed the William Rae award in honour of Bill Rae of HBOG after his death.)

In 1967, the CNGPA's support for education was expanded to include two $50 book prizes, awarded to one third-year engineering student at both the University of Calgary and the University of Alberta. The students would be chosen by their respective Deans and the prize would be a framed certificate and a voucher for the purchase of books at each university's book store. The first prizes presented, at the September quarterly meeting of 1967, went to Johan W. F. Klein of the University of Alberta, and W. E. Prater of the University of Calgary.

The next scholarship established by the CNGPA was the result of a tragedy. In 1969, not long after he had delivered what would, by the end of the year, be recognized as the best member paper, Dr. Alexander Petrunic was killed in an air crash. Prior to emigrating to Canada, Dr. Petrunic had been a distinguished professor at both the University of Vienna and the university at Zagreb. It was fitting, then, that the CNGPA honour his memory and his contributions to the Canadian processing industry by creating a university scholarship in his name. The Dr. Alexander Petrunic Memorial Scholarship is presented annually to a second-year student of engineering at the University of Calgary.

During the 1970's, the Association extended its scholarship program still further. A CNGPA scholarship was created at the U of A to correspond to the U of C's Dr. Petrunic scholarship. In 1978, in honour of the late Jim Armstrong who had so ably covered the oil and gas industry and the activities of the CGPA and CGPSA as a journalist, the Associations jointly sponsored a journalism scholarship in Mr. Armstrong's name at Grant MacEwan College in Edmonton. Finally, the two book prizes were replaced in 1984 with cash scholarships to third-year engineering students at the U of A and U of C in the amount of $400. In honour of the anniversary celebrated by this book, the scholarships will be known henceforward as the CGPA Silver Anniversary Scholarships.

Clayton Edgelow, CGPA President, 1969.

AWARD OF MERIT

In most of the years since its creation in 1964, the Award of Merit has been presented to an individual who has served the gas processing industry in an extraordinary manner.

1964
Dr. George Govier
ERCB

1965
Walter Gabert
PITS

1966
Jim Belding
Belmac Supply

1967
Dr. Don Baker Robinson
University of Alberta

1968
Frank McMahon
Westcoast Transmission

1969
Dr. Andy Younger
HBOG

1970 — Not awarded

1971
Dr. Andy Younger
Dome

1972
Ralph Archibald
Shell

1973
1. Jim Armstrong
Energy Processing/Canada
and
2. Les Rowland
Oilweek

1974
Dr. Jim Hyne
University of Calgary

1975
John Halls
Workers' Compensation Board

1976
Tony Neidermayer
Amoco

1977
Herb Bagnall
Shell

1978
Howie Thom
Exchanger Sales and Service

1979 — Not awarded

1980
Gordon Barnes
Alberta Natural Gas

1981
Ray Dobberthien
Dome

1982
Gerry DeSorcy
ERCB

1983
Jim Gray
Canadian Hunter

1984
John Martin
Canterra Energy

As part of his Award of Merit, Herb Bagnall (left) receives from 1977 CNGPA president Don Weiss a picture of Turner Valley as it looked in 1926.

TRAINING THE CANADIAN WAY

The contribution to education made by the Associations goes beyond scholarships and beyond the universities as well. The encouragement of members to serve as lecturers for the Petroleum Industry Training Service was the beginning of another kind of educational promotion that grew over the years from the liaison between the Associations and PITS.

The PITS gas technology course which started in 1962 and the gas processing correspondence courses offered through PITS were hampered somewhat in the early years by the manuals used as textbooks. The only texts supervisor Gabert could find were a set of Texas A & M manuals which naturally made no allowances for the peculiarities of operation in Canada. At the Edmonton quarterly meeting of 1962, mention was made of developing a set of Canadian gas processing textbooks under the auspices of the Associations and, hearing of this, Walter Gabert swiftly followed up with a letter to CNGPA president Dan T. McDonald. Gabert expressed pleasure that interest existed in developing such a set of texts:

> I am of course very interested in this project because I believe a Canadian
> text is needed by the industry for general informational purposes, and
> also can see extremely good use of such literature in our gas plant course.

The Texas A & M manuals were in fact lecture notes which had been gathered, edited and published. Probably because this had been shown to work, and because it relieved anyone of the chore of creating a text from scratch, the same approach was taken when the CNGPA proceeded with the textbook project in 1963. Dr. Martin Winning had inherited the special projects committee chair and he began to collect and edit notes from lectures delivered at the PITS gas technology course. The idea of the project was that the "Notes" would be used in conjunction with the data book on physical properties of hydrocarbons produced by the American NGPSMA.

The "Notes" were first published in 1964, but each year brought with it changes in the industry and fresh sets of lectures at PITS. This translated into an almost constant need for expansion and updating of the "Gas Technology Notes". Ron Nicholls of Pan Am was the first to inherit this task from Dr. Winning, and he worked on the notes throughout 1965. B. D. Garrison was in charge of *errata* during 1966. Among the numerous others who worked on the "Gas Technology Notes" over the years were Shell's Bill Fisher and Frank Wood.

Not surprising given Elmer Berlie's already demonstrated enthusiasm for education in the industry, projects to improve Canadian gas plant training continued to flourish in 1964 under Berlie's CNGPA presidency. The Association undertook two more training projects that year (besides the "Gas Technology Notes"), both in conjunction with PITS. Elmer Berlie and R. G. "Bob" Naden of Shell took a look at the PITS Gas Plant Operators Correspondence Course and decided it could be made better. Naden volunteered to revise it under the auspices of the CNGPA. In order to do this, Naden had to drop out of another Association project, the CNGPA/CNGPSMA/PITS engine and compressor school.

In the spring of 1964, Walter Gabert had asked the CNGPSMA if it would organize such an engine and compressor school and the Association had consented, striking a joint committee for the purpose with the CNGPA. Bob Naden was on this committee until claimed by the task of revising the PITS correspondence course. When he dropped out of the engine and compressor school committee, Howard Geddes of Home Oil took his place. Bill Sage eventually became chairman of the working committee and the engine and compressor school was first offered in early 1965 at the Northern Alberta Institute of Technology. It became an annual affair, usually a five day course at NAIT. Notes from these schools were also compiled and published.

It may seem that the Associations were giving a lot of service to PITS, but those who did so were never in doubt about its being a two-way street. Contributions to the education of personnel for the industry were investments that paid back multi-fold to the industry. It is intriguing, though, to see how willingly people worked for the overall good of their industry. With no quick, personal remuneration in sight, many in the Associations gave up a great deal of free, or at least discretionary time, to serve that goal. That the industry got from PITS as good as it gave was a message cried loud and clear in 1966 when Walter Gabert, the tireless supervisor of PITS,

Les Rowland, Oilweek senior editor and winner of the CNGPA Award of Merit, noted the "remarkably non-competitive exchange of information" at Association functions.

became only the second person ever to receive the Award of Merit. In 1967, Gabert returned the favour in a sense by presenting the Associations, on behalf of PITS, $400 in appreciation of their work on the "Gas Technology Notes" and the annual compressor schools.

The idea of translating lectures into hard copy was a method of publishing well suited to an organization relying on volunteer time. Eventually, all the technical papers and panel discussions too began making their way into print in some form that would last and could be utilized by those wanting the information farther down the road. In response to demands for copies of the technical papers delivered at the quarterly meetings, the CNGPA established a lending library at PITS. The panel discussions at the quarterly meetings were taped and published in Jim Armstrong's *Gas Processing/Canada* magazine. In 1967, Armstrong's magazine was given the exclusive right to reprint the panel discussions in their entirety. As this did not preclude another magazine from covering the same event in paraphrase form, the Associations usually received double coverage. Les Rowland of *Oilweek* regularly attended Association functions and reported on them faithfully. In 1973, the Associations saluted these energy writers by presenting both Les Rowland and Jim Armstrong with Awards of Merit.

With the Associations so well established in the publishing business, safety chairman Ralph Archibald suggested in 1967 that a comprehensive Canadian gas plant safety manual be prepared and published. As is the almost universal convention within organizations, he who recommended the job got to do the job. Archibald was charged with working the idea into a solid proposal that could be presented at the next Annual Meeting. On October 16, 1967, Ralph Archibald held a meeting on the safety manual project which was attended by nine industry safety reps. Shell and B.A. made their company safety manuals available as resource material.

The safety manual took five years to complete. Titled "Guidelines for Safety — Gas Processing" and published in 1972, it is a very useful manual which Ralph Archibald feels has generally stood the test of time. In the manual, safety chairman Archibald thanks several people for their help:

Ralph Archibald (l) accepts a small iron man on crutches as his Award of Merit from John Martin.

Elmer Berlie, Clayton Edgelow, Bill Fisher, Bob Naden, Don Sargent and Andy Younger. The year the book was published, Ralph Archibald received the CNGPA Award of Merit.

A few years later, after a solid decade as safety chairman, Ralph Archibald called it quits. He was replaced by safety man Ray Dobberthien of Dome. Dobberthien also earned an Award of Merit for his services as chairman and for his general contribution to industry safety in 1981.

THE CANADIAN GAS PROCESSORS' RESEARCH FUND

In most years of CNGPA history, the Association has taken a direction at least partially obedient to the personal views and aims of its president. This is as it should be in that presidents are elected for what they believe in and what they promise to do. When Dr. Andy Younger stepped into the presidency in 1968, he brought with him a respect for research and higher education which his administration expressed by creating the Canadian Natural Gas Processors Association Research Fund. To quote Dr. Younger, "The fund was set up to sponsor and encourage research at Western Canadian universities that would be of particular interest to the natural gas processing industry."

Companies involved in the industry were asked for contributions, the size of contribution being determined by the size of the company's operation in Canada. For example, when the Fund solicited a donation from Dome through Dome's vice-president Don Wolcott, it asked for the Group I rate of $1000 a year. Dome was in Group I because it was among the

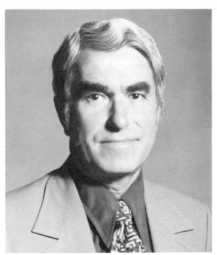

Bob Smith of Travis Chemicals; Supply Men's president in 1966; on the first board of directors of the CNGPA Research Fund in 1968.

largest companies in Canada in total plant capacity. On the first Board of Directors of the Fund were Bob Smith of Travis Chemicals, Bernie Coady of Delta Projects, Howard Geddes of Home Oil, Andy Younger of HBOG and Frank Manyluk, deputy-chairman of the Oil and Gas Conservation Board; that is, two suppliers, two processors and a representative of the Conservation Board. The Fund has always operated under the auspices of the Conservation Board as well as the two Associations. Gerry DeSorcy, now vice-chairman of the Conservation Board, took over from Frank Manyluk, serving as the Fund's secretary-treasurer for many years.

In 1969, the Research Fund collected $19,800. $15,000 was used to fund four projects at Alberta's universities. At the University of Alberta, Dr. Iwo G. Dalla Lana's work on the catalytic reactions between hydrogen sulphide and sulphur dioxide received support; and at the University of Calgary, three projects were funded. Dr. M. Mohtadi, the head of the department of chemical engineering at U of C, was directing study of sulphur recovery from low concentrations of SO_2 and H_2S in flue gas; this research received help from the CNGPA Fund. Also at the University of Calgary, a study of wear characteristics in compressor rings, directed by Dr. G. Walters, was supported. The Fund also funded a study under the direction of Dr. Khalid Aziz in search of a computer method of calculating compressibility in sour gas mixtures. At this time, the University of Calgary was offering a new program by which practising engineers could do graduate work without leaving their jobs. One of those taking early advantage of the opportunity was Ed Wichert who was currently working for Canadian Fina at its Wildcat Hills plant. Under Dr. Aziz' supervision, Wichert chose the search for sour gas compressibility factors suitable for computer as his Master's Degree project. He came up with the Wichert Method, a modification of the Reidlich-Kwong equation of state suitable for computer application. He also developed a chart method of calculating the compressibility factors, based on the Standing and Katz chart.

It is not possible or practical in a book like this to detail all the research sponsored in the last decade and a half by the CGPA Research Fund. The largest and most on-going of the projects sponsored were probably Dr. Don Robinson's investigations into the behaviour of sour gas mixtures and the work of Dr. Dalla Lana in search of better catalysts for the sulphur recovery process. A pilot reactor was built for the latter research and was installed first at the Petrogas Balzac plant and later at Gulf Nevis. Research projects such as these require large amounts of money and have not been solely sponsored by the CGPA. The CGPA Research Fund often functions as a money raiser, encouraging funds from other sources to enable the work to go forward.

As the industry boomed in the 1970's, so did contributions to the Research Fund. A decline in the size of the fund during the 1980's would seem to confirm a not too surprising tendency for the Fund to track industry prosperity. The Research Fund still brings in over $40,000 per year, seeding and enabling much basic research at our universities which would not otherwise be done. Dr. Younger received the Award of Merit for the first time in 1969 for initiating the Fund and it remains a tribute to Dr. Younger's commitment to higher education and the improvement of knowledge in gas processing.

Dr. Andy Younger, (centre) 1968 president of the CNGPA and the only two time winner of the Award of Merit to date.

THE ASSOCIATIONS IN HINDSIGHT

In 1962, CNGPA president Dan T. McDonald gave a parting address to the Association that contained much encouragement and a sound advice:

> This association should not fall into the limbo of *just another technical society*. On the contrary, you will build real stature as you continue to keep in focus a well-balanced program of action which recognizes the important interrelationship between personal development, management, safety, marketing, transportation, and technical development. All have a definite place in our industrial and professional careers. We must give varied emphasis to each of these toward the end goal of individuals and contemporary growth in the challenging days ahead. This association is a wonderful forum through which each of us can be an active participant in meeting and conquering these challenges.

Year by year, the two Associations gained ground on McDonald's vision. From the beginning, the Associations maintained a broad angle of perception. The latest advances in processing technology were presented in technical meetings alongside the latest in safety, the latest in management. More important, the integrated nature of these subjects was stressed. Good safety was seen as a product of good management, for example, rather than something which could be achieved only through the proper use of equipment. The realization that the processing industry can never live in isolation from its environment was expressed in numerous ways: by invitations to political spokesmen, by technical papers on air pollution monitoring and control and, most recently, (at the 1984 4th quarterly meeting) by an NFB film and panel discussion on the subject of acid rain.

This industry which was compelled into existence by a government determined to stop wanton waste of gas has become an industry that consciously conserves more than the gas; it conserves its people and it conserves the world it lives in. Again, it is amazing to see how modern a view Dan T. McDonald was urging on Association members back in 1962:

> Conservation is too often viewed in the industry as *putting out the flares.*
> In fact, conservation of men, materials and energy are the real areas all of
> us can be cognizant of. Build a better plant with less materials, that
> destroys less fuel gas in its operation, and that permits men to do a safer
> and more intelligent job of processing gas. Our responsibility is to use
> wisely all the resources which have been entrusted to us by our Creator,
> the Nation, the Public and Our Employers. It is in our power to do so.
> We must be alert and intelligently venturesome to be true con-
> servationists.

Based on philosophies like these, the CGPA and CGPSA kept themselves at the centre of change in the Canadian gas processing industry. Progress on the search for reliable sour service materials was charted by technical papers and panel discussions throughout the 1960's, as was progress in gas analysis, progress in the safe handling of H_2S, progress in the efficiency of the modified Claus process for sulphur recovery. In the 1970's, when environmental regulations jacked sulphur recovery standards into the high nineties, and energy crisis created a spiral in the price of the industry's products, the Associations provided a place to discuss and debate the politicization of the industry and to study the means by which the more exacting regulations could be met. Through the Research Fund, the Associations began to generate answers to their problems as well as communicating the answers that were being found elsewhere.

For early presidents of the Supply Men's Association, men like Jim Belding and Jim Carveth, the challenge was to increase participation by Canadians in the supply of goods and services to the fast growing Canadian

Bob Bowser, vice-president of Alberta Gas Ethylene and Novacor, was CGPA president in 1979, the Associations' 20th anniversary year.

processing industry. The vast improvement in the fortunes of Canadian suppliers since then must in many ways be credited to the diligence of the CGPSA. When the Associations celebrated their twentieth year in 1979, Murray Ross, 1979 Suppliers' president, described the change this way:

> Twenty years ago the Canadian gas industry and our association were new enterprises. As suppliers we served this fledgling industry by importing mostly U.S.A. materials and equipment. There were, perhaps, a half-dozen independent Canadian gas industry consultants. Engineering, design, purchasing and construction companies were predominantly local offices of major engineering firms. This was all as it should be. We were at the bottom of a learning curve.

Into this atmosphere the CNGPA and CNGPSMA were born and, thanks in part to them, a change took place:

> As suppliers to the industry, we have seen member-companies move from distribution into primary and secondary manufacturing. Many of the products we sell to the industry today are truly "made in Canada".

Canadian engineers have likewise taken their place in the front pew, giving away nothing to foreign competition. As Ross puts it:

> There are now a number of large Canadian engineering firms that can compete on an equal basis with foreign firms. Our member companies are supplying technical inputs to the 'mega-projects' like Syncrude.

Looking back from 1984 to the needs and problems that caused the two Associations to be created, it would seem that most of those needs have been met, most of those problems solved. The question must be asked then, have the Associations fulfilled their mandate and, thus, outlived their need to exist?

If there was ever a test of viability, the recent recession in the Canadian oil and gas industry has certainly provided one for the CGPA and CGPSA. During that recession, membership in the two groups slumped from boomtime highs of around 600 for each Association to approximately 500 in each. Contributions to the Research Fund fell from a 1981 high of $65,602 to around $40,000 in 1984.

But the organizations did survive. If, as most hope, the worst for Canadian processing is past, it is not likely that either Association will be bushwacked at some future turning of the road. In 1962, Dan T. McDonald said, "Nothing will stop us but our own apathy." Looking at the Associations in 1984, there is little sign that apathy has taken root. The fourth quarterly meeting of 1984 was extended to two days in honour of the silver anniversary. On the first day the luncheon drew 210 people; on the second day, the luncheon drew 230 people. There were scant symptoms of apathy among the 500 or so people who attended the sold out President's Ball.

John Martin of Canterra, Award of Merit winner in the 25th anniversary year of the CGPA.

At the plant level, apathy would probably translate rather quickly into sloppiness and thus into poor safety practices, but the 1983-84 CGPA safety awards competition showed a strong safety performance across the industry. Safety chairman Don Elves was able to report the participation of 191 plants (24 companies). Of that number, 158 qualified for trophies or certificates (indicating accident-free status in at least the last year). The trophy winners in order of size from large to small were Canterra Ram

River, Home Carstairs and Sulpetro Minnehik-Buck Lake. Six plants won awards for completing their fifth straight accident-free year and five plants were awarded ten year plaques. Five plants achieved the incredible plateau of fifteen straight years of perfect safety and have surely earned a mention in this book. They are: Dome Consort, Dome Sturgeon Lake South, Gulf Rimbey, PanCanadian Bassano-Lathom, and PanCanadian Ferrybank. There is not much apathy evident in records such as these.

All in all, the signs and portents indicate robust health for the two Associations. Their enthusiastic following surely means that the CGPA and the CGPSA are still perceived by the Canadian industry as doing important work.

THE ASSOCIATION AND THE INDUSTRY TAKEN TOGETHER

One sign of the vibrancy of the CGPA and the CGPSA in their 25th year is the undertaking of this book: a history not only of themselves but of the entire Canadian gas processing industry. That industry is so large in Western Canada that a history of it naturally overspills the banks and becomes a partial history of Western Canada itself.

The gas processing industry is one of those few-and-far-between industries on which a nation can truly build. It is not a quick-kill industry passing over the landscape like a fire, that supplies short-term work and short-term cash and then is gone. The gas processing industry lasts. Oil and gas exploration alone would not have created a lasting town at Turner Valley. The shack towns of the drilling industry were exactly as mobile as the rigs they followed. When the flurry of exploration finally ceased, they vanished almost overnight. The communities that lasted at Turner Valley and elsewhere were often those that grew up around the gas plants, immobile structures guaranteed long life by the firmness of government conservation policy and by the length of time it takes a plant to pay out.

Veteran gas processors and supply men have a feeling toward Western Canada that is not dissimilar from that of veteran farmers and ranchers. An elderly farmer or rancher is usually good for a story of the way it used to be before there were good roads and automobiles. And, when he or she speaks of the relatively luxurious way it is now, there is a proprietorial tone in the voice, a tone that tells you the person is taking just a bit of personal credit for the improvement.

So it is with processors and supply men as well. The stories of epic journeys through muskeg and gumbo to frontier plants like Whitecourt and Judy Creek; the tales of bitter cold and lonely winters at isolated Fort

In 1985, the historic Madison gas plant (above) will close. Western Decalta's new Diamond Valley plant near Longview will take over the task of processing Turner Valley's remaining gas reserves.

A road near Leduc in 1947. It is different now and the gas processing industry helped make it so.

Nelson or Rainbow Lake; these are generally told with the same air: "It's different now of course, and we helped make it so."

The gas processing industry has indeed spread good roads and healthy communities far and wide across Western Canada. Cities like Calgary and Edmonton would look considerably different had, say, gas export been indefinitely postponed or refused. From each plant and from each office tower involved in the work of processing gas, concentric ripples of economic activity spread, investment begetting investment, jobs begetting jobs, so that today, for all its ups and downs, Western Canada enjoys the benefits of a modern industrialized society. If we compare that to the situation five decades ago when our natural gas was burning to oblivion in the flares of Turner Valley, it can well and truly be said that the gas processing industry in Canada has helped our society progress from *Waste to Wealth*.

APPENDIX 1:
IMPERIAL TO METRIC
CONVERSION FACTORS

Volume:

cubic feet × 0.2832 = cubic metres

Pressure:

pounds per square inch × 703.1 = kilograms per square metre

Length (Depth):

feet × 0.3048 = metres

Distance:

miles × 1.609 = kilometres

Temperature:

(°F − 32) × 0.556 = °C

Energy:

BTUs (British Thermal Units) × 1054.6 = joules

Power:

HP (imperial horsepower) × 1.014 = HP (metric Horsepower)

HP (imperial) × 0.7457 = kilowatts

APPENDIX 2:
GRAPHS

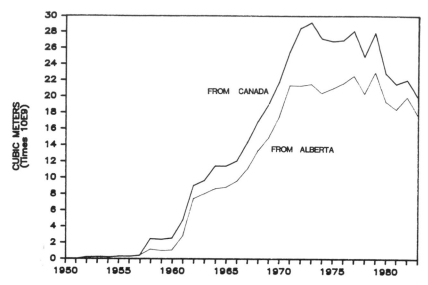

Graph 1: Exports of Natural Gas from Canada to the United States.

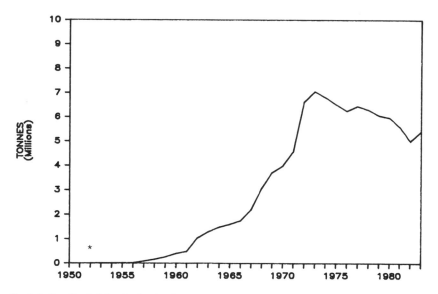

Graph 2: Canadian Sulphur Production from Gas Processing Plants.

*Sulphur production from Canadian processing plants actually began in 1952 at the Jumping Pound and Madison plants. Their combined production of 60 long tons per day does not show up clearly on the above graph.

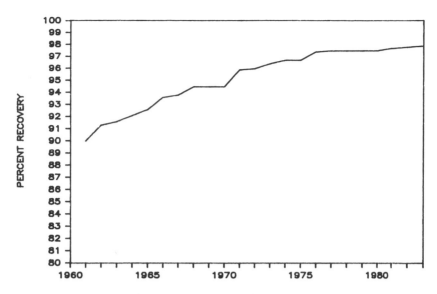

Graph 3: Sulphur Recovery in Alberta Sour Gas Processing Plants.

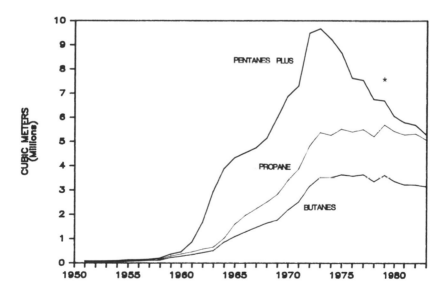

Graph 4: Production of Natural Gas Liquids from Canadian Gas Processing Plants.

*The downward trend in pentanes plus production after 1973 reflects the behaviour of cycled retrograde condensation reservoirs. After production from such reservoirs hits its peak, the decline is very rapid. The major reservoirs of this type in Alberta were brought into production in the late '60's, peaking at approximately the same time in the early '70's and declining rapidly thereafter. No new reservoirs of this sort were brought into production during the period.

ON SOURCES

Much of the information in this book has been gleaned from personal interviews. Most of these interviews were done specifically for the book. The balance came from the Petroleum Industry Oral History Project and the Glenbow Archives collection. Quotations in the text not ascribed to any other source can be assumed to have come from interviews.

Of the print sources relied upon, two magazines, *Oilweek* and *Canadian Oil and Gas Industries*, were particularly useful. The two together provide a "diary" of processing industry activities extending from the early 1950's to the present. These periodicals were used to such an extent that the author refers researchers to *all* back issues of both rather than to specific numbers.

In piecing together the early history of natural gas use and the processing industry, the following books (published and unpublished), articles and papers were of great service:

— Beach, Floyd, K. *Alberta's Petroleum Paternity* (reprinted in booklet form by National Business Publications Ltd., Gardenville, Que., after having been serialized in *Canadian Oil and Gas Industries*).

— Beach, Floyd, K. and Irwin, J. L. *The History of Alberta Oil*. Department of Mines and Minerals, Alberta, 1940.

— Canadian Western Natural Gas. *History and Information Book*. (available through Canadian Western Natural Gas).

— Cannon, R. E. and Sutton, C. B. "Four Eras Highlight Gas Processing History", *Petroleum/2000,* August, 1977.

— de Mille, George. *Oil In Canada West*, Calgary, 1970.

— Gould, Edwin. *Oil: the History of the Canadian Oil and Gas Industry*. Hancock House Publishers, B.C., 1974.

— Keller, David N. *Cooper Industries, 1883-1983*. Cooper Industries Ltd., 1983.

— Lauriston, Victor. *Blue Flame of Service*. Union Gas Co. of Canada Ltd., 1961.

— Natural Gas Processors Association. *The First Fifty Years*. N.G.P.A., Tulsa, 1971.

— Schmidt, John. *Manuscript re: Oil Well Drillers, Frosty Martin and Tiny Phillips*. (Glenbow-Alberta Institute Archives).

— Sheep River Historical Society. *In the Light of the Flares: History of the Turner Valley Oilfields*. 1979.

Information on the early natural gas conservation efforts in Alberta and on the development of the Petroleum and Natural Gas Conservation Board were largely obtained through the ERCB library. The two Floyd Beach books mentioned above were also helpful. Materials available through the ERCB include:
— Calder, W. "Alberta Oil Conditions, 1932". *The Canadian Institute of Mining and Metallurgy*, 1932.
— Calder, W. and Owen, R. M. S. "Alberta Oil and Gas Development", *Journal of Institutional Petroleum Technologists,* September, 1935.
— Goodall, D. P. "An Historical Sketch of Oil and Gas Conservation", 1957.
— Weymouth, Thos. R. "The Conservation of Gas in the Turner Valley Field."

Sources for the fifth chapter on the development of the TCPL and Westcoast pipelines principally were:
— Gray, Earle, *Wildcatters: The Story of Pacific Petroleums and Westcoast Transmission.* McClelland and Stewart, Toronto, 1982.
— Kilbourn, William. *Pipeline.* Clarke, Irwin and Company Ltd., Toronto, 1970.
— McDonald, D. P. *The Westcoast Story* (manuscript).
— Raborn, Smiley. *"The CanDel Story"* (presentation paper).

Magazines devoted to the oil and gas industry and personal interviews were the main sources for charting the development of the Canadian conservation plants and the later series of plants brought to life by the completion of the pipelines. A good source of reference information was the annual report *Natural Gas Processing Plants in Canada* brought out by the Mineral Resources Division of the Department of Energy, Mines and Resources, Ottawa. R. E. Doyle's presentation "CIGAS — BTUs on Wheels" provided a good basis for the story of early LPG sales in Western Canada. A Shell Oil of Canada Limited publication *The Canadian Petrochemical Industry* (Ryerson, 1956) was relied upon for Alberta's early development in the petrochemical area.

An almost complete source for the technological history of Canada's gas processing industry is found in the CGPA Lending Library of technical papers available to the public through the Petroleum Industry Training Service. Other sources on processing technology included:
— Archibald, R. G. *Guidelines For Safety — Gas Processing.* CGPA, 1972.

— Berlie, Elmer. "The Canadian Gas Processing Industry" (paper). 1966.
— Berlie, Elmer. "A History of Environmental Control for the Petroleum Industry in Alberta" (paper). 1981.
— Berlie, Elmer. "The Power Engineer and the Natural Gas Industry" (paper). 1962.
— Berlie, Elmer. "Processing of Natural Gas" (lecture paper). 1971.
— Berlie, Elmer and Estep, James. "Sulphur in Alberta" (paper). 1969.
— Lukes, Norman. *Corrosion in the Petroleum Industry* (manual). 1950.
— Paskall, Harold G. *Capability of the Modified Claus Process.* Western Research, 1976.
— Richardson, J. A. "A Spectacular Past — and Future" (CNGPA paper). 1969.
— Richardson, J. A., Smith, R. F. and Younger, A. H. "Gas Processing During CGPA's History" (CGPA paper). 1979.

The final chapter on the history of the CGPA and CGPSA relied heavily on the minutes and correspondence of the Associations, on personal recollections and on the coverage of the Associations' functions by *Oilweek* and *Gas Processing/Canada* (later *Energy Processing/Canada*).

PHOTO ACKNOWLEDGEMENTS

Alaska Highway News — 120
Alberta Energy and Natural Resources — 53
Alberta Sulphur Research Ltd. — 195
Amoco Canada Petroleum Company Ltd. — 148, 149, 168, 182, 264
Archibald, Ralph — 270
Bagnall, Herb — 187
Barber Engineering and Controls Ltd. — 69, 296
Beer, Reg — 288 (left)
Berlie, Elmer — 64, 193, 273, 274, 276, 288, 332
Canadian Western Natural Gas — 7, 9, 11, 13 (bottom), 15 (both), 17, 26,
    35, 36, 52, 106, 184
Dome Petroleum Ltd. — 132, 188, 212, 230, 232, 240, 251, 327
Energy Resources Conservation Board — 58 and 59 (nine portraits)
Esso Resources Canada — 66, 74, 84, 111, 234, 278, 333
Gabert, Walter — 280
Gas Processors Association, Tulsa — 61, 308
Glenbow-Alberta Institute Archives — viii, 5, 13 (top), 18, 20, 21, 22,
    28, 31, 32, 37, 39, 41, 43, 44, 46, 50, 55, 62, 82, 89, 97, 98, 100,
    102, 108, 138, 176
Graves, R. K. — 48, 268
Gulf Canada — 112, 127, 128, 142, 207, 257
Kiernan, Al — 236
McDowell, John — 30, 164
Milne, Kevin — 117 (a and b), 318
Novacor Chemicals Ltd. — 252, 329
Oilweek — 115, 141, 180, 246, 317, 323, 330
Photos provided by persons depicted — 73, 87, 116, 119, 124, 145, 146,
    154, 198, 203, 216, 218, 220, 223, 254, 277, 301, 305, 319, 325
Provincial Archives of Alberta — 51 (P.5359), 227 (P.1170), 247 (J.502/18)
Richardson, Jim — 136, 300
Rowland, Les — 205, 208
Scott, Earl — 90, 304
Shell Canada Ltd., CRC — Photographic Services — 77, 79, 80, 150,
    162, 173, 174, 177, 209, 266, 283, 285, 292, 293, 316, 324
Trans-Canada Pipe Lines — 92, 105
Weiss, Don — 321
Western Decalta Petroleum Ltd. — 191, 214, 332

INDEX

Oklahoma, State of, 28, 33, 40, 125, 214,
216-7, 266
Oklahoma A & M, 126
Okotoks, Alta., 14, 19, 21, 29, 31, 46-7, 52
Okotoks field, 130, 165-6, 172, 177-9, 308
Olean, N.Y., 185, 299
Old Glory, 8-10
Ontario, 2-4, 16, 18-9, 27, 29, 34, 46, 49,
85, 103, 106, 133, 190, 231
O'Rourke, Leo, 129
Osler, Hammond and Nanton, 95
Owen, R. M. S., 50

Pacific Empress (plant), 228-33, 235, 239,
241-2, 250
Pacific Gas and Electric, 99, 133-4, 238, 245,
249
Pacific Northwest (region), 68, 93-4, 99, 103,
243
Pacific Petroleums Limited, 89, 114-6, 121,
139, 159, 192, 228-33, 237, 241, 260, 261
Packer, Joe, 192
Pakowki Lake, 95
Palmer, Harry, 122
Palmer, Morris, 177, 178, 308
Palmer, Ned, 47
Palmer, Wally, 86-7, 146
Pan American Petroleum Corporation, 131,
147-50, 151-2, 167-8, 201, 233, 234,
238-40, 243, 303-4, 306, 310, 315, 322
Pan Am East Crossfield (plant), 182
Pan Am West Whitecourt (plant), 143, 147-50,
167-8, 316, 331
PanCanadian Petroleum Limited (See Also
Canadian Pacific Oil and Gas), 123, 331
Partec-Lavelin, 242, 255
Paskall, Harold, 202
Pauls, Ron, 125-6, 129
Peace River, 117-19
Peace River (region of), 29, 94, 99, 104
Pearson, Bud, 36
Pelican Rapids, Alta., 22
Pembina field, 130-2, 224, 228
Pembina Pipe Lines Ltd., 225
Pepper, Spence, 83, 215-8, 221, 231-2
Percy, Elwood, 218
Petro-Canada, 146, 251, 260-2
Petrofina S.A., 144-6
Petrogas Balzac (plant), 152, 172-3, 179-80,
199, 201, 210, 235, 291, 326
Petrolane Gas Services, 218
Petroleum and Natural Gas Conservation Board
(See ERCB)
Petroleum Institute Training Service (PITS),
278-9, 281, 311, 320-1
Petroleum Refiner, 27
Petrunic, Alexander, 145, 161, 196-9, 203-4,
309, 319
Pew, H. P., 307

Phillips, A. P., 8-10, 16
Phillips, Alan, 109
Phillips, Dale, 283
Phillips Petroleum, 114-21, 228, 231, 260-1
Phillips, R. S., 159-61, 176
Pincher Creek, Alta., 5, 39, 154-5, 285-7
Pincher Creek field, 68, 96, 101, 103, 125-9,
170
Pine Creek field, 147-8, 167-8
Plotke, Nes, 314
Plotkins, Leon, 215
Plum, Ed, 318
Polysar, 244
Poole-Pritchard Canadian Ltd., 142, 182
Port Alma, Ont., 27, 34, 113, 175
Pouce Coupe field, 94, 113, 119
Powell River Company, 78
Prairie Fuel Gas Co., 12
Prairie Gas Ltd., 218-9
Prairie Pipe Lines Ltd., 94
Prater, W. E., 319
Princess Margaret, 119
Pritchard, Ken, 314
Progas of Canada, 83, 217-8
Progas Acheson (plant), 217
Progas Big Valley (plant), 83, 217
Propane Gas Association of Canada, 233
Provincial Producers Pipeline Ltd., 225-6
Provo Gas Producers Ltd., 85, 122
Provost field, 108, 122-3
Prudhoe Bay, Alaska, 246
Pryde, James Morrison, 70-73, 215, 300
Purdue University, 116
Pure Oil Co., 309
Purvin and Gertz, 131

Quebec, 103, 133, 231, 263
Queen's University, 116, 137, 158

Rae, William, 318
Raborn, Smiley, 101, 103, 110, 144
Rainbow Lake field, 129, 199, 333
Ralph, M. Parsons Co., 152, 178, 192, 200
Rankin, Charles, 53
Rankine, Robin, 202
Redwater field, 68-9, 84
Regas, 214, 215
Regina, Sask., 123, 215-6
Richards, Bill, 123, 222, 243, 250
Richardson, Jim, 136, 181, 182, 192, 237,
242, 300
Richardson, Sid, 221, 222
Robb, Alta., 255-8
Robinson, Dr. Don, 197, 320, 326
Rockefeller, John D., 29
Rock Gas, 214
Roman, Bill, 80-2, 151, 172-3, 181-2
Ronicker, Fred, 193-273, 276
Ross, Charles, 50
Ross, Murray, 314, 329